THE
HOME
PLUMBER'S
BIBLE

To the do-it-yourselfer
in every home

No. 914
$10.95

THE HOME PLUMBER'S BIBLE

by Ramesh Singhal

TAB BOOKS

BLUE RIDGE SUMMIT, PA. 17214

FIRST EDITION

FIRST PRINTING—SEPTEMBER 1978

Copyright © 1978 by TAB BOOKS

Printed in the United States of America

Library of Congress Cataloging in Publication Data

Singhal, Ramesh P
   The home plumber's bible.

   Bibliography: p.
   Includes index.
   1. Plumbing—Amateurs' manuals. I. Title.
TH6124.S54   696'.1   78-12496
ISBN 0-8306-8914-1
ISBN 0-8306-7914-6 pbk.

Thumb Index Contents (please see page 6 for itemized Contents)

Contents

Acknowledgments

A large number of individuals and organizations have enthusiastically furnished information, photographs, and other material for use in this book. I wish to acknowledge their contributions and to express my deep appreciation for their cooperation.

I particularly wish to thank the following firms who supplied me with photographs of their products and granted permission to use illustrations and quotations from their published material:

Sears, Roebuck and Company; General Electric Company; White-Westinghouse Appliance Company; Delta Faucet Company; Kohler Company; Eljer Plumbingware, Wallace Murray Corp.; Tyler Pipe; Imperial-Eastman Corp.; Cascade Industries; Connecticut Precast Corp.; Bradley Corporation, Faucet and Special Products Division; Toledo Tools; The Ridge Tool Company; and Parco Pools.

Published literature was reviewed in detail, particularly that dealing with recent advances in the field of plumbing and plumbingware. A bibliography of suggested further reading will be found at the end of the book.

It took several years of effort to develop the material to its present form. The original draft was critically reviewed by several professional and literary persons including Anil and Mala who deserve my sincere appreciation.

Credit goes to Eleanor Moser for her patience in reading and figuring out my handwritten pages and typing them into a perfect copy.

And finally, I wish to thank my understanding wife, Swarn, without whose cooperation and patience this project would not have been possible.

Introduction

If you are a homeowner or intend to be one, this book is for you! Not only will it furnish you with sufficient know-how to carry out common maintenance and repair jobs, but it will also prepare you for undertaking more adventurous projects such as adding a new bathroom, or remodelling your old plumbing system.

Most homeowners cry for help when any plumbing-related emergency develops. Such help usually does not arrive in time and is quite expensive. The blame is not your plumber's, either! He is constantly getting distress calls and has to set priorities and work accordingly. Like any other professional, he puts all his training and experience into the job he does. So if you are standing in a flooded basement, and he just flips a gadget and stops the flow, you can't really feel bad; he knows which way to turn the valve, and you don't!

Being a do-it-yourselfer, particularly in the plumbing field, is very rewarding. It saves a considerable amount of money and gives you a sense of accomplishment every time you successfully tackle a job.

Whether your house is new or old, problems like clogged toilets and drains, freezing and bursting of exposed pipes, leaking faucets, overflowing sewage disposal systems, and noises in pipelines are quite common. Also as the size of the family increases and more and more modern appliances are added, the design capacities of both the water supply and drainage lines are exceeded. This may lead to lower water pressure at the fixtures and frequent cloggings in the drain lines. At this stage you will want to replace some of the undersized pipelines with larger ones. Perhaps you would also like to install a larger water heater or a bigger sewage disposal field. In time, the fixtures in your kitchen and bathrooms become obsolete and aesthetically unacceptable to you. This is when you will want to intall new fixtures and undertake a remodelling or modernizing job.

Having read this book and familiarized yourself with the components of your domestic plumbing system, you will find that common plumbing emergencies will present no problem to you. In fact, with the help of your toolbox and a few rented tools, you will be able to do everything mentioned in the previous paragraphs and many, many more.

The first three chapters of this book explain how your plumbing system works, and how the sewage is disposed of by the septic tank and leaching system. The next three chapters describe tools, pipes, and other plumbing materials; they explain how to replace old pipelines with new ones, and deal with various problems which may arise.

Toilets, faucets, tubs, and showers are described in Chapters 7 through 9, and appliances are discussed in Chapter 10, with emphasis on installation procedures and troubleshooting.

In Chapters 11 and 12 you will find material to enable you to do major renovations, improvements, and remodellings. Chapter 13 deals with plumbing for swimming pools and other outdoor facilities.

Prevention is always better than cure. Chapter 14 explains how you can keep the plumbing system running trouble-free with some elementary precautions. Finally, if you are closing down your home for a considerable period of time and will be away during the winter months, this chapter explains how you can prevent your plumbing from freezing and your water seals from evaporating.

It is my conviction that, after reading this book, you will be a semi-professional in the plumbing field and will be able to carry out most repair and installation jobs.

Ramesh P. Singhal, Ph.D., P.E.

How Your Plumbing System Works

How Your Plumbing System Works

Many homeowners tend to look upon the plumbing of their home as a mysterious setup working in ways beyond their comprehension. They think it runs into problems and emergencies at its own whims and at most unearthly hours. You don't have to join their ranks once you understand that plumbing is a scientifically designed system that works according to the basic laws of nature. You can easily study the entire system section by section, learn to diagnose the troubled spots, and carry out the common, run-of-the-mill repairs. In fact, if you are the more enterprising type, you may even master the art of plumbing to the extent that you can make improvements and additions to your bathrooms and kitchen and install or repair plumbing-related fixtures. As a homeowner you owe it to yourself and to your family to learn at least how to do the following:

1. Identify and deal with a plumbing emergency
2. Carry out basic repairs
3. Plan improvements and additions to the plumbing system
4. Determine when it is necessary to seek the help of a plumber.

Over a long period of time this will save you a considerable amount of money and prevent lots of worries and frustrations. Also it will give you a feeling of satisfaction and accomplishment every time you complete a job. However, a note of warning is appropriate here: not everyone is trimmed to be his own plumber. Most handymen can do very good and useful plumbing jobs, and chances are that with a little effort, you can be a good one, too.

In any event, you will have to read the instructions on how to do a particular job before actually starting to tackle it. If you still don't feel confident or if you feel a particular job is too complicated, by all means call your plumber. He has the necessary know-how and technique to do the planning, servicing, and installing that may be needed.

Another thing you have to know about is the *plumbing code* applicable to your community. Every city or town has a plumbing code. The county plumbing code applies to rural areas which don't have their own codes. A copy can be obtained from the town hall or the county courthouse. In areas where no plumbing code applies, it will be safe to work according to the National Plumbing Code—you may get a copy of this from your local library. Some codes will not allow you to work on the installation of pipes, fittings, fixtures, etc., even though you may be fully capable and experienced; they require a licensed plumber to do all the plumbing jobs except minor things like clearing clogged toilets and drains.

Most codes lay down specifications for:

- Types of pipe for various uses—water supply, drainage, vents, soil stacks, etc.
- Minimum pipe sizes for various purposes
- Requirements for waste connections and venting
- Requirements for fixture traps

The home plumbing system starts either at the well in your yard or at the water supply main near the street curb in front of your house. The system brings the required quantity of potable water inside the house, heats part of it, treats it if necessary, and carries it to every fixture. In addition, it collects the soil and waste waters and conveys them to the street sewer or to the private disposal system in your yard, without causing any inconvenience, noise, or nuisance. It is a pretty big setup with a large number of pipes, valves, gauges, fixtures, and controls. An average home has more than 350 feet of piping hidden within the floors and the walls, or buried underground.

There are three main parts of the home plumbing system:

1. The water supply system
2. The fixtures
3. The drainage system

The major portion of the repair work you will be doing will probably involve the fittings and fixtures you can see without opening up the floors and walls. Yet it will be worthwhile to try and understand how the whole thing works, particularly if you are ambitious and look forward to undertaking major additions and alterations like remodelling a bath or kitchen or installing a dishwasher, an automatic washer, or a garbage disposer. Let us start with the water supply system.

THE WATER SUPPLY SYSTEM

The water supply system should furnish good quality water at the correct pressure and in enough quantities to meet the requirements at all the fixtures. In addition, it should provide hot water. If you live in a rural area or in a part of town where there is no municipal or company water supply, you have to install a well in your own yard from which water is pumped into your home water supply system. In urban and suburban localities, streets have water mains owned by municipalities or private water companies. These mains supply water which is already purified, treated, and raised to the required pressure so that when you open a faucet in the home, potable water gushes out. It is this pressure which carries water through the *risers* (vertical pipes) to the upper floors. Sometimes the pressure in the municipal water mains is not adequate, particularly if your home is situated far away from the overhead tank or from the pumping station. In such a case, you will have to install a pump in your basement to boost the pressure; it will be just like the one for pumping water from a private well.

Valves

Figure 1-1 illustrates a typical domestic water service installation, starting from the street main. There is a meter to register the consumption of water in your home, and there are three shut-off valves: the curb valve within a stop box, the meter valve, and the main shut-off valve.

The *curb valve*, which belongs to the municipality or water company, is operated by a *street key*—a long-handled wrench. The home water supply system starts from the curb valve.

The *meter* is often installed in the basement or garage, and has a remote sensing device somewhere outside. This device is sometimes buried in the yard. The *meter valve* is located between the foundation wall and the water meter, near where the pipeline enters

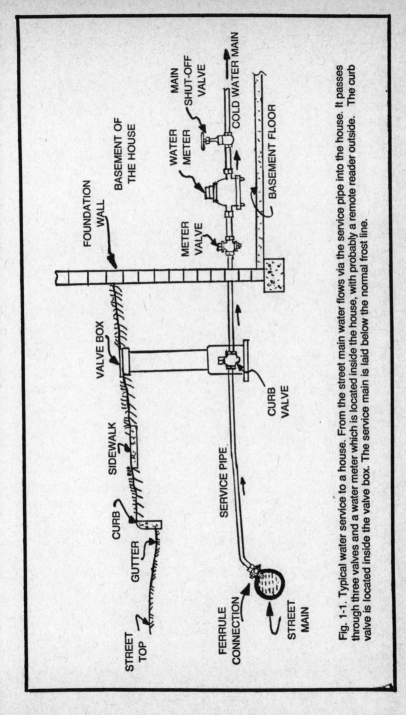

Fig. 1-1. Typical water service to a house. From the street main water flows via the service pipe into the house. It passes through three valves and a water meter which is located inside the house, with probably a remote reader outside. The curb valve is located inside the valve box. The service main is laid below the normal frost line.

the cellar or basement. It comes in handy when the meter needs repairs.

The *main shut-off valve* is located on the other side of the meter. It is the most important valve, from the handyman's point of view, and every member of your family should know where it is located. If a leak suddenly develops at a fixture or in a water supply line, for instance in the case of a pipe burst, this valve should be shut off immediately. Remember, however, that if the emergency is at a fixture which has an individual shut-off valve, like a toilet, tub, or lavatory, you should not stop the supply to the entire house by unnecessarily rushing and closing the main valve.

In case you have never seen or worked shut-off valves, you should locate them and try to shut off water both at the fixtures and on the main line. Sometimes you will find that a valve has rusted and does not work freely. A little lubrication will help. Another important point to learn by trying the valves is the direction in which each one opens and closes. Most will open when turned counterclockwise.

Distribution

The water distribution system in a house consists of a cold water main which starts from the water meter, a water heater, perhaps a water softener, several branches of cold and hot water lines running across the house and vertically through *risers* that lead to various fixtures, room shut-offs, fixture stopcocks, and air chambers behind the fixtures located within the walls. Figure 1-2 illustrates a typical layout of a water distribution system in a two-story house. Close to the water meter, the cold water main splits into two: one line leads to the water heater, the other to the cold water main (a riser). Branches take off from the cold water main to supply water to individual fixtures like sinks, toilets, lavatories, tubs, washing machines, and showers.

A hot water main starts from the hot water heater and runs parallel to the cold water. It sends similar branches to those fixtures which need hot water. Toilets and boilers need only cold water, while most dishwashers use only hot water. The main or branch that is untapped merely runs by such fixtures. Whenever necessary, shut-off valves are provided on the branches and the mains. Small-diameter fixture supply lines connect the individual fixtures to the branches. The mains generally maintain the same size diameter all along their runs. Branches are smaller in size than mains; the actual diameter depends on the number of fixtures they serve.

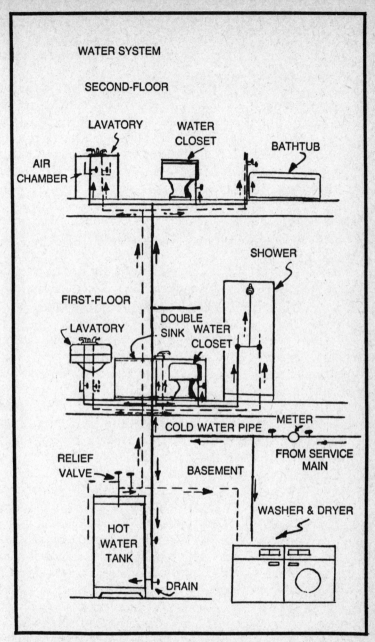

Fig. 1-2. Cold water main splits in two—one branch going to the hot water heater, the other to the cold water riser and fixture branches. Hot water lines start from the heater and run parallel to cold water lines. Toilets need only cold water, dishwashers only hot water. Other fixtures use both.

Pressure

The pressure of water in the lines is a very important feature—too much or too little may cause problems. A good working pressure is between 30 p.s.i. (pounds per square inch) and 45 p.s.i. A pressure of 60 p.s.i. or higher may cause pipes to bang, and the joints to come loose or even break. At higher pressures the velocity of flow through the fixtures is very large. This results in unnecessary waste and loss of money. What's more, when you draw a glass of water from your faucet, the high velocity, turbulent flow makes the water seem milky.

The water pressure can be measured by mounting a pressure gauge at a faucet and taking an average of several readings during the day and the night. To get correct results make sure there is no flow of water through any line or fixture just when you are noting down the reading.

Pressures of 60 p.s.i. or higher should be reduced by installing a pressure-reducing valve on the water main. The device is inexpensive and can be easily installed with the help of the union fittings that come with it. Once installed, the valve can be set to a desired value of pressure, for instance 30 or 35 p.s.i.

Low water pressures are not as easy to correct. Unless you wish to go to the expense of installing a booster pump, building your own water tower, or ripping off all the walls and floors and changing the old pipes with new ones, you will have to live with the situation. If it is really impossible and the upper floors have practically no flow from the fixtures most of the time, you'll have to take the more drastic measures, however.

Temperature

The temperature of the hot water you get at your tub, shower, sink, or appliances is another important feature of your system. There is a thermostat control at the water heater which you may set at a desired value. The temperature is then maintained within reasonable limits as the heating elements turn on and off automatically. In some installations, there are two hot water systems. One, operating at a temperature of approximately 180°F, goes to the washing machine and the dishwasher; the other one carries a mixture of hot and cold water at about 120°F for other fixtures. There is a mixing valve at the hot water heater. Separate pipes carry the water at the two different temperatures to the fixture and the appliance branches.

In a big or long house (like a country ranch) there is a substantial run of hot water pipes between the heater and some of the fixtures, with the result that you may have to run the faucet or shower quite a while before getting really hot water. It may be advantageous, in such a case, to lay the hot water main as a continuous loop of pipeline within which hot water from the heater constantly circulates. Every outlet will then give instant hot water.

THE FIXTURES

Fixtures are devices that enable you to use water safely and conveniently. The shower, tub, toilet, sink, lavatory, dishwasher, and automatic washer all serve a specific purpose for which they are suitably designed.

All these fixtures come in different qualities and price ranges. It is a good policy not to compromise quality, when buying a fixture, just to save a few dollars—you may have to spend much more on repairs in the years to come, and face inconvenience whenever there is a breakdown. So buy the best you can afford.

Most fixtures come in three materials— vitreous china, enameled cast iron, and enameled stamped steel. The first two are very durable and give a solid ring when struck with a metal. China is the best material and usually the most expensive. Toilets come only in vitreous china. Other fixtures may be made of any of the three materials. Try to avoid stamped steel fixtures unless price is the only consideration possible. Appliances like automatic washers and dishwashers are normally made of stamped steel only, and there is nothing wrong with it. More about fixtures and their selection will be found in Chapter 12.

THE DRAINAGE SYSTEM

The basic purpose of a drainage system is to collect soil and waste water from the fixtures and convey it through the *vertical soil stack* and the *horizontal house drain* to the septic tank or street sewer (Fig. 1-3). The soil stack in a residential house is generally four inches in diameter, and extends up through the roof. The portion AB (See Fig. 1-3) is called the *main vent*. Pipes of the drainage system which carry human waste from toilets are called *soil pipes*; those carrying liquid wastes from lavatories, sinks, tubs, showers, etc., are termed *waste pipes*. The soil stack that receives flow from a toilet is called a *main soil stack*. Every house has to have at least one main soil stack. Unlike the water supply system, a

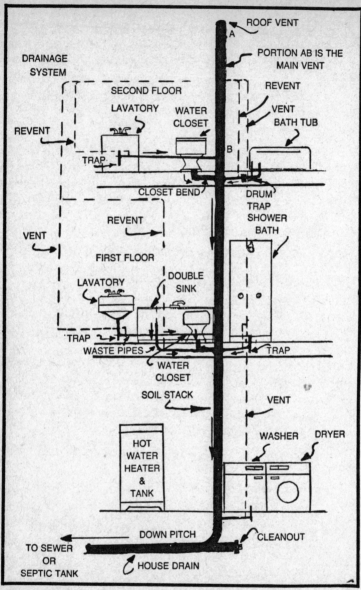

Fig. 1-3. The drainage system flows under gravity. The horizontal pipes are not truly horizontal—they have a small downward pitch. The soil and waste pipes in the figure above are shown by solid lines; vent pipes by dash lines. The long vertical pipe is the soil stack to which other pipes connect. The bathtub has a drum trap. All other fixtures have regular traps. Vent pipes prevent breakdown of water seals and entrance of sewer gases into the building. Revents are those which connect to other vents instead of to the main vent. Venting of fixtures on top floor is generally unnecessary.

drainage system flow is dictated by gravity. All the pipes except the vertical risers have a small downward pitch.

Figure 1-3 illustrates the drainage system for a two-story house with a basement. There are three basic parts of any drainage system:

1. Soil and waste pipes, including the main soil stack
2. Traps
3. Vent pipes

In Fig. 1-3 the *soil and waste pipes* connecting the fixtures to the stack, as shown by solid lines, have a slight downward pitch and are sized according to the quantity of flow they must carry. Toilets are connected to the soil stack by a large-diameter pipe called a *closet bend*.

The *trap* is a U- or S-shaped pipe which always remains full of water. Traps serve a very important function in the drainage system. Septic tanks and street sewers always contain gases produced by decomposition of sewage. These gases are foul smelling; some are poisonous and others explosive. The column of water in a trap does not allow these gases to enter the building through the drainage pipes and the fixtures. When you flush a toilet or open a faucet, water runs down the drain and replaces the column of water present in the trap. As the flow stops, the bend in the trap retains some water which acts as a seal. Toilets have a built-in trap, while all other fixtures have to be provided with traps on the drainage lines close to them. Bathtubs have drum traps.

Figure 1-4 illustrates a U-shaped trap at a lavatory. Every trap needs a vent pipe connection to maintain the water seal. The functions of a vent pipe are as follows:

1. It prevents the water seal from being siphoned out of the trap when there is simultaneous flow in connected drains.
2. It carries gases away to the atmosphere, thus relieving back pressure acting on the traps. (In the absence of a vent connection, a high gas pressure could wash the seal out into the house drain, allowing the gases to enter.)
3. It ventilates the house drainage system. Circulation of fresh air in the house drain and in the sewer prevents the lines from becoming corroded or having slime deposit.

You have probably seen the soil pipes and vent pipes sticking out at the top of your roof. That portion of the soil stack which extends above the highest fixture connection and through the roof of

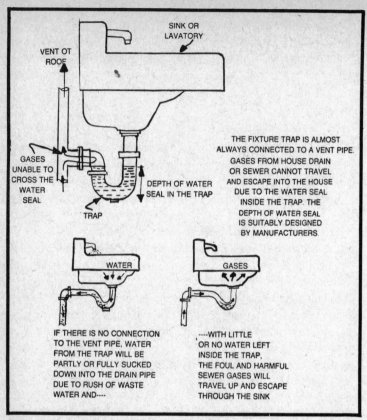

Fig. 1-4. The fixture trap is almost always connected to a vent pipe. Gases from house drain or sewer cannot travel and escape into the house due to the water seal inside the trap. The depth of water seal is suitably designed by manufacturers.

your home serves as the *main vent pipe*. According to the provisions of the National Plumbing Code, fixtures may be vented by connecting their waste pipes to the soil stack, provided they are close enough to it. This system is called *wet venting*. A tub or shower can be so vented if the distance between its trap outlet and the soil stack is 3 1/2 feet or less. If a lavatory is 2 1/2 feet or closer to the soil stack, it also qualifies for wet venting.

Separate vent pipes are required for fixtures that are farther away from the soil stack. These vent pipes either extend from the fixture through the roof to the outside atmosphere, or they are connected through horizontal pipes to the soil stack at some point higher up than the connection of the highest fixture draining into the stack. Such vent-only lines are called *revents*. The horizontal sections of the revent pipes are given a slight upward pitch from the fixture to allow condensation to drain back into the fixture. The venting of fixtures on the top floor is not necessary unless required by the local plumbing code. The sizes of the vent pipes and drain-pipes are determined by the flows they carry.

THE HOT WATER SYSTEM

The cold water pipe entering your house forks, as has been explained, with one branch leading to the cold water main and the other to the hot water heater and the storage tank. The hot water coming out of the heater and running to the fixtures is termed *domestic hot water*. It is simply the domestic cold water that has been heated. Generally, this is a completely separate system from that which heats the house, even if hot water is used in the space-heating process.

During the process of heating domestic water, the domestic hot water retains the original pressure existing in the service main, or the pressure developed by a domestic well pump. The hot water lines in your home run parallel and adjacent to the cold water lines, and are generally of the same size.

Although any metal pipe can be employed to convey hot water, copper pipe is normally used for the small sizes required in homes. Plastic pipe can only be used by communities whose local codes permit it. *CPVC* pipe (Chlorinated Polyvinyl Chloride) is the most heat-resistant plastic pipe, yet it can only be used for temperatures of water up to 180°F. The water close to the heater is at a higher temperature than 180° and gradually cools down during its run to the fixtures. It may be a good idea, therefore, to install a few lengths of copper piping next to the heater and use CPVC pipe for the rest of the run. If the hot and cold water pipes are made of different metals they should not be allowed to touch, or else they will corrode very quickly when they get wet.

Selection of Water Heaters

A water heater is an essential part of the plumbing system in most countries. It comes in two basic designs: the instantaneous or tankless type, and the storage or tank type.

Although some *instantaneous heaters* may use electricity as their heat source, most get their heat from the home's furnace. The furnace contains copper coils that are supplied with water. As the water inside the coils gets heated it runs into the hot water system of the house. There is no storage of this hot water in a storage tank, and hence such heaters are called *tankless*. If you don't draw too much hot water at a time, such heaters work very efficiently and you never run out of supply.

The rating for an instantaneous heater is reckoned in terms of gallons of hot water per minute, computed for a certain rise of temperature—generally 100°F. If a unit is rated or specified to produce four gallons per minute (g.p.m.) and raise water temperature by 100° F, this means that if the entering water has a temperature of 50° F the unit will continuously deliver water at the rate of 4 g.p.m. at 150°F. If the incoming water is cooler than 50°F you will get water at a temperature correspondingly lower than 150° F. Also, if you try to draw water at a rate higher than 4 g.p.m., the temperature of the water will go down.

The *storage* or *tank* type heaters are the ones most commonly used. They have a heating device and a storage tank with capacities of 30, 40, 50, and 60 gallons or more. The heating device consists of gas flame or electrical heating coils which are built inside the tank. The choice between a gas and an electrically operated heater depends both on the economic concerns and the location of the heater.

Electrically operated heaters can be located anywhere, and may be in contact with the outer walls. Gas-fired heaters, on the other hand, need fresh air inlets and also a flue to carry away the exhaust fumes. Building codes specify these details for gas-fired heaters as well as the separating distances from combustible material all around. The materials of construction for the walls, ceilings, and floors have to be fireproof.

The average quantity of hot water consumption in a home is indicated by the following figures, which vary with the equipment and the water temperature:

Shower	4 to 10 gallons
Bathtub	10 to 15 gallons
Automatic washer	12 to 25 gallons
Automatic dishwasher	6 to 15 gallons
Hand dishwasher	2 to 5 gallons

Because water cannot be heated instantaneously at the rate of use, some storage capacity has to be provided in the tank of the water heater. To decide what size heater you should have, the following figures may be used as a guide:

Minimum ....20 gallons
For family of four ....30 gallons (min.)
For family of four using dishwasher
    and/or automatic washer...........................50 gallons (min.)
Larger families......................................60 gallons or more

Hot water costs depend on the amount of fuel used. With increasing costs of fuel, water bills are also going up every year. Rough estimates of fuel requirements are given in Table 1-1.

The consumption of fuel in your home may be substantially different from the figures in the Table, depending on the number of family members and their use patterns. One water waster may use as much water as three normal users. The total yearly cost of fuel consumption can be found simply by multiplying the average figures in Table 1-1 by the unit cost of fuel in your area.

If your old water heater is worn out or leaking, it has probably given you long service and needs to be replaced. Before looking at a new heater, find out the particulars of your old one by referring to the specification plate attached to it. This plate will give you important data like capacity in gallons, recovery per hour, warranty-period, and BTU rating. The recovery per hour is a very important specification. Forty gallons recovery per hour for a 100-degree rise means that if cold water enters the tank at say, 35° F, then you will get, in one hour, 40 gallons of hot water at $100 + 35 = 135°$ F.

If your old hot water heater has given you enough hot water for the entire family, a new heater of the same capacity and with the same recovery value will probably be enough. But if you expect additions to the family or wish to install some more fixtures and appliances like a shower, dishwasher, or automatic washer and dryer, it will be desirable to have either a water heater of the same

Table 1-1. Fuel Consumption of Water Heaters.

Type of Fuel Used in a Hot Water Heater	Approximate Yearly Consumption for a Family of Four
Electricity	7000 kWh
Oil	300 Gallons
Natural Gas	35,000 Cubic Feet
Manufactured Gas	70,000 Cubic Feet

capacity as your old one but with larger gallons per hour recovery for 100-degree rise or one with a larger storage capacity and the same recovery as the old unit.

You also have to be careful about the recovery rate specified by some manufacturers. Instead of the usual 100° F rise, they may specify in terms of, say, 60° F only. Simple arithmatic will show that a heater with 40 gallons recovery per hour for 60° F rise is equivalent to only about 25 gallons recovery per hour for 100° F rise, and is no good or at least not as good as will appear from the claim in the specifications. So be careful of what you are getting. Obviously, a high recovery heater should cost more than a low recovery one. Products by well-known manufacturers may be a little more expensive, but they are, at least, reliable.

Water heaters are usually covered by a warranty extending for a period of 7 1/2 years to 15 years or more. The longer the warranty on your new heater, the better the heater will be. The type of lining inside a heater tank is very important. Glass linings are clean and the most durable. Copper linings also last for a pretty long time. A galvanized tank is the least expensive of all and works satifactorily only when the water supply does not contain chemicals likely to corrode the tank.

Mechanism and Working Principles of a Water Heater

Basically a hot water heater consists of the following parts (See Fig. 1-5):

1. An insulated water tank.
2. A source of energy: a gas burner or electric element encased by a cabinet.
3. Cold and hot water connections at the top with a dip tube carrying water to the bottom of the tank. (Dip tube is not necessary if the cold water inlet is at the tank bottom itself.)
4. Thermostat control, also a pilot light in the case of a gas heater.
5. Electric or gas connection.

The hot water exit leading to the building's plumbing system is always at the top because hot water, being lighter, rises; cold water remains at the bottom while in the process of being heated by the burner. Both electric and gas heaters have thermostats to control the water temperatures.

A gas water heater has a pilot light burning continuously, with its flame playing on a device known as a *thermocouple*. Should the pilot light go out at any time, the thermocouple will immediately signal the gas valve that the pilot has stopped functioning. The gas valve will shut off supply to the burner when there is no pilot flame to burn it. Normally pilot lights do not go out; but if wind blows down the vent, or if the pilot light orifice collects some lint, the pilot may fail. When this happens, clean up the orifice area with a lint brush or an old toothbrush, and relight the pilot. Very often the failure is due to a defective thermocouple, in which case a replacement part should be obtained with the same exact length of tube. Detailed installation instructions come with thermocouples.

There are *baffles* inside the flue running from the burner to the vent at the top of the tank. The vents convey the flue gases to a point outside the building. The baffles catch much of the escaping heat and transfer it to the interior of the tank to provide additional energy for heating water.

All water heaters have a safety feature called a *relief valve*. These come in two types: the pressure type and the temperature-cum-pressure type. Mounted at the top of the tank, these valves open up and let cold water run into the top of the tank (where the hottest water is contained) if the temperature rises to a dangerous level (more than 200° F). The valve is always set at safe, predetermined valued of pressure (around 70 p.s.i.) and temperature. If there is no relief valve or if the existing one has developed some defect, dangerously high temperatures and pressures can build up leading in some cases to explosions. Install a relief valve if your water heater does not have one.

There is always some overflow from the water heater (maybe a couple of gallons daily) due to the expansion of cold water as it heats up. A drain line should convey this water to a sump or house drain. Don't run the line outside, however, because it might freeze during winters and stop functioning. All tanks have a magnesium rod (an anode) that prevents corrosion of parts that may not have been corrosion-proofed during manufacture. Faulty anodes can be easily replaced after opening a plug at the top of the tank.

Electric water heaters have bimetal thermostats to maintain preset levels of temperature. The element automatically goes off and on. You can adjust the thermostat to a desired temperature; in some cases, though, the power will have to be turned off and the access panel removed before you can work at the dial of the thermostat unit. Normal temperature setting is between 140° F and 150° F. Rather than indicating the exact temperature, some thermostats just have settings for warm, normal, and hot.

In a large house or a long ranch, water has to run a considerable distance before reaching fixtures at the farthest end. The thermostat in these houses should be set at the temperature desired at the fixtures, plus one degree per linear foot of pipeline between the heater and the fixtures. Dishwashers and laundry units require a temperature of 140° F to do an efficient job.

The heating elements of an electric water heater are either contained within the tank itself, with connecting bolts going onto a flange outside, or they are wrapped around on the outer surface of the tank. There are usually two sets of elements and thermostats—one located towards the top and the other towards the bottom. As hot water is drawn out of the tank, the water temperature inside the tank starts to fall, and the upper thermostat kicks in its element. When the temperature goes up to the dial setting, this upper element shuts off. At the same time, the lower element starts, since the water lower down must still be heated up. The two elements are interlocked so that the lower element does not start until the upper one has gone off. After the water in the lower portion attains the desired temperature, the lower element also shuts off.

Heaters manufactured by some good companies often have a safety interlock device which automatically turns off power to both the elements should water be overheated. To reset the device, open the front access panel after shutting off all power, and push a red button you will see there. Then, to verify if the heater is actually overheating, you may run hot water from a faucet close by, and measure its temperature with a thermometer. If the temperature is lower than that of the thermostat setting, and the safety device again shuts off the supply of power, there must either be a malfunction in the tank or some other problem which needs to be investigated.

Installing a Hot Water Heater

Installation of hot water heaters mainly consists of making connections to the following: the cold water line, the hot water line, and the gas line or electric outlet. Figure 1-5 illustrated the installation details of a natural gas water heater. Before starting the installation, make sure that the building code in your community permits homeowners to install heaters. Some codes require that the job be done by a licensed plumber only.

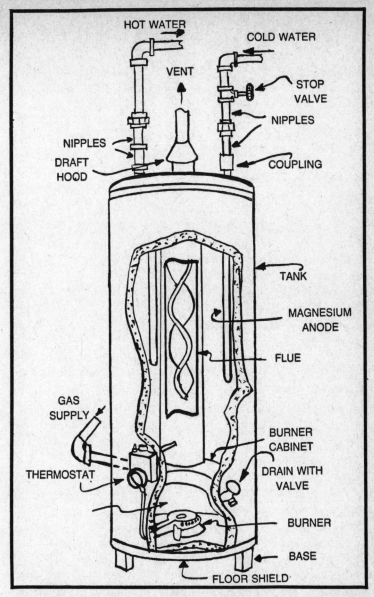

Fig. 1-5(a). To install a new gas water heater connect the cold water, hot water, and gas lines. Use old safety valve if in good condition, or else get a new one. Install a sediment trap on the gas line. This will prevent sediment deposits which may lead to thermostat malfunction. Follow manufacturer's instructions for the installation including the start of pilot light and the burner. Make sure the tank is not hanging in the air from pipelines instead of sitting on the floor. This may break the pipe joints and start leakage.

The following pipes and fittings will be required for the installation shown in Fig. 1-5:

1 Coupling
3 Nipples
2 Unions
1 Gate Valve
1 Tee
48 inch length of 3/4 inch galvanized pipe.

In addition, the gas supply line may need some pipe length and fittings if it is very old and rusted. Also, the flue line will need a galvanized furnace pipe and an elbow of 3 inch size for a 30 gallon recovery heater, or 4 inch size for a 40 to 50 gallon recovery heater.

First disconnect and remove the old water heater. Close the gate valve on the cold water line at the top, and attach a garden hose to the drain valve located towards the bottom. Let the water run out till the tank empties. If you break loose the union on the hot water line and let air in, water will run out much faster. Disconnect the hot water and cold water lines, and the gas line, by shutting off the gas valve, and disconnecting the union. Take off the flue pipes. The old water heater is now completely disconnected.

Place the new heater in the correct position and connect the cold and hot water lines using the various pipes and fittings tabulated previously. Pipe joint compound should be used at the fittings to provide watertight joints. If the old safety valve is in good condition, you don't need to buy a new one. Also, if the pipe and fittings in the gas line of the old heater are in good condition, with the insides practically free of rust or scale deposits, you don't have to change them either.

The function of a *sediment trap* is to prevent scale and rust from traveling to the thermostat and depositing there. Such deposits are likely to interfere with proper functioning of the thermostat. If there was no sediment trap on the gas line before, it will be a good idea to install one. You can easily make such a trap by using a 1/2 inch cap, a 1/2 inch × 6 inch nipple and a 1/2 inch T. After connecting the gas line, install the flue line. The installation procedure varies with different designs put out by various manufacturers. Before starting the job, it will be advisable to familarize yourself with the instruction sheet that will come with your new unit.

To light the burner on a gas heater, first turn the pilot knob and the thermostat off, and then turn the pilot knob to the point marked

Fig. 1-5(b). Always buy a water heater with high recovery ratio and long warranty period. To deal with common malfunctions, refer to the troubleshooting chart at the end of the chapter. This photo shows a gas water heater. Courtesy Bradford-White Corp.

with the word *pilot*. Light a match and hold it at the pilot, keeping the red button depressed for half a minute. Now release the red button and see if the pilot light remains on. If so, turn the pilot knob to the *on* position. If the pilot goes out, light it again. Finally, adjust the thermostat dial to its normal position. This will ignite the burner. Normal setting corresponds to 140° F.

The hot water heater should not hang in the air from the hot and cold water lines without resting on the floor. Such a situation will cause excessive stress on the pipelines and may break open the joints.

It is possible to use two or more tanks to heat the water by connecting them in series (Fig. 1-6). This will provide more heating capacity. The tanks, which need not be of the same size or capacity, should be interchanged at least every year.

To facilitate this, use union connections. The first tank (the one with the inlet for a cold water line) will be doing the maximum amount of heating because its temperature will be falling down first.

It is also possible to connect two heaters in parallel provided they are similar in capacity and recovery rate. If dissimilar in size, the net hot water capacity will only be equal to that of the smaller tank.

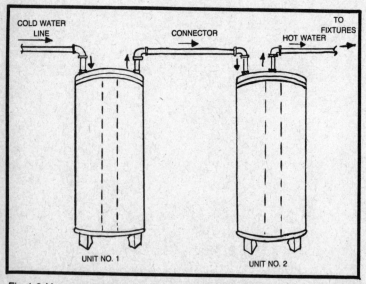

Fig. 1-6. You may obtain larger hot water capacity if necessary by connecting two hot water heaters in series. The tanks need not be of same size or even same recovery ratio. Unit No. 1 does most of the heating. Provide union joints on the lines so you may interchange the positions of the heaters every year or so.

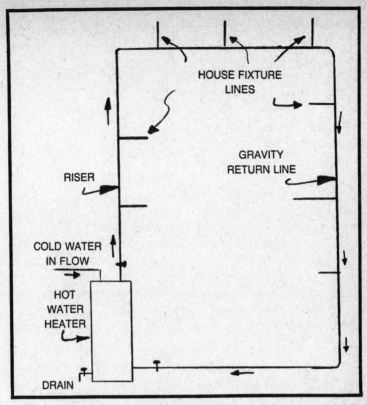

Fig. 1-7. Adding a gravity return line to the hot water system will provide good circulation and instant hot water at the faucets with no wastage. You won't have to run the faucet or fixture and wait till hot water arrives.

It is a common experience to have to run a hot water faucet, shower, or other fixture for a few moments before really hot water arrives. The farther away the fixture, the longer you have to wait; meanwhile the not-so-hot water is being wasted. This situation can be prevented if the *upfeed and gravity system* is used for the layout of hot water lines. A riser pipe takes the water up as usual to the various fixtures, but, in addition, there is a gravity return pipe through which the cooler (less hot) water returns (Fig. 1-7). In fact there is a constant circulation of water from and to the water heater which assures instant hot water at the fixtures, and stops usual wastage. The best time to install the upfeed and gravity system is during the construction of a house.

Another method commonly employed to reduce the hot-water waiting period is to wrap the pipes with an insulating tape that uses

Table 1-2. Usual Malfunctions of Water Heaters and Suggested Repairs*

MALFUNCTION	PROBABLE CAUSE	SUGGESTED REPAIRS
Abnormally long recovery time	Calcium deposits in the heating element	Take out the heating element and remove the calcium with vinegar and a brush
Water collects under the tank	1. Condensation may be forming on the heater surface	1. It is nothing to worry about. Collect drip in a pan.
	2. Tank may have developed a hole	2. Start looking for a new heater—stop the leak temporarily with a boiler plug.
	3. Leakage at plumbing connections	3. Repair as necessary
	4. Element may be leaking	4. Replace the element.
No hot water reaching the fixtures	1. The circuit breaker may have tripped or a fuse may have blown out	1. Reset the circuit breaker or replace the fuse. If it goes out again, take the help of a professional.
	2. Thermostat may be defective	2. Replace the thermostat
	3. Calcium build-up on heating element (electric heater)	3. Heating element should be removed and cleaned.
	4. Upper heating element burned out	4. Replace upper heating element.
	5. Thermocouple malfunctioning (gas heater)	5. Check pilot light, clean the orifice. If pilot does not stay lit, thermocouple is defective; replace it.
Water at fixtures not hot enough	1. The temperature setting at the thermostat may be low	1. Set within the normal range of 140° to 150° F.
	2. Capacity of water heater tank insufficient.	2. Get a unit of larger capacity or add another one in series.
	3. Lower heating element may have burned out (electric heater)	3. Replace defective element
	4. Dip tube may have developed a hole.	4. Remove dip tube and install a new one.

Table 1-2. (continued)

Usual Malfunctions of Water Heaters and Suggested Repairs*

MALFUNCTION	PROBABLE CAUSE	SUGGESTED REPAIRS
Steam coming out with hot water	1. Thermostat not functioning due to stuck contact points (electric heater) 2. Burner does not shut off 3. Thermostat set at a very high temperature.	1. Replace shorted or burned out terminals 2. Set thermostat lower; if it still fails to shut off, replace thermostat. 3. Set thermostat at normal setting of 140° to 150° F.

*NOTE: ALWAYS SHUT OFF POWER BEFORE STARTING REPAIRS.
IF YOU DON'T FEEL CONFIDENT, CALL AN EXPERT FOR REPAIRS.

aluminum foil and prevents heat loss. Again, this is best done during construction.

More Hot Water For The Money

If suddenly your gas or electric bill goes up and you feel that the hot water heater system may be a fault, check for possible leaks in the lines. Sometimes leaks within the walls or under the floors may go undetected indefinitely. If any hot water faucet is leaking, the loss may be considerable. Repair the faucets as explained in Chapter 8.

There are several tricks that can be used to actually increase the quantity of hot water available from a water heater, or to economize its use. One very common method is to use a *mixing valve* at a tankless water heater. This valve connects the cold water inflow line and the hot water outflow line of the heater. The temperature of outgoing hot water is reduced by the mixing process, and more water is thus available at this lower temperature than would be available at the higher temperature in the absence of the mixing valve. Such valves are seldom used on tank-type heaters unless their outflow temprature is 180° F rather than the normal 140° F.

Another method for obtaining more hot water from the same heater consists of *preheating*. An uninsulated boiler may be placed ahead of the water heater on the incoming cold water line. The air in the cellar, being at a higher temperature than the incoming cold water, heats the water in the uninsulated boiler by a few degrees.

The same result can be achieved by installing heating coils on the roofs of buildings in localities with hot climates; the cold water gets heated to some extent before it enters the water heater, and there is a resultant saving in the operation of water heaters. In other words, more hot water is obtained for the same amount of money.

Water Heater Maintenance and Repairs

Water heaters, unless they get very old, do not usually give much trouble. Also, they are covered with a warranty which may run up to 15 years. As mentioned before, it is good policy to pay a little more and buy a heater made by a well-known manufacturer. A warranty is good only if the manufacturer is in business.

The problems, when they do arise, often cannot be easily handled by a do-it-yourselfer; you will have to decide whether to do the repairs yourself, or seek outside help. One thing that you should not attempt to repair is the burner on a gas heater. It takes special repair equipment and very great care to avoid explosions and fire hazards. If you are convinced the problem involves the burner, check with your utility company for suggestions.

If you have an electric heater, always turn off the power before you tackle any repair job like changing a burned out heating element. Power should also be shut off if you are temporarily stopping the cold water supply to your home. If the heating elements remain on, and the water level goes down, the elements are likely to burn out.

The most disturbing problem occurs when you don't get any hot water at all. If you have an electric heater, a circuit breaker switch may have tripped, or a fuse may have blown (in older installations). Replace the fuse or reset the switch on the circuit breaker. If there is a short circuit in the element, it should be located and corrected. Examine the wires also; a loose wire may be causing the short circuit. If you don't discover any short circuiting, the possibility is that one or both heating elements have burned out. After shutting off the water supply and power, empty the tank by opening the drain valve. Take out and examine the elements. If they show large amounts of calcium deposits, clean them with vinegar and a soft brush. Test by reinstalling them. If they still don't work, get and install replacements. If your heater has two elements, one at the top and the other at the bottom, it is rather unlikely that both will go out simultaneously, however.

If you have a gas-operated water heater, and you are getting no hot water, it is possible the pilot light has gone out. Check the gas unit and ignite the pilot if it is not burning. Also make sure the valve is not *off*. Turn the temperature control to its maximum, and fully open a nearby hot water tap. If the burner does not start in a while, it indicates a clogged or defective thermostat. Slide out the control knob and after opening up the screws from the front of the thermostat unit, take it out. If it looks corroded or clogged with dirt, blow some air into it with a plastic squirt bottle. If there is no dust or foreign matter present, most likely the thermostat is defective and needs replacement. Get a new one with the same specifications as the old one. Screw it in and slide the control knob on. The burner should now function properly. Sometimes you may hear funny noises coming out of the tank. These may be caused by a buildup of steam or sediment deposits. The steam buildup will subside if you just turn down the thermostat to the normal setting of 140° F to 150° F. Make sure the thermostat is actually functioning; a defective thermostat may fail to shut off the elements or the burner, and this failure may result in overheating of water. Turn off the thermostat completely and observe the elements or the burner. If they have not gone out, the thermostat is malfunctioning and should be replaced. In an electric heater, the thermostat may fail due to a short circuit. Check it as explained before. If the unit has developed short circuiting inside it, get a replacement unit and install it.

Sediment deposits will build up in a water heater tank if it is not drained regularly. Every other month, shut off the water supply and power, and open the drain valve that is located towards the bottom. Check the flow—if it is clear, close the valve and restore the water supply. In most cases you will find the water is dirty in the beginning but clears up in a few minutes. After you start getting clean water, shut off the drain valve and restart the heater. After running this draining procedure a few times over a period of several months, you will be able to determine at what intervals the cleaning should be done. The amount of deposit depends on the amount of sediment the water carries, and may change from season to season. A regular cleaning program will insure efficient working, as well as elimination of sediment-connected noises.

Sediment deposits in a water tank may lead to discolored water flow from the hot water faucets and fixture taps. Also, when the magnesium anode (Fig. 1-5) gets corroded over a long period of time, it may give out particles that cause the discoloration. If this has happened, replace the anode with one of equivalent size and length. The recovery rate of a water heater is reduced when sediment builds up in it. Drain the tank if you observe a marked drop in the recovery rate.

You should always keep the owner's manual that comes with the unit when you purchase it. Some of the troubles and defects are peculiar only to certain designs, and the owner's manual helps in dealing with them. Most water heaters, however, have a long life and will seldom give you much trouble until they get very old. If your unit is pretty old and you notice a leak somewhere, start looking for a new unit—apparently the inside of the tank has corroded. If you repair a leak at one spot, another will probably spring at some other location. To keep the heater in working condition temporarily, insert a *boiler plug* in the hole and turn it down tightly.

Water Supply Sources: Wells and Pumps

Chapter 2

Wells and Pumps

If you live in a city or a suburb, your water supply will most probably come from the supply mains owned by a water company or the water department of your municipality. In localities like Hartfor, Conn., and Boston Mass., the water organizations cover a large area and go by the name of Metropolitan Districts. The sources of water may be surface runoff from controlled watersheds collected in lakes and reservoirs, or deep wells that pump water from undergound, or a combination of the two. The surface water quality varies, and requires purification and sterilization to various degrees. In most cases, the water is filtrated, and chemicals like fluorides, lime, and chlorine are added. (Chlorine is provided to destroy pathogenic bacteria.) Water from the street main enters your house through the service pipe and goes to the network of distribution pipes feeding the various fixtures like bathtub, toilet, and sink.

DOMESTIC WATER REQUIREMENTS

In order to determine the sizes of the pipes leading to fixtures, the *unit method* is used. A unit is one cubic foot of water flowing per minute, which comes to approximately 7 1/2 gallons per minute. Table 2-1 gives the unit values for various fixtures as determined during actual tests by the Uniform Plumbing Code Committee.

Not all the fixtures will be running simultaneously. To find the maximum flow expected at any instant in your main supply pipe, multiply the total number of units by a suitable factor from Table 2-2 to give the maximum flow rate.

Table 2-1. Fixture Unit Values.

NAME OF FIXTURE	UNIT VALUE
Toilet	6
Bathtub	2
Shower	2
Lavatory or washbasin	1
Slop sink	3
Kitchen sink	2
Laundry tray set	2
Clothes washer	3
Dishwasher	3
Bathroom group with	8
toilet, lavatory, tub, and shower	

To illustrate the use of the unit method, let us take an actual example of a home and work out the demand. Table 2-3 shows the compilation:

The total of 127 1/2 gallons per minute is the maximum flow. Not all the fixtures will be running simultaneously, however, so a suitable multiplying factor from Table 2-2 (0.25 for residential homes) should be used. Accordingly, the probable flow will be 127 1/2 × 0.25 = 32 gallons per minute.

Total Number Of Fixtures	Multiplying Factor to Give Simultaneous Flow
1 to 5	1.0 to 0.5
6 to 50	0.5 to 0.25
More than 50	0.25 to 0.10

Table 2-2. Flow/Fixture Relationship.

Table 2-3. Determining Maximum Flow.

Number of Fixtures	Units	Maximum Flow in Gallons Per Minute (Units × 7½)
1 Toilet 6	6	45
1 Bathtub 2	2	15
1 Lavatory 1	1	7 1/2
1 Kitchen sink 2	2	15
1 Dishwasher 3	3	22 1/2
1 Clothes Washer 3	3	22 1/2
Total 17	17	127 1/2

PIPE SIZES

Sizes of the water mains, branches, and individual fixture supply lines depend on the probable flows through them. From a practical standpoint, some minimum sizes for various services have been fixed, and pipes smaller than these sizes are not employed. Table 2-4 gives the flows that different lengths of galvanized and copper pipes can carry when pressure at the water main is 50 pounds per square inch (an average value). Flows will be somewhat different for other pressures.

Table 2-4. Flow in Gallons Per Minute Carried by Various Lengths and Sizes of G.I. and Copper Pipes with 50 P.S.I. Pressure at Water Main.

Size/Length	20′	40′	60′	100′	140′	200′
3/8″ G.I.	10	9	7	6	5	4
1/2″ G.I.	-	16	13	10	8	7
3/4″ G.I.	-	34	28	21	18	15
1″ G.I.	-	65	57	40	33	27
1/2″ COPPER	-	12	9	7	6	5
5/8″ COPPER	-	22	16	12	10	8
3/4″ COPPER	-	34	28	20	16	14
1″ COPPER	-	75	60	45	36	30

Lastly, Table 2-5 gives the sizes of galvanized iron and copper pipes most commonly used in small homes when there is medium pressure in the water main—30 to 60 p.s.i.

WELLS

If you live in a rural area or a locality that is not served by a community water system, you must install a private well and keep it in good shape. There are two types of wells: a shallow or dug well, and a deep well.

Shallow Wells

While the supply to both types of wells comes from ground water, there is one basic difference between the two. The shallow well does not go down very deep; in some cases it may go down only 15 feet to 25 feet. These wells collect water that has seeped through the subsoil or the uppermost layer of soil to form what is generally called the *ground water table*. Rarely ever will a shallow well be dug through an impervious stratum or rock layer. Also, because the well is shallow, there is limited percolation or filtering of the water through the soil, and the water, therefore, does not undergo much natural purification. The water quality will depend on the location. In open rural areas with practically no source of contamination, the quality will be sufficient.

Table 2-5. Sizes of G.I. Pipe and Copper Tubing Commonly Used in Small Homes.

Purpose of Supply	G. I. Pipeline	Copper Tube Between Fixture and Cut-Off Valve
Service line in the house	3/4″	—
Toilet, Flush Tank	1/2″	3/8″
Toilet, Flush Valve	1″	1″
Lavatory	1/2″	3/8″
Bath or Shower	1/2″	1/2″
Kitchen Sink	1/2″-3/4″	1/2″
Dishwasher	1/2″-3/4″	1/2″
Washing Machine/Laundry Tray	1/2″-3/4″	1/2″
Service Sink	1/2″-3/4″	1/2″
Water Heater	1/2″	1/2″
Drinking Fountain	1/2″	3/8″
Sill Cock/Wall Hydrant	1/2″	1/2″

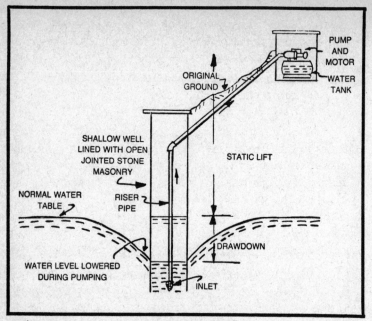

Fig. 2-1. Shallow well may give good quality water in areas with no sources of contamination nearby. A shallow well pump will lift water through a total head of about 25 feet, which is the sum of the actual static lift, the draw-down during pumping, and the head loss in pipes and fittings.

Shallow well pumps are used to draw water from such shallow wells. The pumps can lift water through about 25 feet, which includes the static lift, the head loss in the pipes and fittings, and also the maximum draw down in the well during pumping, plus seasonal variation in the water level (Fig. 2-1).

Deep Wells

Deep wells are required in cities and other localities where there are possible sources of contamination in the upper stratum of soil. These wells are drilled down to a water-bearing stratum, called an *aquifer*, which furnishes a sufficient quantity of water when pumped. The aquifer is overlain by at least one stratum of impervious material that prevents contaminated water in the water table of the top soil from seeping through. Depth of a deep well may vary from 75 feet to 300 feet or more, depending on the locality. In some places, like in the Southwest, you may drill down several thousand feet and still strike little or no water. In many instances, more than one aquifer has to be tapped to furnish sufficient water.

Drilling is a highly technical and professional job best done by an experienced contractor who uses a drilling rig. Depending on the type of soil or rock encountered, the contractor may use one or more of the following methods:

1. Percussion method
2. Rotary drilling
3. Water jet drilling

A wrought iron casing, 2 to 8 inches in diameter, is driven throughout the depth of the well. This casing prevents contaminated water from entering the soil. When several aquifers are tapped, perforated pipe surrounded with mesh screen is substituted for the blind pipe over the runs through each aquifer. If found necessary, a screen is installed at the end of the casing. Figure 2-2 illustrates two drilled wells with pumps installed at different locations—above

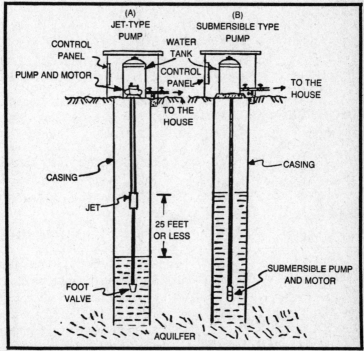

Fig. 2-2. Deep wells go down to a water-bearing stratum. The pump may be of the jet type or submersible type. Jet type pumps are located at ground level. Submersible pumps have their controls outside the well. The casing consisting of wrought-iron pipe may be from 2 inches to 8 inches in diameter.
Note—Often the pump and/or water tank may be located away from the well, say in the utility room or basement of the house. Pipes from the jet or submersible pump will run from top of well to this location.

ground in one, and under water in the other. The submersible pumps are more efficient and more dependable.

PUMP TYPES

In water supply systems for buildings, pumps are used for raising water from wells into the storage tank or directly to the distribution system. Booster pumps may be necessary when you have a municipal or utility water supply which provides water at low pressures and you wish to have better pressure at your fixtures—particularly on the upper floors.

Wells are fitted with the following types of pumps:

Shallow Well Pumps

1. Reciprocating or piston type
2. Centrifugal type
3. Centrifugal jet type

Medium-to-Deep Well Pumps

1. Centrifugal jet type
2. Submersible type

Reciprocating or Piston-Type Pump

You have probably seen the old hand-operated piston pumps. As the handle is pushed down and pulled up, a piston moves inside a cylinder. There are two valves, one at the bottom and another at the top. During the upward stroke, a vacuum is created which opens the lower valve and draws water up from the well (Fig. 2-3). In the downward stroke, the upper valve opens and water flows out. The cycle is then repeated with each successive set of strokes, and more and more water is lifted up and out.

The automatic, shallow-well piston pump has a double-acting piston and four valves. During each stroke, water is both drawn up and pushed out; this results in a steady flow. These pumps also have the usual automatic and safety features, and an air chamber along with a storage tank (Fig. 2-4).

Straight Centrifugal Pump for Shallow Wells

This pump has only one moving part, a fan-type blade called an *impeller*. The size depends on the required flow and the total head. As the impeller is turned by the motor at speeds of 1350, 1750, or a larger number of revolutions per minute, water is sucked up from the well and delivered to the outlet pipe. Normally, centrifugal pumps cannot suck air from the pipes because their parts don't fit tightly.

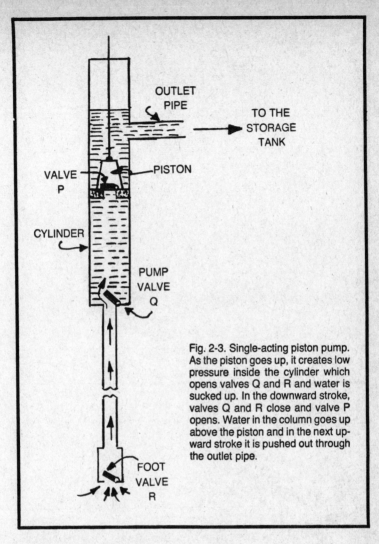

Fig. 2-3. Single-acting piston pump. As the piston goes up, it creates low pressure inside the cylinder which opens valves Q and R and water is sucked up. In the downward stroke, valves Q and R close and valve P opens. Water in the column goes up above the piston and in the next upward stroke it is pushed out through the outlet pipe.

Priming is needed, which consists of filling the suction pipe with water before the motor is started. Specially designed self-priming pumps are also available at somewhat higher prices. They have an impeller constantly immersed in water contained in the chamber; so long as this water does not disappear by evaporation or other causes, the pump quickly primes itself when the motor is turned on (Fig. 2-5A). Air inside the pipe bubbles through the chamber full of water and is gradually driven out of the system. The pump then starts working at full speed (Fig. 2-5B).

SHALLOW-WELL
PISTON PUMP

HORIZONTAL TANK

Fig. 2-4. Shallow Well piston pump and storage tank.

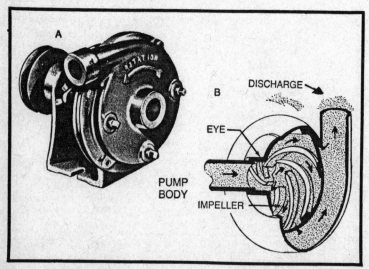

A

B

DISCHARGE

EYE

PUMP
BODY

IMPELLER

Fig. 2-5. Working pump.

Centrifugal Jet Pump for Shallow Wells

Where higher flows and increased pressures are desired at a shallow well, a centrifugal jet pump is used. Figure 2-6 illustrates a shallow-well centrifugal jet assembly. It consists of a centrifugal pump with an added feature, a water jet arrangement consisting of:

1. A restriction to capture some of the water from the discharge end of the pump, and to bring it back towards the inlet side.
2. A small-diameter nozzle in the water passage to increase the velocity of this water.
3. An expanding *venturi flume* (a small pipe length of increasing diameter, like an increaser) through which this high velocity water passes, causing suction pressures which drag an additional quantity of water from the well pipe.

There is thus an appreciable increase in the flow due to the jet action, which results both in higher gallons per hour and increased water pressure at a shallow well. If the jet arrangement is added to an existing standard centrifugal pump, it can be used to draw water from a medium-depth well going to, say, 75 feet below ground.

Centrifugal Jet Pump for Deep Wells

The principle for these pumps is the same as that for a shallow well arrangement, only the nozzle and venturi are located lower down

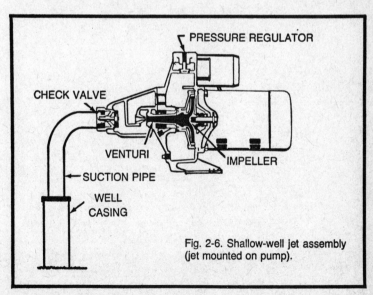

Fig. 2-6. Shallow-well jet assembly (jet mounted on pump).

49

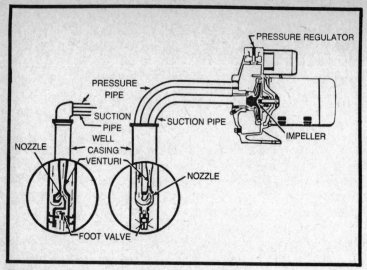

Fig. 2-7. Deep-well jet assembly (jet installed in well).

in the well pipe, and a foot valve is provided at the bottom of the venturi. Figure 2-7 shows the details. The arrows pointing downwards in the circles indicate the flow back which runs from the outlet end of the impeller, and enters the nozzle at the lower end of the venturi. From here this high-velocity jet travels upward. Due to its high velocity, it has pressures much lower than atmospheric pressure. This disparity causes water from the well to rush up. It is this additional water which adds to the overall flow thrown out by the impeller, and raises its pressure. This arrangement works very satisfactorily for wells down to a depth of 110 feet.

For deeper wells (down to 260 feet) *multi-stage jet pumps*, similar to the one described in the previous paragraph, are used. A single shaft carries several impellers which create pressures as high as 40 to 60 pounds per square inch. This additional pressure causes water to be sucked up from greater depths. Such pumps are not very efficient if used at shallow or medium depth wells; they produce higher pressures rather than increased flows.

The only moving part in a centrifugal pump with or without the jet system is the impeller. It can be easily repaired or replaced as need be, since the pump is located above ground (as was shown in Fig. 2-2A). This is the major advantage over the submersible system (Fig. 2-2B), in which the pump is located deep down. The jet system itself will seldom give any trouble. If it does, you can easily pull up the flexible plastic pipes by which it is suspended, and do the repairs. The jet unit is connected to the pump above ground through two pipes; one brings down the water and feeds it into the jet and the venturi, while the other one leads up from the venturi back to the impeller. If at any time the plastic pipe gets damaged, replacement will not cost much.

Submersible Pump

Though the initial cost of a submersible pump is higher than that of a jet type, the submersible pump is coming more and more into use. It can pump water from wells as deep as 500 feet; it requires only one flexible plastic pipe for suspension; and, being located inside the well casing, it needs little space above ground. Only the electrical control box and a tank must be placed above ground. These can be accommodated in a corner of the utility room or kitchen. Also, you don't even hear the pump running, so there is no noise pollution! Basically, it consists of a long, thin centrifugal pump with a motor connected to the lower end of the supply pipe. Being immersed in water, it needs no priming. Submersible pumps can also be used for wells as shallow as 20 feet. The integral pump and motor look like a cartridge. They can go within casings of 4-inch diameter or larger (Fig. 2-8). The multi-stage centrifugal pump gives a reliable quantity of flow at very satisfactory pressures.

Booster Pumps

A booster pump (Fig. 2-9) is used to improve pressures in a home water supply system, in a sprinkler system, in a line leading to an annex or barn, or anywhere else needed. It is fitted on the main supply line or on the particular branch where pressures are low. The usual design features an integral motor and an automatic flow switch. As the demand for water builds up and pressure falls down, the motor kicks in automatically.

SELECTION AND INSTALLATION OF PUMPS

If your new well has enough of a water supply, determined by the drilling contractor during actual tests, the only other thing you need to deliver the maximum necessary flow is the correct pumping equipment. As already discussed, the water requirement is based on the total number of fixtures and their flow rates. It is reckoned in gallons per hour (GPH). Minimum recommended pump capacity for an individual home is 540 GPH.

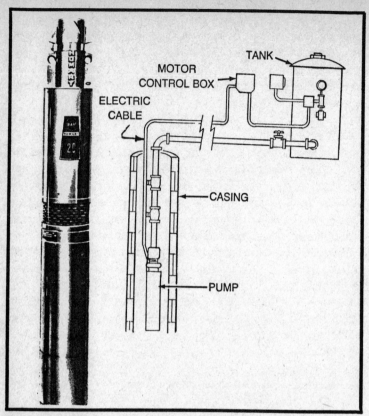

Fig. 2-8. Submersible pumps, though somewhat more expensive, can draw water from depths of 500 feet. The integral pump and motor, shaped like a cartridge, stay within the casing and require no overground space. The control box can be placed in the kitchen or the utility room. There is no pump noise outside.

If the well has limited water supply, you should not use a high-power pump that would dry it up in minutes. A well driller will be able to tell you the yield of a well. When the pump starts, there is always a *drawdown*—a dropping down of the water level inside the well. The pump runs intermittently; as soon as the storage tank fills to its maximum level, the pump shuts off automatically. Water level in the well then gradually returns to its normal level as more and more water seeps into it from the aquifer. The drawdown should not expose the intake foot-valve, or the pump will lose its *prime*. If it runs dry for some time, it will seriously damage itself. In short, pump capacity has to be determined so that drawdown stays within reasonable limits.

Selection of the type of pump to be used depends on its individual features and your specific requirements. If space is limited and you cannot construct a pump-house, or if you want completely silent operation, the obvious choice is a submersible pump (although it will cost more than other types). On the other hand, if you have ample space where the pump-house can be constructed, or if the pumps can be located in the basement without any noise problem, use a centrifugal jet pump and save some money. Again, if the depth of the well is more than 25 feet, you should get a medium or deep well pump and not experiment with a shallow well type.

Plastic pipe is easy to work with, so you should select a pump that can use plastic pipe. Most submersible and centrifugal jet pumps will be able to do so. If you are doing the installation yourself, read the pump manufacturer's instructions and use the recommended pipe sizes only. Make all the joints watertight. Use only those clamps which go with the type of pipe you are using.

If installing a centrifugal jet system, you will notice that the diameter of one pipe leading from the pump to the jet is larger than that of the other. Make connections to the correct size fittings at both ends. The length of tailpipe between the jet and the foot-valve should not be more than that suggested by the manufacturer in the instruction booklet.

Be careful not to damage the plastic pipe when lowering the submersible pump cartridge or the jet of the centrifugal pump into

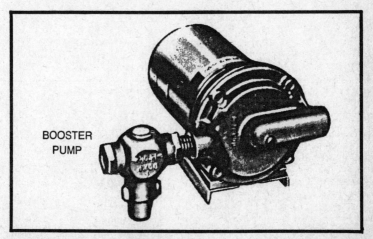

Fig. 2-9. A booster pump can be fitted on a main or branch line to improve water pressures. The motor automatically kicks in as the consumption of water increases, resulting in a lower pressure.

the well. Use a large bending radius and don't let the pipe strike against the sharp edges of the casing.

After the installation is complete, prime the pump fully before starting, following priming instructions given in the instruction booklet. After you start the motor, a few minutes will elapse before all the entrapped air is driven out and the inlet pipe starts running fully.

Table 2-6. Well-Pumping Machinery Troubleshooting Chart.

Malfunction	Probable Cause	Suggested Cure
No water pressure in tank after a very cold night	1. Slim tube to pressure switch has frozen and switch is not working at low pressure.	1. Heat the copper tube by flame from a candle or cigarette lighter.
	2. Pipe between pump and tank has frozen.	2. Thaw pipe as explained in Chapter 5.
Pump starting and stopping very frequently.	Tank is waterlogged with no air cushion at top due to:	
	1. Loose and leaky fitting at the top (test by applying soap suds solution)	1. Open fitting, apply Teflon tape and retighten.
	2. Defective air regulator or stuck part.	2. Tap air regulator lightly with a small wrench to free the stuck part. If air regulator is damaged, repair or replace it.
		Re-establish air space at top by draining off some water from tank.
Though no water is being used, the pump keeps starting and stopping at long intervals during the night.	1. Leak in plastic pipe.	1. Remove sanitary well cap and inspect the pipe. If found defective, replace.
	2. Foot-valve leaking	2. Watch for a day or two. If problem persists, take it out and have it repaired.

Once normal running starts, your storage tank will get filled in a few minutes, and the pressure will build up. The motor will then shut off automatically.

To cut down noise at above-ground installations, attach the pump base to the floor with bolts that have rubber washers above and below their holes. Also, provide rubber ferrules inside the holes. You will have to use bolts slightly smaller than the ones that came with the unit. To protect the upper set of rubber washers use metal washers at the tops. To prevent pump vibration noise from being transmitted to the water supply pipes, use a couple of feet of plastic pipe between the pump and the supply pipes.

If the capacity of the well is satisfactory and the pumping equipment has been properly designed and installed, there is no reason that the system should not work practically trouble-free for a long time to come.

PROBLEMS RELATED TO WELLS AND PUMPS

Minor problems will sometimes arise at the pumping machinery and the water tank. These can be tackled with a little common sense and some experience. Table 2-6 contains a troubleshooting chart which will prove helpful.

Private Sewage Disposal System: Septic Tanks, Disposal Fields, and Seepage Pits

Chapter 3

Private Sewage Disposal System:
Septic Tanks, Disposal Fields, and Seepage Pits

There is a continuous movement of population in the U.S., and the expansion of existing sewerage systems can hardly keep pace with the ever-increasing demands on their capacity. The individual septic tank & soil absorption system continues to be a very important method for sewage disposal in areas where it is feasible and acceptable to the authorities.

Improper or careless disposal of human excreta may result in serious health hazards like the spread of typhoid, diarrhea, dysentery, and infectious hepatitis. Such diseases soon spread from one person to another when there is fecal contamination of food and water supply. To safeguard against such epidemics, wastes should be disposed of in such way that:

1. The drinking water in the wells or pipelines does not get polluted.
2. The facility is not open to rodents, insects, and other disease carriers which, after picking up the disease bacteria, may contaminate our food and water supply.
3. The wastes do not pollute the waters of streams, beaches, lakes, or shellfish breeding grounds. If any of these clean waters are used for drinking or recreational purposes, the waste disposal system should be located far away from them.

4. The disposal ares is not accessible to children and pets.
5. The system is in conformance with the local and state health codes.

All these requirements are best met by properly designed sewerage and sewage treatment systems. In the absence of these systems, the septic tank and disposal system is the only alternative left to an individual homeowner. The septic tank system, too, can give good service if the soil, the water table (or level) and the depth-to-ledge (the distance from the surface to ledge rock) are satisfactory, and if the system is properly designed, installed, and maintained. Most towns, cities, and states have health codes which lay down requirements for proper investigations of a site, detailed design of the system, and actual installation. The following extract from one such code will give a general idea of such requirements:

"No subsurface sewage disposal system shall be laid out in an area where high ground water, surface flooding or ledge rock will interfere with its effective operation. The bottom of any leaching system shall be at least eighteen inches above the maximum ground water level and at least four feet above ledge rock. The following minimum separating distance between any part of the sewage disposal system and the item listed shall be provided:

Well or spring or domestic water suction pipe (Greater separating distance shall be required for wells with higher rates of pumpage than for single residential use) ------75 feet
Human habitation, other than building served ------50 feet
Building served to leaching system ------25 feet
Building served to septic tank ------15 feet
Tributary to a drinking water supply (including surface water, ground water, cellar drain and building footing drain) ------50 feet
Any other stream, pond, lake, or tidal water, surface water, ground water, cellar drain or building footing drain unless such drain is extra heavy cast iron pipe with leaded joints or equal ------25 feet
Top of embankment ------15 feet
Property line ------10 feet
Water pressure line ------10 feet

No water service line shall cross any portion of a leaching system. Sewer shall be tight pipe for a distance of at least ten feet on either side of water service."

A TYPICAL SEPTIC TANK SYSTEM AND HOW IT WORKS

In essence, the septic tank system consists of (Fig. 3-1):

1. A sewer pipe connecting the house, the septic tank, and the distribution box.

2. A grease trap between the kitchen line and the septic tank, if considered necessary.
3. The disposal field, consisting of several trenches with perforated or open-jointed pipes surrounded by porous material. (Alternatively, there may be rows of concrete seepage galleries, rectangular in section, with holes on two sides and with open bottom.)
4. One or more dry wells to dispose of excess flow from the distribution lines.

Figure 3-1 shows the plan and the elevation of a typical septic tank and disposal system. The separating distances do not conform to the particular code cited previously. The building sewer, usually four inches in diameter, conveys the sewage and drainage from the house drain to the septic tank. The joints on it are made watertight to prevent any ex-filtration. The septic tank capacity depends on the expected sewage flow from the house. This flow is linked to the number of bedrooms in the house. Local health codes generally lay down the minimum capacity requirements. If you live in a rural area with no health code, you may use the following guidelines:

Three bedrooms or less	1000 gallons
Four bedrooms	1250 gallons
Five bedrooms	1500 gallons
Each additional bedroom, add	250 gallons

The above figures represent the actual liquid capacity, which is less than the total cubic contents of the septic tank. In no case should a septic tank with capacity smaller than 1000 gallons be used.

THE SEPTIC TANK

Figure 3-2 shows a septic tank with a liquid capacity of approximately 2500 gallons. The inlet is 3 inches higher than the outlet and the inside tank dimensions are 10' 10" × 5' 4" × 6' 4". There are two cleanout covers at the top. The inlets consist of either down-pointing sanitary Ts or openings with baffles hanging down about 18 inches which prevent sewage from flowing at the surface from the inlet to the outlet without being properly decomposed. The incoming

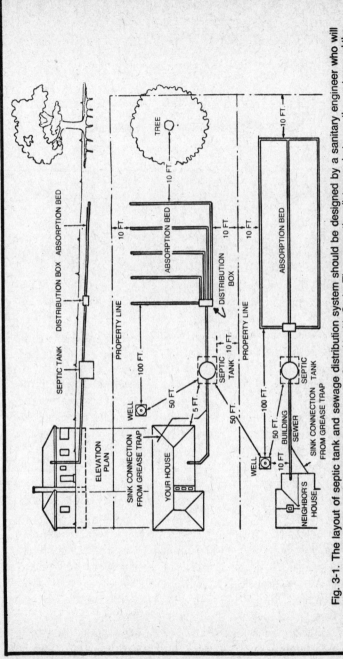

Fig. 3-1. The layout of septic tank and sewage distribution system should be designed by a sanitary engineer who will investigate the permeability of soil and follow the State Health Code. The separating distances between the system and the drinking water wells both on your property and those of your neighbors are very important.

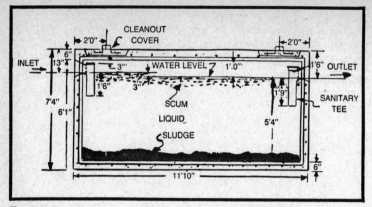

Fig. 3-2. The sewage separates out into scum, liquid, and sludge inside the septic tank. The sludge is reduced in volume due to bacteriological action. Cleaning of septic tank is needed at long intervals of time.

sewage flows down towards the tank bottom and gets decomposed, by bacteriological action, into liquid, gases, and mineral sludge. The liquid flows out through the outlet into the disposal field. Gases travel back through the house sewer to the vent stack and escape to the atmosphere, while the mineral sludge gradually settles down at the bottom and has to be cleaned every few years. The anaerobic bacteria, which thrive in the absence of oxygen, decompose the incoming sewage in just 24 hours.

Because the liquid effluent running out from the septic tank is foul-smelling and full of bacteria, it should never be allowed to run above-ground or come in contact with wells, springs, or other water supply sources. It should be carried underground in pipes with watertight joints that lead to the disposal field (also called a *leaching field* or *absorption bed*).

The bacteriological action going on in the septic tank all the time is slowed down by strong detergents and bleaches that kill the bacteria. When oversized washing machines and other appliances discharge large volumes of water saturated with such chemicals, the bacteriological action is disrupted. Also, the large quantities of water churn up both the sludge and the solids which are in the process of decomposition. What's more, when these detergents and bleaches arrive at the disposal field, they enter the pore-spaces of the soil and slow down the absorption rate. In extreme cases, the disposal field flows over and causes nuisance and health hazards.

Some simple precautions can go a long way. Do not use strong bleaches or detergents. Avoid washing several loads of clothes in succession or within a short period of time, and do not run several appliances simultaneously. Also, try to do the laundry at a time when there is no other water consumption in the home, particularly in the bathrooms or kitchen. This will prevent the dumping of large volumes of water in the septic tank at one time. There is, however, no objection to sprinkling your lawn or using water in the yard or anywhere else if it does not enter the sanitary drainage system.

If at any time your disposal field flows over, the problem can be tackled in several ways. A professional sanitary engineer experienced with septic tank systems can give you the best advice. In some cases it may be necessary to put in additional trenches, while in others a larger septic tank may be required. Installation of a grease-trap on the line from the kitchen arrests greases and oils and prevents them from coating the walls of the dry well, and clogging the pores of soil. This will improve the absorption rate to some extent. If, however, the problem persists even after you have taken all these precautions, including the replacement of your appliances with those using smaller quantities of water, one good solution is to separate the toilet waste lines from the remaining drainage system in your home. Send only the toilet waste line to the septic tank itself, while the rest of the flow is carried to dry wells or drainage pits for disposal. You have to be careful, though; not many local health codes will permit this. Check with your town sanitarian before you plan to make these changes.

As mentioned before, state or local health codes specify various separating distances. You have to follow these to the letter when siting the septic tank and the disposal field. The most important single item is the distance between the disposal field and your water supply well.

Pre-cast concrete septic tanks are most commonly used. Manufactured on a large scale, these tanks are the least expensive. Capacities start from as low as 500 gallons and go up to 15,000 gallons or more. Welded steel tanks are also available, and, of course, you may choose to construct your own tank from solid masonry blocks set in cement to make a watertight construction. Metal tanks are good under normal conditions, but soon get corroded if certain corrosive salts are present in the soil. If you still prefer the lower-priced metal tank, coat it with a corrosion-resistant material like an asphalt-based roof coating.

The excavation for the tank should be done to a depth which will provide a downward pitch of about 1/4 inch per foot run on the sewer

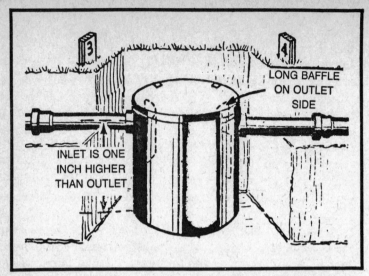

Fig. 3-3. The excavation for the septic tank should provide suitable pitch on the house sewer. The inlet has to be 1 to 3 inches higher than the outlet.

pipe leading from the house to the tank inlet. The inlet is 1 to 3 inches higher than the outlet, depending on the length of the tank. The tank should be set level in the hole (see Fig. 3-3 which shows a round, metallic tank). The top of the tank should be buried at least one foot deep but not more than three feet. Larger depth makes cleaning operation difficult. The opening at the top should be large enough to permit a tank-cleaning crew to loosen the sludge with a shovel and turn the contents into a slurry which can be easily pumped out.

THE SEWAGE DISPOSAL FIELD

For satisfactory functioning of a sewage disposal field, the following basic requirements should be met.

1. 4 to 6 foot depth of good, permeable soil.
2. Water table at least 4 1/2 feet below ground.
3. No ledge rock down to a depth of about 7 feet.
4. Sufficient area of land with above characteristics available for present requirements, and a reserve for possible future expansion.
5. Proper design and layout of the distribution trenches and the pipes.

How big will the field be? All depends on the results of what is commonly knows as a *percolation or perc test*. This test determines the *permeability* of the soil, or, in other words, the rate in gallons per minute at which the soil can continuously absorb the flow from the septic tank without letting it break out of ground or flood. Sometimes your town sanitarian will simply ask for the results of such tests, but more often he or his representative will want to be present when these tests are being run. Some towns even insist that their own official or a professional engineer actually perform the investigations of soil conditions, and carry out suitable tests, particularly in areas with problem soils, high ground water, or shallow ledge rock.

The procedure used to run a perc test in the area proposed to be used as a disposal field is as follows:

1. Using a hand auger and a pickax if necessary (or other suitable equipment), dig test holes 4 to 12 inches in diameter extending to the depth of the proposed leaching system. Remove loose earth particles from inside the holes, and drop onto the bottom about a 2-inch depth of coarse sand or fine gravel, to avoid scouring action.

2. Fill the holes with clean water to a minimum depth of one foot over the bottom. Wait till all the water is absorbed by the soil. Unless the soil is very porous and all the water runs out quickly, it will be preferable to leave the holes as is, absorbing the water overnight.

3. Next morning refill the holes with water to a depth of one foot above the bottom.

4. Start the test by measuring the initial water level below some reference point on the ground. A flat piece of wood or metal placed across the hole at the top will serve as an excellent reference surface. After every 10 to 15 minutes, depending on how rapidly the level falls, note and record the depth of the water surfaces in the holes. Continue for two to four hours for soils of medium to low absorption, and one to one-and-one-half hours for porous soil.

5. From the above data, work out the time in minutes during which water level fell down through depths of one-inch intervals. Take the slowest uniform rate of drop for one inch as the *seepage rate*. Seepage rates should be determined for each hole.

Table 3-1 gives data to determine the required area of the disposal field for various seepage rates, as determined at the site.

The trenches of a disposal field should follow ground contours. It is preferable that the trench bottoms be level. If a slope is

Table 3-1. Data for Calculating the Area of the Absorption Field at Various Rates of Seepage.

Seepage Rate in Minutes Per Inch Drop in Water Level	Required Minimum Absorption Area in Square Feet at Trench Bottoms	
	Up To Three Bedrooms	Additional Area For Each Bedroom Above Three
5 or less	375	125
6 to 10	495	165
11 to 15	570	190
16 to 20	675	225
21 to 30	750	250
31 to 45	870	290
46 to 60	990	330
More than 60	Special design required to avoid nuisance conditions. In some soils it is impossible to use absorption trenches. Consideration may be given to seepage pits or an absorption bed.	

provided, it should not exceed 0.5 percent. Normal depth is 2 1/2 feet to 4 feet and normal width is 3 feet. The trenches should run parallel to each other, with center-to-center spacing not less than 4 times the width of the trenches. Thus, for three-foot-wide trenches, the spacing will be at least 12 feet from one center to the next center, or 9 feet between adjacent trench sides. The length of a trench should not exceed 75 feet unless automatic siphons are used to intermittently pump out excess water that might accumulate. If these siphons are used, trenches may be as much as 100 feet long.

Before digging the trenches, the disposal field area should be graded, if necessary, so that no water stands in any depressions or hollows. Also, if the natural water table measured during spring months is high, a *curtain drain* may be constructed on the upstream side of the trench to carry excess water to an area where it will drain better. This will lower the water table.

In a flat area the trenches may be connected, as in Fig. 3-4, to produce a continuous seepage system. The bottoms of the trenches should be level or almost level. (Normally the construction uses a distribution box, as shown in Fig. 3-1, with trenches that are not interconnected.) In areas with sloping ground, the individual trenches should run along contours with level bottoms and should be connected to each other through solid, non-perforated pipes. A typical layout in sloping ground is shown in Fig. 3-5.

A cross section of an absorption trench with the distribution pipe (with perforations) is shown in Fig. 3-6.

Depending on your local code, you may use one of the following types of pipe: perforated plastic pipe, perforated fiber pipe, drain tile with 1/4 inch to 1/2 inch open joints, or perforated tile.

The first two types are easy to lay. They should be laid with perforations at the bottom. The different lengths are joined in the same manner as solid plastic pipe; fittings and couplings are also the same. However, on fiber pipes, a snap coupling is used instead of a tapered one.

The trench between the septic tank and the distribution box carries the sealed-joint pipe, while the trenches beyond this carry perforated pipes which distribute the septic tank effluent into the soil. The distribution boxes, made of concrete, are available ready-made with any number of knockouts through which connections can be made to various lines (Fig. 3-1).

The 4 inch diameter perforated or open-jointed pipe is laid over a 12-inch to 14-inch depth of 3/4 inch to 1 inch size crushed stone. If open-jointed tile is used, the upper half of the joint is protected by strips of tar paper or any other suitable material. The distribution lines are covered with a 2- to 4-inch depth of 1 inch size crushed·

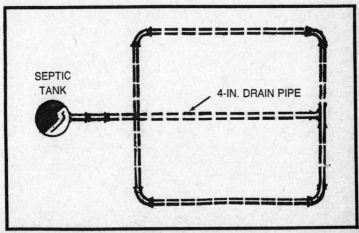

Fig. 3-4. The absorption trenches in a flat area can be interconnected to make a continuous system.

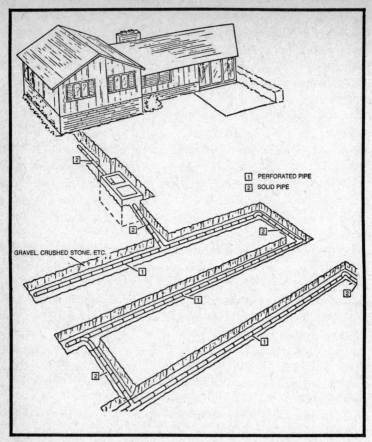

Fig. 3-5. On sloping ground, individual lines can be laid along contours and connected through blind pipes. The bottoms of trenches should be level.

stone or screened gravel. A layer of salt hay, three layers of #15 tar paper (or any other suitably pervious barrier) will come next, and then the trench will be backfilled.

The grass roots of your lawn absorb some of the moisture that the soil receives from the distribution system, so do not lay the lines deeper than 36 inches. The end portions of the distribution pipes should be filled with broken stones over a length of about six inches; or, large pieces of concrete or masonry should be placed at the ends. This will prevent too much flow from going out at the ends; otherwise the flow might over-saturate the soil and break out of ground.

One word of caution about the slope of the distribution pipe when it is made of open-jointed tile: it is easy during installation to end up with reverse slope or slope steeper than 0.5 percent, which is the maximum allowable. To prevent this, first lay slope boards (6-inch sheathing lumber) on edge over the 12-inch layer of crushed stone, and give the boards the required downward pitch. The distribution pipe will have the same pitch when laid over the boards. After you are fully satisfied that everything is in position, place the remaining 4-inch layer of crushed stone on top, and backfill the trench.

A very easy procedure can be adopted to provide the required slope to the grade boards: get a straight, flat board, 8 feet long, and place it on a level floor to see that it is not warped. Tape a plumber's level to it in the middle and drive a nail at one end so that it protrudes exactly 1/2-inch from the lower edge. Place it over the top of the grade boards and raise or lower their ends till the bubble in the plumber's level comes to the center. This will indicate that the grade board over which you are working is lying exactly at a pitch of 1/2 inch per 8 feet, or about 0.5 percent. If you want a flatter pitch,

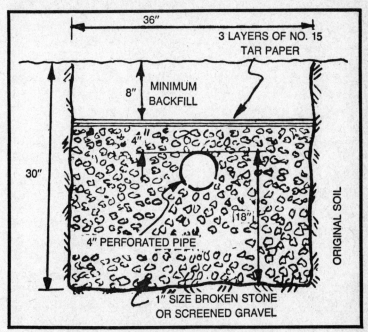

Fig. 3-6. The distribution trenches are generally excavated 36″ wide and 30″ deep. 4″ diameter perforated plastic or fiber pipe, or open-jointed tiles are laid over a bed of at least 12″ depth of 1″ crushed stone or screened gravel. There is a 4″ deep cover of same material at top, finished with 3 layers of tar paper. Minimum backfill is 8″ thick.

reduce the angle from 1/2 to 1/4 inch and you will get a 0.25 percent grade. Start from the upper end of each line and work down to the lower end.

If the soil is good and the system is carefully installed, it should give good service almost indefinitely without any repairs. The sludge at the septic tank bottom deposits very gradually and it will be many years before you have to call a septic tank cleaning contractor.

THE SEEPAGE PIT

A seepage pit is one alternative to be investigated when a regular disposal field cannot be laid out. Seepage pits or dry wells are hollow structures, 6 to 10 feet deep, with tight covers and open-jointed or perforated walls. There is a cleanout manhole cover at the top. Figure 3-7 illustrates one such precast concrete structure 77 inches high, with top and bottom diameters of 60 inches and 78 inches, respectively. The 3-inch thick walls have 12 rows of perforations through which the septic tank effluent flows out into the soil. After digging a suitable hole in the ground, the structure is carefully lowered into it and packed all around with one-inch size broken stone or screened gravel, forming a layer 12 to 24 inches thick. The diameter of the pit is limited to 10 feet.

When several seepage pits are used they are spaced at distances three times the pit diameter; this distance is measured between the sides of adjacent pits. Not more than two such pits should be connected in series. Seepage pits should not be used re the ground water table is high and there is a chance of contamination. Also, if better quality soil exists at shallower depth, a regular disposal field should be laid out. Sometimes seepage pits are used as supplements to the regular disposal system. The same separating distances dictated for the regular disposal system should be observed for these supplementary pits as well.

If you don't want to use precast dry wells, you can dig a hole of required diameter through at least 4 feet of permeable soil and then line the sides with stones, bricks, or precast concrete blocks laid dry with open joints (Fig. 3-8).

The lining should be constructed after a layer of 12 inches or more of gravel is laid on the bottom of the hole. Six to 12 inches of gravel should be packed on the outside of the lining, all around it. The septic tank effluent should be brought to the pit by tight-jointed sewer pipe. A removable slab or a smaller manhole cover should be provided at the top for future cleanings or repairs.

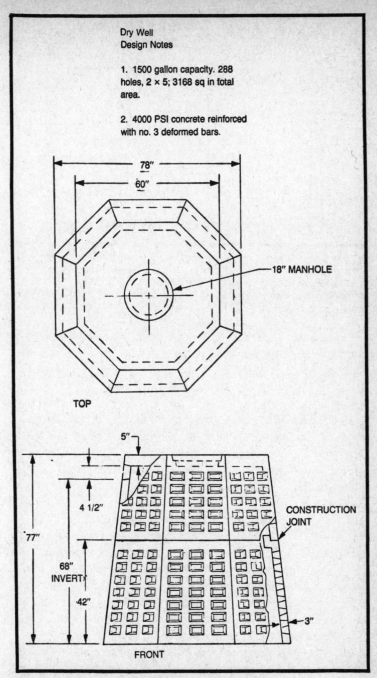

Dry Well
Design Notes

1. 1500 gallon capacity. 288
holes, 2 × 5; 3168 sq in total
area.

2. 4000 PSI concrete reinforced
with no. 3 deformed bars.

78"

60"

18" MANHOLE

TOP

5"

4 1/2"

77"

68"
INVERT

42"

CONSTRUCTION
JOINT

3"

FRONT

Fig. 3-7. A dry well. (Courtesy Connecticut Precast Corp.)

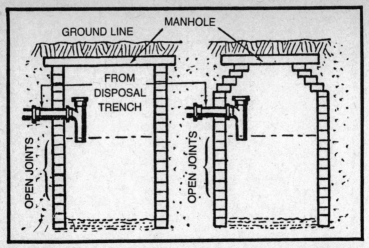

Fig. 3-8. Seepage pits can be made by digging through at least 4 feet of porous soil and lining the side walls with stones, bricks, or concrete blocks laid dry with open joints. A manhole cover or concrete slab is provided at top. The lining is surrounded by a 12 inch thick layer of 1 inch size crushed stone or screened gravel.

The effective seepage area of a seepage pit is considered to be equal to the sidewall area only. To compute this area, you must multiply the depth of the pit by the permimeter. The perimeter is computed by multiplying the diameter by π (we'll use 22/7 as π, for easier computation). For instance, an 8-foot deep pit with an average inner diameter of 6 feet will provide a sidewall area of $8 \times 22/7 \times 6$, or about 151 square feet. If the percolation rate of the soil is determined by field tests as 15 minutes per inch, this will require a 570 square foot area for a three-bedroom house (refer to Table 3-1). Thus, you will need four seepage pits to give a total area of 4×151 or 604 square feet.

Sometimes seepage pits are constructed to receive drainage from roofs, areaways, foundation drains, and basement drains. The construction of these pits is similar to that described above. Such pits should be 10 feet away from the building, 20 feet from the disposal field or sanitary seepage pits, and at least 50 feet from any water supply source. Under no circumstances should these drainage pits be connected to the sewage pits or the disposal field.

Where soil is good but the area of land is not sufficient to lay a regular disposal system, *seepage galleries* may be considered. The trade name for a seepage gallery is *galley*. Available in 2-foot and 4-foot heights, the gallery construction resembles that of precast

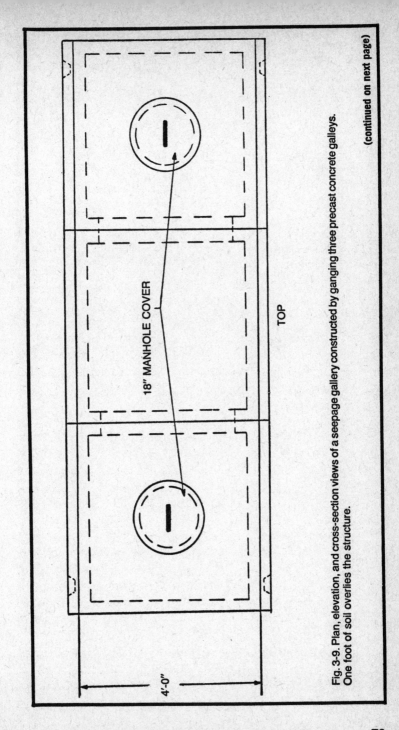

TOP

18" MANHOLE COVER

4'-0"

Fig. 3-9. Plan, elevation, and cross-section views of a seepage gallery constructed by ganging three precast concrete galleys. One foot of soil overlies the structure.

(continued on next page)

(continued from previous page)

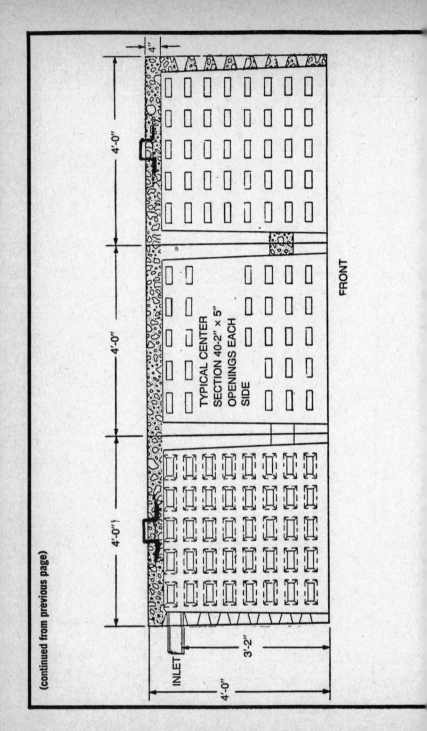

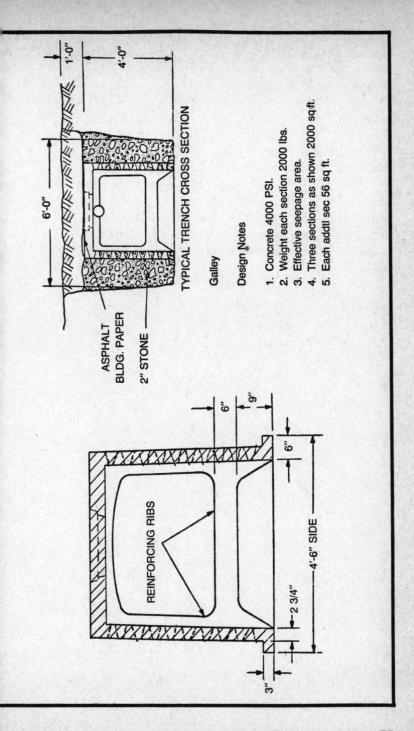

TYPICAL TRENCH CROSS SECTION

ASPHALT
BLDG. PAPER

2" STONE

Galley

Design Notes

1. Concrete 4000 PSI.
2. Weight each section 2000 lbs.
3. Effective seepage area.
4. Three sections as shown 2000 sq.ft.
5. Each addtl sec 56 sq ft.

REINFORCING RIBS

4'-6" SIDE

concrete dry wells. Figure 3-9 illustrates a 4-foot high gallery. It comes in 4-foot long sections with perforated sidewalls, solid top, and open bottom. A typical trench cross section with the gallery set in place is shown in the illustration at the bottom right of Fig. 3-9. There is a one-foot soil cover at top, and 12 inch thick layers of 1 inch to 2 inch size stones or gravel against the two sidewalls. Any number of sections can be joined to make up the required length. Each section comes with two manhole covers in the roof. The pipe carrying septic tank effluent connects towards the top.

The effective seepage area of a gallery is the total area of its perforated sidewalls. A 4 foot high, 4 foot long gallery section (with two sides) provides 2 (4 × 4) = 32 square feet of seepage area. To provide a 570 square foot area, as in the example discussed in the previous section, you will need 18 of these 4-foot long gallery sections.

Tools and Pipes

Tools and Pipes

As a do-it-yourselfer, you will need only a few commonly used tools to start with, and a thorough understanding of their use. Simple jobs like changing a faucet washer, unclogging a drain, fixing a singing or overflowing toilet, or repairing a stuck garbage disposer can be done with the help of a screwdriver, pliers, adjustable wrench, force or suction cup, and a plumber's snake or auger. You probably have some of these already, and can buy the rest for a few dollars. Electrician's tape and a supply of faucet washers in assorted sizes will come in handy when you are repairing faucet leaks. If a washer does not cure the drip problem, the valve seat will have to be faced with a seat-dressing tool which does not cost much either.

PLUMBING TOOLS

As you grow familiar with your plumbing system and feel confident to handle different tools, you may wish to tackle more elaborate repair and remodelling jobs. Additional tools will then be needed. These may be purchased, or if you feel you will not require them very often, some of the expensive ones may be rented. In short, you will add more and more items to your tool box as time goes on and as you become involved in various plumbing projects.

The type of tools you buy depends on whether your water lines consist of copper tubing with soldered joints or steel pipes with caulked-in joints. Drainage pipes need still other types of tool. A propane gas torch is used to make soldered joints on copper pipes while a gasoline blowtorch will be required if you are assembling a soil stack, house drain, or any other soil pipe from cast-iron materials. A small lead-melting pot and a few caulking tools with caulking yarn will also be needed when making the joints. A pair of Stillson wrenches is used for making threaded joints. When cutting a pipe, it will be necessary to get a pipe cutter, a reamer, and a vise. To cut threads at the pipe ends, a threader will be used. All these are among the comparatively higher priced items to be bought or rented if needed.

The most frequent plumbing problem is a clogged sink or toilet. It can be handled with what is called the *plumber's friend*. Also known as a *force or suction cup*, this tool consists of a rubber suction cup mounted on a wooden handle. The ball-type version with a rounded bottom is very effective in creating high pressures on the clog. If it fails, the *plumber's snake* or hand auger should be used.

Following are two lists of tools, one for the usual maintenance and repair jobs and the other if you want to undertake major repairs and remodellings like adding a toilet, a shower, or even a new bathroom.

Tools Required For Normal Maintenance	Tools Required For Major Repairs and Remodelling
Plumber's friend (suction cup)	Plumber's vise
Hand auger or snake	Pipe and tubing-benders and cutters
Screwdriver	Pipe threader
Pair of pliers	Pipe reamer and file
Fixed wrench	Tools for cast-iron pipe
Adjustable wrench	Flaring tool
Seat removal tool	Hacksaw
Seat facing tool	Rachet wrench
	Propane torch

Normal Maintenance

The suction cup and the hand auger will be described in detail in Chapters 6 and 7. A discussion of the other tools needed for normal maintenance follows:

Screwdrivers—Everyone is familiar with screwdrivers. They come in various sizes to fit different screw heads. It is important to use the correct size. A smaller one will not have enough

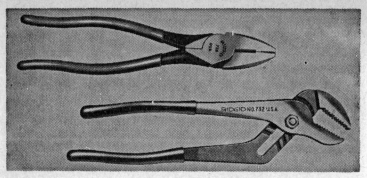

Fig. 4-1. Household pliers and slip-joint pliers. Courtesy Ridgid Co.

turning force while one substantially larger than the screw head may damage it and make further turning impossible. If you do happen to snap off the head of a screw, drill a hole through its body lengthwise and unscrew it with a screw remover.

Pliers—Pliers have jaws to hold and grip; but if used in place of wrenches to turn nuts, they quickly damage the heads. The common type, called the household plier or gas plier, 6 inches to 8 inches long, is convenient for working on small fittings or for holding or unscrewing small size pipe after it has been loosened a little by appropriate wrenches. For pipes larger than 1 1/2 inches in diameter, a pair of slip-joint pliers is used. This type has several channels cut across the side of one arm which enable its jaws to be set pretty wide apart without losing their grip when under pressure (see Fig. 4-1).

Two other types of pliers are sometimes used: the water-pump plier and the vise-grip plier. The former has one jaw that is adjustable to seven positions. Both jaws have teeth consisting of deep grooves. The arrangement is ideal to grasp cylindrical pipes or similar objects. The vise-grip plier can be clamped in place, which eliminates the necessity of holding it. This leaves both hands of the worker free. A screw is provided at the end of the handle to adjust the jaw opening. This type of pliers is good for holding small sized pipes. If used on nuts or other fittings, the teeth may cause damage to the contact surfaces.

Wrenches—Wrenches used by plumbers are of two types: fixed and adjustable. Illustrations A and B in Fig. 4-2 show open-end wrenches whose head sizes can be adjusted within certain limits. Figure 4-2C and Fig. 4-3 show examples of fixed-size wrenches of the open-end and box type, respectively. Although the use of fixed-size wrenches is rather limited, a good set with sizes ranging from

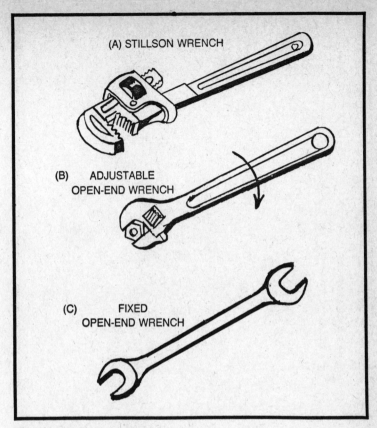

Fig. 4-2. Open-end wrenches.

about 3/8″ to 1 1/4″ is worth having in your tool box.

A *closet spud wrench* with open ends is very useful in working under sinks and lavatories. In such limited spaces these thin wrenches are more convenient than others. When working on a faucet or fixture connection in tight spots you will have to lie down on the floor face up. If necessary, use a flashlight or an electric lamp.

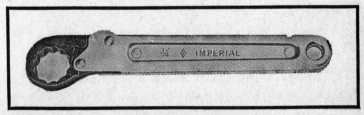

Fig. 4-3. Fixed-size rachet wrench. Courtesy: Imperial-Eastman.

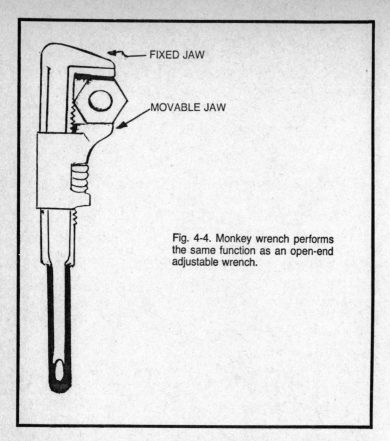

FIXED JAW

MOVABLE JAW

Fig. 4-4. Monkey wrench performs the same function as an open-end adjustable wrench.

For tubs and shower valves, the *packing-nut socket wrench* is used. It is hexagonal in shape, so will fit the faucet stem. The faucet nut and valve assemblies made of brass are quite delicate; if an ordinary wrench is used on these, the assemblies may get damaged. The packing-nut socket wrench distributes the pressure evenly and does a much better job.

Adjustable wrenches— A large variety of adjustable wrenches is available to meet different requirements. Like fixed wrenches, they are used on nuts, bolts, and pipes of water supply and drainage systems. Figure 4-2B shows an *adjustable open-end wrench*, which is used for square and hexagonal nuts particularly inside faucet and valve assemblies. A 12-inch size will do most such jobs. Sizes like 6- or 8-inch are useful for working on smaller parts. To prevent an adjustable wrench from slipping off a nut, always feed the nut all the way into the jaws, and make sure the jaws are screwed

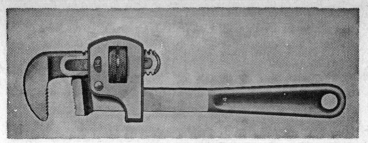

Fig. 4-5. A pipe wrench will do a variety of jobs.

on to fit tightly. Also the wrench should engage the nut in such a way that when you start to turn it, the force should be applied towards the adjustable jaw (see the arrow in Fig. 4-2B). A monkey-wrench performs the same function as an open-end adjustable wrench.

The *pipe wrench* (Fig. 4-5) and *Stillson wrench* (Fig. 4-2A) both have jaws, made of hardened steel, which provide a very good grip on pipes. Ideal for working with iron pipes, these wrenches are often used in pairs, one type to turn the pipe and the other to hold it tightly in place. A set of 12-inch, 14-inch, and 18-inch pipe wrenches will suffice for all pipe sizes between 1/2-inch and 2-inches. Both the pipe wrench and the Stillson wrench bite into the pipe and leave marks. They should therefore not be used on nuts, copper tubing, or chrome-finish pipe. Flat-sided or delicate fittings like brass or copper valves may get damaged by a pipe wrench or a Stillson wrench, so an *adjustable spud wrench* (Fig. 4-6) is used for turning these. Another use for this wrench to to turn the large, flat-sided nuts found on drainpipes under a lavatory or a kitchen sink.

The *strap wrench* consists of a heavy webbed strap attached to a handle. After being looped around the pipe, the strap is passed

Fig. 4-6. Adjustable spud wrench is used for large hex-shaped parts.

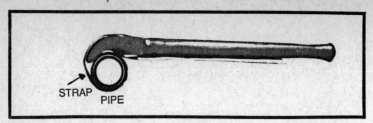

STRAP PIPE

Fig. 4-7. Strap wrench is used on delicate pipes likely to be damaged by the jaws of other wrenches.

through a slot in the handle and drawn tight. When you pull the handle, the loop is tightened further. This makes a very firm grip on the pipe, which starts turning under the force. A strap wrench is very suitable for working on plastic, aluminum, brass, lead, or soft metal pipes (Fig. 4-7). When you are unable to reach pipes and fittings with a pipe wrench because of limited space, a *chain wrench*, being light and slim, will probably do the job (Fig. 4-8). It is particularly suitable for large pipes like those on cast-iron drains. The wrench consists of a length of heavy sprocket chain attached to a steel handle. Like a strap wrench, it grips the circumference of the pipe and holds it firmly. It works in one direction only. However, when you want to turn the pipe around substantially, the handle can be backed up without removing the chain. Turning can be re-started with a new hold.

The *basin wrench* is used on nuts that hold faucet assemblies and spray attachments in place under a wash basin or sink (Fig. 4-9).

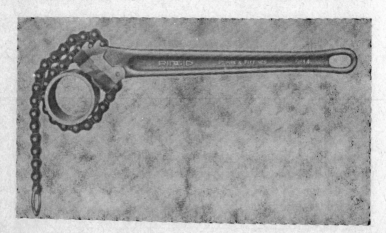

Fig. 4-8. The chain wrench, being light and slim, can reach pipes and fittings which are inaccessible to a pipe wrench. Courtesy: Ridgid Co.

Such narrow spaces are difficult to reach with other types of wrenches.

Seat removing and refacing tools—A discussion of these two tools will be found in the chapter on faucets (Chapter 8).

Major Repairs

The following tools are needed for major repairs and remodelling:

Plumber's vise—Its serrated jaws go around a pipe and hold it firmly in place. The vise you select should fit all the pipe sizes you will normally be using. You can convert a standard bench vise to a pipe vise by attaching to its jaws suitably shaped pieces of hardwood or aluminum. Many designs of pipe vises are available. The yoke vise shown in Fig. 4-10 is the best one to use on pipes it can hold securely between its V-shaped jaws. It is usually mounted on a stand or bench. Another type of pipe vise is illustrated in Fig. 4-11. A chain vise can sometimes be used on steel and cast-iron pipes.

Tube bender—This is used to bend copper tubing without flattening it out. Figure 4-12 shows a tube bender manufactured by Imperial-Eastman. After the upper handle is flipped to one side, the

Fig. 4-9. Basin wrench is used in tight places, as for turning recessed nuts beneath lavatory. Two working positions are shown.

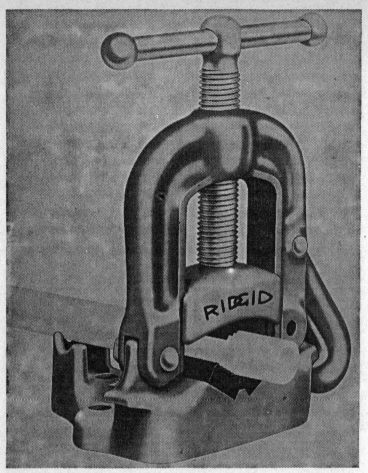

Fig. 4-10. A yoke vise having V-shaped jaws is best suited to plumbing work. Courtesy: Ridgid Co.

tubing is fed in. As the handle is turned gradually, the tubing bends. The graduations indicate the turning angle.

Pipe and tube cutters—You can use a hacksaw to cut pipes and tubes but for sharp, straight cuts, a pipe cutter and tube cutter are needed. A tube cutter (Fig. 4-13) cuts copper and plating tubing. It has one cutting wheel and two rollers. The tube is fed in between them and turned round and round. The handle is gradually tightened till the cut is deep enough. The pipe and the cutting wheel should be lubricated frequently during the job.

A *pipe cutter* is similar to the tube cutter, only it is larger and heavier. Thick-walled iron, brass, copper, and steel pipes are cut by

Fig. 4-11. Another type of pipe vise.

a wheeled pipe cutter. When cutting by hand, the cutter is rotated round the pipe, but for power cutting, the cutter stays steady while the pipe is rotated by the machine.

Pipe threaders—Unless you buy pieces of pipe already cut to size and threaded, you will have to cut the pipe and thread it yourself. External threads on the type of pipe that you will generally need are

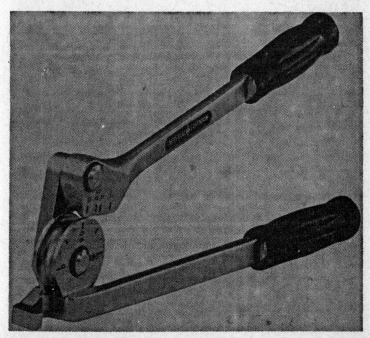

Fig. 4-12. A tube bender is used to bend copper tubing without flattening it. Courtesy: Imperial-Eastman.

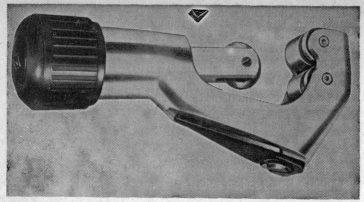

Fig. 4-13. A tube cutter has one cutting wheel and two rollers. After inserting the tube between these parts, apply sufficient pressure by tightening the handle and turning the cutter round and round.

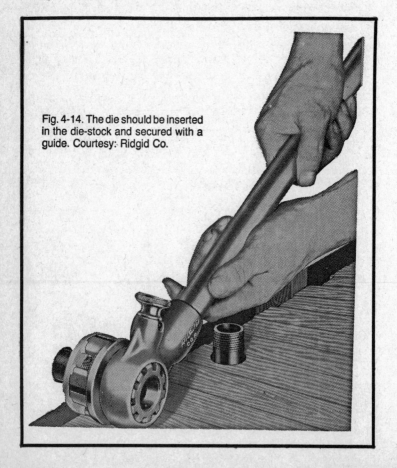

Fig. 4-14. The die should be inserted in the die-stock and secured with a guide. Courtesy: Ridgid Co.

cut by dies held in a die-stock which has long handles to turn it. The same stock can hold dies for pipes of different sizes. Stocks come in two designs: the two-handled type and the ratchet type. Normally dies for one stock cannot be used on another. You should buy a set of dies and a die-stock with handle for pipes of different sizes.

To insert a die in the die-stock, loosen the thumb nut located on the stock, slide the cover plate and insert the die, taking care that the printing on its top faces up towards the cover plate. Replace the plate and tighten the nut. Next clamp the pipe in the vise and slip the die-stock over the pipe end with the guide on the inside (Fig. 4-14). Push it further over the pipe till you feel that the die has caught the pipe surface. With the die pressed firmly against the pipe, turn the stock gradually in a *clockwise* direction. When you have cut a few threads and the die has taken a firm hold on the pipe, apply a generous quantity of cutting oil to the pipe end and the threads of the die (Fig. 4-15). Proceed with the thread cutting. For every one-half turn forward that you move the die, back it one-quarter turn. This will clear off the metal chips. Continue cutting the threads, with occasional lubrication, till the pipe end emerges from the face of the die. Now turn the tool *counterclockwise* so that it disengages and can be taken off. Before starting to join the threaded pipe to the next

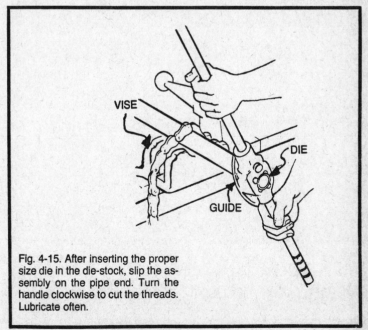

Fig. 4-15. After inserting the proper size die in the die-stock, slip the assembly on the pipe end. Turn the handle clockwise to cut the threads. Lubricate often.

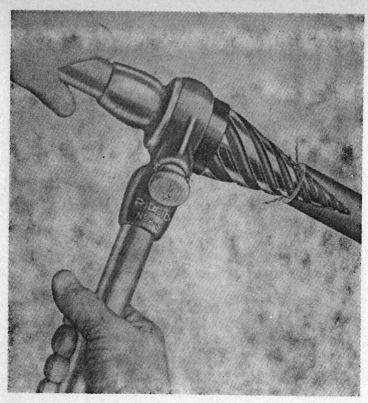

Fig. 4-16. A spiral reamer is used to remove burrs from inside a pipe after it has been cut. Burrs interfere with proper flow of water. Courtesy: Ridgid Co.

section, remove any excess cutting oil and metal chips from the pipe surface and the threads by wiping with a piece of rag.

Pipe reamer and file—After cutting a pipe you will find that both the inside and outside surfaces of the pipe have burrs. The ones on the inside interfere with proper flow of water and may lead to clogs or obstructions. Burrs on the outside surface prevent proper threading and may cause injury to your hands. The outside burrs are removed by a flat file, while those on the inside need a spiral type reamer (Fig. 4-16) which may either have a turning handle or may be fitted in a brace. After inserting the reamer inside the pipe, turn it round till you feel it has started to turn smoothly and the burrs have been removed (Fig. 4-17).

Tools for cast-iron pipes—To cut cast-iron pipe, a *hammer*, a *cold chisel*, and a *hacksaw* will be needed. The cutting process is described later in this chapter along with the method for making poured joints. For the latter type of joint you will need a *melting pot, yarning iron, a blowtorch, a ladle,* and *caulking tools.*

Flaring tool—When copper tubing has to be attached to valves and fittings of the flare type, you have to flare or expand its end and turn it outward. A flaring tool, shown in Fig. 4-18, does this job. It consists of: (a) a split die block of hardened metal with holes of various sizes to take the tubing; (b) a clamp (shown on the right hand side in Fig. 4-18) which locks the tubing in place after it has been inserted; (c) a vertical yoke with a compressor screw and drive handle; and (d) a solid metal cone fitted to the lower end of the screw, to form a 45° flare or bell shape. To make the flare, insert and clamp the tubing into the appropriate hole from below, after the sleeve nut of the fitting has been slipped over it. Turn the compressor screw so that the cone moves down and engages the end of the tubing. The flare will form as increasingly greater pressure is applied by turning the handle.

Propane torch—This is used for making soldered joints on copper pipes and tubings. You can buy a bottle-powered propane torch; this consists of a bottle of liquid gas to which a nozzle and valves are attached (Fig. 4-19). When the bottle has exhausted its fuel it is discarded and a new one is obtained. Various sizes of nozzles can be bought to produce different amounts of of heat and shapes of

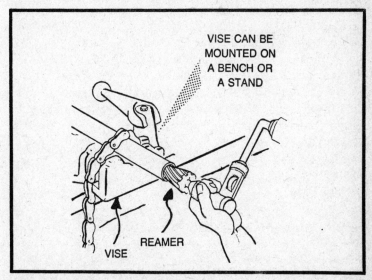

VISE CAN BE
MOUNTED ON
A BENCH OR
A STAND

REAMER

VISE

Fig. 4-17. Hold the pipe in a vise and insert the reamer inside one end. Turn the handle round till the burrs are removed.

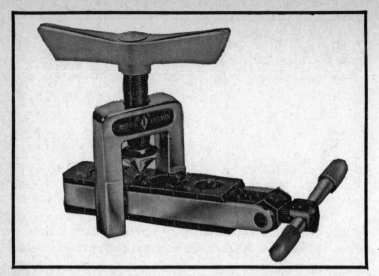

Fig. 4-18. Flaring tool is used to produce flare on the ends of copper pipe or tubing when connection is to be made to a flared fitting. Courtesy : Imperial-Eastman.

flame. You will find that for almost all your plumbing jobs a straight nozzle, 1/2 inch in diameter, will suffice. Larger size torches come with cylinders instead of bottles. To play it safe, always read and follow manufacturer's instructions. If you don't have access to them, follow these general directions: The gas cylinder should not be stored in the living area. When not in use, the burner should be disconnected from the cylinder. When you want to start the flame, connect the torch burner tightly to the cylinder by screwing it on. Open the control valve a little so that the gas starts to come out with a low hissing sound. Ignite it immediately with a match or cigarette lighter. After the flame has burned for a couple of minutes and the burner is fully heated up, open the control valve to get the required size of flame. The gasoline blowtorch is not used today because it is very dangerous. If you have an old one, discard it.

Hacksaw—This is used for cutting metal pipes. Blades of fine, medium, or coarse variety are used, depending on the thickness of metal. When mounting the blades in the frame, see that the teeth point forward, and away from the handle. During cutting, apply very little pressure on the forward stroke and none when turning back. When working on steel or iron pipes, use cutting oil. This oil may be a commercial lubricant, a mixture of kerosene and light oil, or even light oil alone.

PIPE TYPES AND REQUIREMENTS

Almost a dozen different kinds of pipe are available for use in the plumbing system of your house, be it new construction or a remodelling job. Normally you have a choice of several in any given situation, and your decision, like that of a builder, will be dictated by your budget. One kind of pipe may be used for the entire job or several kinds may be mixed if it suits the requirements better or results in some saving. In an existing building, though, the choice is limited by what is already there. Also, there are limitations imposed by the local plumbing code. Sometimes the characteristics of soil and water, like the presence of salts and chemicals which corrode a particular type of pipe, will significantly influence the choice.

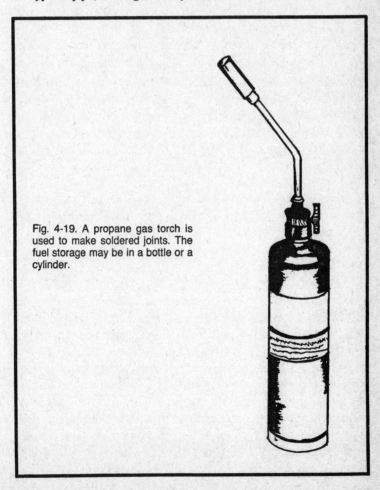

Fig. 4-19. A propane gas torch is used to make soldered joints. The fuel storage may be in a bottle or a cylinder.

COPPER PIPE

Currently, rigid copper pipe is the most popular kind, and it appears on the approved list of almost every local plumbing code. It is lightweight, easy to work with, and very durable. Its inner smooth surface offers little resistance to flow of liquids and therefore it has a larger carrying capacity compared to the same size pipes of cast iron, clay, or concrete. In other words, often a smaller size copper pipe will deliver the same quantity of flow as a larger size pipe of another material with a less smooth surface. Rigid copper pipe comes in four different thicknesses:

Type K: Heaviest—used for underground work.

Type L: Medium weight—used for interior plumbing work.

Type M: Lightweight—also used for interior plumbing if the local plumbing code permits.

Type DWV: Thinner than type M—used only for vent, waste, and drainpipes. Many local plumbing codes forbid its use.

Both type M and type DWV pipes are made from thin copper sheet. Type M is used for carrying water under pressure, but the thinner DWV pipe is used only for the vent, waste, and drainpipes which do not run under pressure. If your plumbing code forbids the use of either type M or DWV, there is no alternative but to use types L or K, unless you decide to use pipes of some other material.

Copper pipe comes in 20-foot lengths, although some mail-order houses offer 10-foot lengths too. When asking for copper pipe at your plumbing store, use the trade term *tube*.

Flexible Copper Tubing

Flexible copper tubing comes in two varieties—type *K* for outdoor use and underground installations, and type *L* for indoor use. Coils are normally sold in lengths of 15, 30, and 60 feet. Sometimes larger coils, even up to 250 feet long, can be obtained. Flexible copper tubing has an obvious advantage over the rigid type: flexibility of working. It can be bent easily and taken around corners or obstructions, and passed through walls or ceilings with much less effort. Like an electric cable, it can run between studding, and over and under pipes and electric conduits. It eliminates the need to drill holes through ceilings and plastered walls. Joints between various lengths of pipe, however carefully made, are always potential sources of leakage. Flexible copper tubing has the fewest number of joints. In fact, you may unroll the coil and use a single length for the entire run, right from the basement up to the attic, with only two joints—one in the basement with the water system, and the other at the fixture or the faucet. Since there are no joints inside the walls or floors where it runs, there is hardly any chance of a leak developing, except of course in extreme cases when the entire building structure is subjected to forces for which it is not designed, like earthquake, tornado, or hurricane forces, which tend to rupture or tilt the building about its foundation.

When installing flexible tubing, be careful not to cause a kink anywhere over its length. A kink restricts the opening of the tube and reduces its flow capacity. Gradual bends or curves on a line can be made by hand or by maneuvering with your knee. For sharp turns, use a tube bender.

Table 4-1 gives the outside and inside diameters of some common sizes of type L (medium weight) copper water supply tubes.

Copper Pipe Fittings

For the various types of pipe, fittings are available to serve specific purposes: elbows to make 90°, 45°, 22 1/2°, 11 1/4°, and 5 5/8° turns, Ts to connect a branch pipe at right angles to a main pipe, Ys to connect branches to the main at angles other than a right angle, crosses to connect four pipes at right angles to each other,

Table 4-1. Dimensions of Type L Copper Water Supply Tube.

Nominal Size in inches	Outside diameter in inches	Inside diameter in inches
1/4	0.375	0.315
3/8	0.500	0.430
1/2	0.625	0.545
5/8	0.750	0.666
3/4	0.875	0.785
1	1.125	1.025
11/4	1.375	1.265
11/2	1.625	1.505
2	2.125	1.985
21/2	2.625	2.465
3	3.125	2.985

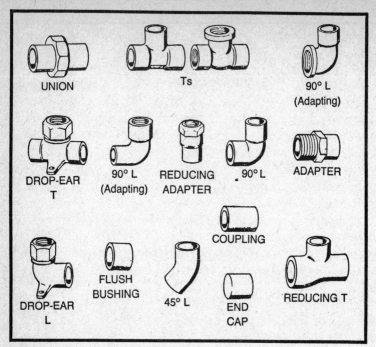

UNION

Ts

90° L
(Adapting)

DROP-EAR T

90° L
(Adapting)

REDUCING ADAPTER

90° L

ADAPTER

COUPLING

DROP-EAR L

FLUSH BUSHING

45° L

END CAP

REDUCING T

Fig. 4-20. Typical solder-type fittings.

reducers and increasers to connect smaller pipes to larger ones and vice versa, adapters and caps, etc. In fact, at your plumbing supply store you can get a fitting for almost every plumbing situation that you may run into. In addition, there are scores of special types of fittings. If you have a tricky situation, check with the plumbing supplier. He may give you a special fitting or some ideas for solving the problem easily with the conventional fittings which might not have occurred to you.

Solder or sweat-type fittings. These are the fittings most commonly employed for general plumbing work. They are used both for rigid and flexible tubing. Figure 4-20 shows the commonly used solder-type fittings. In addition, your store may have reducing Ts, reducing Ls, iron pipe adapter Ls, Ts with male or female iron pipe adapter outlets, and others.

Flare or compression-type fittings. These fittings go only with the flexible copper tubing, mainly for air piping and fuel-oil lines. Being heavier, they withstand vibrations much better than the solder-type fittings. Figure 4-21 illustrates a few of these flare-type fittings. In general plumbing work, where lines are to be sealed in the walls, the use of these fittings is not recommended.

Measuring Copper Pipe

When measuring copper pipe, allowance is made for the distances it is inserted into fittings at both ends, and for the fitting dimensions themselves. The method for calculating offsets is the same as for a threaded pipe, and will be discussed in a later section. Fittings for offsets on flexible copper tubing are normally not required, however, because the tubing can be easily bent.

Cutting Copper Pipe

A hacksaw or a tubing cutter is used to cut both the rigid and the flexible copper tubing. Avoid using a saw for smaller sizes of pipe. When using the hacksaw for larger-sized copper pipe, fit a blade with the finest teeth (24 per inch) and saw straight, with a steady hand. File away any irregularities in the edge and outside burrs. If necessary, use a reamer to smooth the inside surface. If you find it necessary to clamp the pipe in a vise while you are sawing, attach the

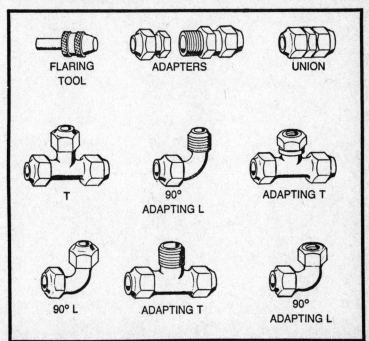

Fig. 4-21. Typical flare-type fittings.

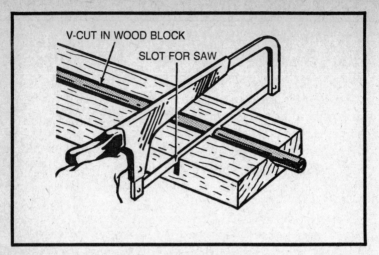

V-CUT IN WOOD BLOCK

SLOT FOR SAW

Fig. 4-22. Jig and hacksaw are used to cut a copper pipe.

vise far away from the point of cut. This will prevent the pipe from getting crushed or dented.

A good joint needs a perfectly round end. Figure 4-22 shows a jig and a hacksaw for cutting a copper pipe. Made of a piece of wood two to four inches long, the jig helps to keep the cut square.

Copper pipe and tubing may also be cut by a tubing cutter, as was illustrated in Fig. 4-13.

Making Copper Pipe Joints

The *soldered joint* is one of the easiest joints to make with copper pipe. First, completely remove all tarnish and dirt from the end of the pipe and from inside the fitting. This can be done easily with fine steel wool or very fine emery cloth which you can buy from an auto-supply shop. Be careful not to cause too much abrasion or the gap between the pipe and the fitting will increase beyond its normal limit and may cause a leaky joint. Check to see that the end of the tube is round and without burrs. Now apply a thin coating of non-corroding soldering flux to the polished surfaces—the inside of the fitting and the outside of the pipe. This flux comes as a thick paste and can be applied with an old toothbrush. Slip the tubing into the fitting and turn it round several times to spread the flux evenly; remove the excess from the outside of the fitting.

Heat the connection with a propane torch, playing the flame evenly all around the fitting, and also on the pipe adjacent to it, till they get sufficiently hot and the flux bubbles out. On tubings larger than 1 1/2 inch size use two torches, one on each side, to get even heating. Remove the torch and touch the end of a length of wire-type solder against the edge of the joint. If the tubing and the fitting have attained the right temperature, the solder will melt and will immediately be drawn into the joint by capillary action. You will be amazed to observe that the molten solder will be drawn in, even if it has to flow vertically upwards. Let it flow till a gleam of solder appears all around the seam. This will indicate that the joint is full (Fig. 4-23). Wipe off excess solder with a cloth, but be careful not to burn your hands. After the joint cools down for a few minutes, wet the joint to bring it to a working temperature. *Don't pour cold water on a hot joint*; it may crack the fitting.

If you are working with a water supply pipe, you may test for a leak by turning the supply on. For a drainpipe, block the outflow at the bottom of the line before you test the upper length by filling it with water. In the rare case when the joint you have made is leaky, it can be easily fixed. After you drain out the pipe completely, bring the joint again to the soldering temperature, as before, and add more solder to the inside of the joint till it appears full again; then let it cool.

Several precautions are necessary during this soldering procedure:

1. When the solder is in the process of cooling, keep the tubing and the fitting motionless, or else the joint that results may be defective. Unless the joint has been overheated, the solder will solidify in a minute or two.

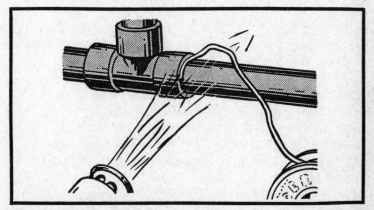

Fig. 4-23. To make a soldered joint on copper pipe or tubing, insert the tube into the fitting after applying a coat of flux or soldering paste. Heat with a blowtorch. When flux bubbles out, touch the end of solder wire to the edge of the fitting. The solder will be drawn in till the joint is full.

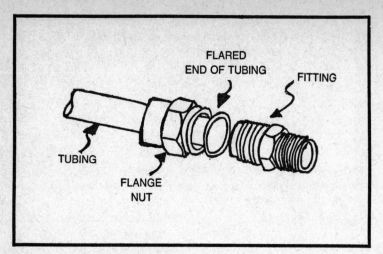

Fig. 4-24. Making a flared fitting joint.

2. Apply the flame over the fitting and the tubing, *never* on the wire solder.

3. If you are making a joint close to wood or other combustible material, guard against fire by placing a piece of asbestos or metal sheet between the combustible material and the fitting.

4. When joining the tubing to a fitting which has already been soldered at its other end to another piece of tubing, as in the case of a T, Y, or a cross, keep the finished joint cool by wrapping it with a piece of wet rag. This will prevent opening up of the joint due to heat.

For a *flared connection* or joint, you need a flare-type fitting and a flaring tool (Fig. 4-18), made of hard metal, with holes that can accommodate various sizes of tubing. First remove the flange nut from the fitting and slip it over the tubing which should then be clamped in the flaring tool. Screw down the cone into the end of the tube. The end will flare out till it fills the recess in the flange nut. Now press this flared end onto the end of the flare-type fitting and make the connection by tightening the nut over the threads in the fitting (Fig. 4-24).

Before starting to make the joint, make sure that the tubing is practically round, and has no burrs. Flaring will, however, re-round the tubing to some extent. When flaring the tubing, put one or two drops of light machine oil at its end.

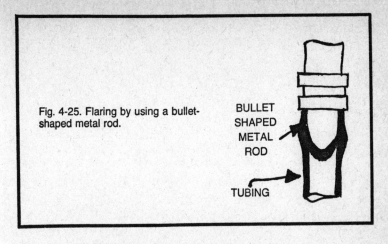

Fig. 4-25. Flaring by using a bullet-shaped metal rod.

BULLET
SHAPED
METAL
ROD

TUBING

A bullet-nosed, solid metal rod, called a *flanging tool* is sometimes used to flare the ends of tubings (Fig. 4-25).

A *compression fitting connection* is similar to the flare fitting connection and costs about the same. No flaring tool is required. There are two parts as before: the flange nut and the compression fitting with threads on both sides. To make the connection, remove the flange nut from the fitting and slip it on to the end of the copper tubing. Also slip on the compression ring which matches the tube diameter. Now insert the tube into the fitting as far as possible and tighten the nut by hand (Fig. 4-26). Take two open-end wrenches; turn the flange nut with one and hold the fitting in place with the other. This will seal the ring against the fitting and will also squeeze it against the copper tubing. Just like with the flared connection, the tube should be neatly cut with a tubing cutter, and any irregularities and burrs should be removed with a file.

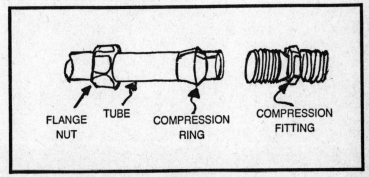

FLANGE
NUT

TUBE

COMPRESSION
RING

COMPRESSION
FITTING

Fig. 4-26. Compression fitting connection.

GALVANIZED STEEL PIPE

A few years back, galvanized wrought-iron or steel pipe was almost exclusively used for home water supply lines, but it has now largely been replaced by copper and plastic pipes. Wrought-iron pipe is no longer manufactured and steel pipe is used instead. Steel pipe's greatest use is for distribution of hot and cold water supplies, for the heating system, for gas and air distribution, for vents, for certain drainage situations, and in locations subject to corrosion.

Steel pipe comes plain (black) and galvanized (zinc-coated), in lengths up to 21 feet; it comes threaded or unthreaded, in three weights: standard (s), extra strong (x), and double extra strong (x x). It is less expensive than other types of pipe, but is easily corroded by acidity or alkalinity of water. Lime and scale deposits gradually build up inside a galvanized pipe and reduce its flow capacity. Even a new galvanized steel pipe does not have a surface as smooth as that of a copper pipe. The fittings that go with it also restrict the flow. Repairs including cutting, threading, and joints are more expensive and time-consuming with steel pipe than with copper pipes. However, steel does offer some advantages because of its strength and toughness. In exposed locations like a basement, garage, or workshop where the line is subject to blows and impacts from tools, garden equipment, automobiles, etc., it will be safer to use the galvanized steel pipe. Plastic or copper pipes might get damaged and need replacement very often if used in these areas.

Table 4-2 gives the standard sizes of steel pipe. For use on long pipe lines it is available in 21-foot lengths, with both ends threaded. A coupling is screwed on one end of each length to make the connection to the next one. For small jobs, you can buy *nipples* as small as six inches in length. Your plumbing supplier can cut the pipe to any length, or you can do it yourself with the help of some rented tools. While doing an add-on job to your plumbing system, don't try to guess the size of existing pipe. Measure the outside diameter with a guage or tighten an adjustable wrench round the pipe and then take this wrench to a plumbing supplier, who will give you the right size pipe based on the wrench opening. Galvanized pipe is always referred to as a *pipe*, not a tube. If you ask for a tube you will get a copper pipe.

Threaded Pipe Fittings

Figure 4-27 shows some of the malleable iron fittings used on steel pipes. Malleable iron can be bent and shaped by beating to

Table 4-2. Dimensions of Steel Pipes, Standard Weight.

Nominal size in inches	Outside diameter in inches	Inside diameter in inches	Wall thickness in inches	Thread engagement of screw-in distance, in inches
1/8	0.405	0.269	0.068	1/4
1/4	0.540	0.364	0.088	3/8
3/8	0.675	0.493	0.091	3/8
1/2	0.840	0.622	0.109	1/2
3/4	1.050	0.824	0.113	9/16
1	1.315	1.049	0.133	11/16
1 1/4	1.660	1.380	0.140	11/16
1 1/2	1.900	1.610	0.145	11/16
2	2.375	2.067	0.154	3/4
2 1/2	2.875	2.469	0.203	15/16
3	3.500	3.068	0.216	1
3 1/2	4.000	3.548	0.226	1 1/16
4	4.500	4.026	0.237	1 1/8
5	5.563	5.047	0.258	1 1/4
6	6.625	6.065	0.280	1 5/16
8	8.625	8.071	0.277	1 7/16
10	10.750	10.192	0.279	1 5/8
12	12.750	12.090	0.330	1 3/4

some extent without breaking. These fittings are of two types: ordinary or pressure type, and drainage or recessed type. The drainage fittings are smoother on the inside; the pipe screws in and fills the recess inside the fitting completely, leaving no pocket where the solid matter which comes with the flow could lodge.

Regardless of the material of construction, or the type of pipe on which used, every fitting performs a specific function as follows:

Couplings connect pipes of the same size that will not be taken apart in future except in some very special situation.

Unions connect pipes that may have to be disconnected from time to time.

Reducing Couplings connect pipes of different sizes.

Nipples come in various lengths and pipe sizes. They are used to connect short sections to galvanized pipelines.

Caps are used at the ends of pipes to close them.

Plugs are used to close the female ends of fittings.

Crosses connect four pipes at right angles to each other.

Ts are used to join a pipe to two others at a 90° angle.

Reducing Ts join three pipes of two or three different sizes.

Bushings are inserted when it is desired to reduce the size of a coupling or any other fitting.

Elbows are used to change the direction of a pipeline by 90° or 45°.

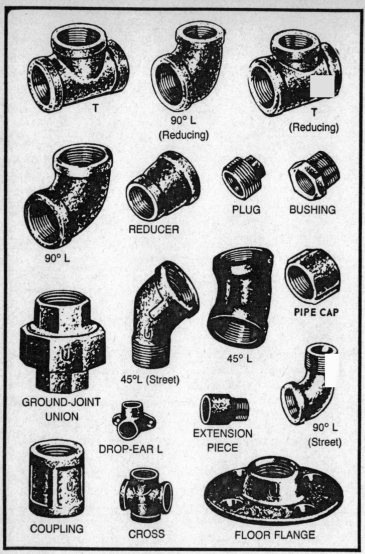

Fig. 4-27. Typical galvanized malleable fittings.

Reducing elbows join two pipes of different sizes at 90° or 45° angles.

Measuring Threaded Pipe

Threaded pipes can be measured in several ways. In each case, the length of the pipe going into the fitting, and the fitting dimensions, have to be considered to arrive at the exact length of pipe needed.

Figure 4-28 shows different methods of measurement. The *end-to-end* measure is the total length of the pipe including the portion which goes inside the fittings at both ends. *End-to-center* measure is used for a length of pipe having a fitting at one end only. The required pipe length is equal to the distance from the far end to the center of the fitting (labelled *end-to-center* in Fig. 4-28B), minus the dimension from the near end of the pipe to the center of the fitting, plus the length of pipe going inside the fitting. *Face-to-end* measure is also used for a pipe length with a fitting at one end only. The pipe length is equal to the measure from one end to the fitting, plus the length of overlap, (the length of pipe going inside the fitting). *Face-to-face* measure is used for a length of pipe having fittings at both ends. The pipe length is equal to the distance from one fitting to the other plus twice the length of overlap. *Center-to-center* measure is used in the same situation as the face-to-face measure. The

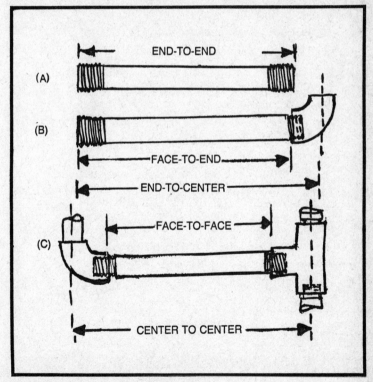

Fig. 4-28. Measuring threaded pipe.

105

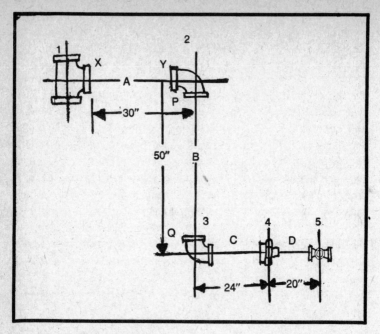

Fig. 4-29. Pipe fitting calculations.

required pipe length is the measure from the center of one fitting to the center of the other, minus the sum of the distances from where the pipe enters the fitting, to the fitting's center, plus twice the length of thread engagement.

Pipe Fitting Calculations

To calculate the exact length of pipe required for any job, one of two approaches can be used: the sketch method and the dry-run method. Figure 4-29 shows the layout of a system starting from a T

Table 4-3. Computations for Pipe Fittings in Fig. 4-29.

1 Pipe label and size	2 Distance between center (inches)	3 Fitting numbers	4 Center to face of fitting, in inches (subtract)	5 Allowance for threads, in inches (add)	6 Total length of pipe required (inches)
A 3/4"	30"	1 - 2	1 5/16 + 1 5/16	9/16 + 9/16	28 1/2 "
B 3/4"	50"	2 - 3	1 5/16 + 1 5/16	9/16 + 9/16	48 1/2"
C 3/4 "	24"	3 - 4	1 5/16 + 1 1/16	9/16 + 9/16	22 3/4"
D 1/2"	20"	4 - 5	1 1/16 + 1 5/16	1/2 + 1/2	18 5/8"

(1), going through two elbows (2) and (3), then through a reducer, (4) and ending at a cross (5). Size of pipe is 3/4 inch all along except for the last run, between fittings 4 and 5, which is 1/2 inch.

Table 4-3 gives the computations. Column 1 gives the sizes of pipes, and column 2 the distance between the centers of the fittings. Column 3 indentifies the fittings at both ends of the pipe. Column 4 is the center-to-face distance of each fitting which you can measure out for each fitting, or you can get the values from the manufacturer's catalog. Column 5 is the distance the pipe goes inside the fittings on either side. Column 6 is the length of each run:

$$\text{Col. } 6 = \text{Col. } 2 - \text{Col. } 4 + \text{Col. } 5.$$

In the example of Fig. 4-29, therefore, the total length of 3/4 inch pipe will be 28 1/2″ + 48 1/2″ + 22 3/4″ = 99 3/4 inches = 8′ 3 3/4″. In addition, an 18 5/8 inch length of 1/2 inch pipe will be required. When going to buy the pipe, it will be advisable to buy a little more to allow for possible wastage.

In case a line has an *offset* at, say, 30° or 11 1/4° (see Fig. 4-30), the length of pipe between the fittings can be calculated with the help of Table 4-4.

The following example will explain how the actual calculation is done for pipes with offsets:

Example. A one-inch pipeline has an offset at 30° and the dimension A is 36 inches. Fittings #1 and #2 are 30° elbows. Calculate the length of threaded steel pipe required between fittings.

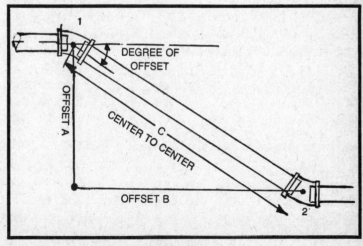

Fig. 4-30. Measurement of pipe for offsets.

Table 4-4. Values of A, B, and C in Fig. 4-30.

Degree of offset	Value of B when A = 1	Value of C when A = 1	Value of A when B = 1
60°	0.577	1.155	1.732
45°	1.000	1.414	1.000
30°	1.732	2.000	0.577
22 1/2°	2.414	2.613	0.414
11 1/4°	5.027	5.126	0.199
5 5/8°	10.168	10.217	0.098

From Table 4-4, the value of C for a 30° offset equals 2 when A = 1. It is given that A is 36 inches. Hence C = 2 × 36 = 72″.

The standard length of elbow for 1 inch line is 2 1/4″, end-to-end (of fitting). Hence end-to-center length = 1/2 × 2 1/4 = 1 1/8″. For the two elbows, the total length = 1 1/8 + 1 1/8 = 2 1/4″. The length of thread engagement for a 1 inch pipe is 11/16″. The total engagement length = 2 × 11/16 = 1 3/8″.

Length of pipe required = 72″ − 2 1/4″ + 1 3/8″ = 71 1/8″

If you don't want to get involved with arithmetic, you may use the *dry run* method: measure the distance between the connection (where your new line has to start) and the first fitting (distance X-Y in Fig. 4-29). You may need someone's help to hold this fitting at the exact spot where you want it to go; then measure the distance X-Y. To get the actual pipe length, you have only to add the screw-in distances at both ends. In the same way, the distance P-Q (face-to-face between fittings 2 and 3 in Fig. 4-29) can be measured, and the required pipe length computed. And so on, till you get the entire length of the pipe for the whole job. The screw-in distance can be taken from Table 4-2. Don't forget that if the pipe size changes along the run of the line, you want to determine the lengths of various sizes separately.

Cutting, Reaming, and Threading Steel Pipe

Careless cutting leads to wastage of pipe, and improper reaming may result in subsequent stoppage of flow in drainpipes. This can be avoided by carefully following the procedures outlined below.

The pipe cutter for cutting the pipe should be checked to insure that it has no burrs or nicks (rough or blunt edges) on the cutting wheels. Pipe cutters have been described earlier in this chapter.

First calculate the lengths of pipe required from fitting to fitting, and then, with a file, a piece of crayon, or a little paint, mark the spots where cuts are to be made. Set up the vise and tightly lock the pipe in it with the first mark about 6 to 9 inches away. Select a suitable cutter, a single-wheel or three-wheel type, depending on the size of the pipe. Turn its handle clockwise to open the jaws, and place it round the pipe from underneath, so that the cutting wheel is exactly over the mark you made on the pipe. When using a three-wheel cutter, the three wheels should stay level and perpendicular to the center line of the pipe. Now turn the handle clockwise so that the jaws close tightly. To get a *bite* on the pipe, turn the handle another quarter turn. A little thread cutting oil can now be applied to the pipe and to the wheels of the cutter. Next rotate the cutter completely around the pipe. This will start the cutting process. Turn the handle a quarter turn and again rotate the cutter one complete revolution. Continue till the pipe is fully cut.

Threading is done with threading sets, as described earlier, in the tools section. Many different types of threading sets are available. If an uncommon one is to be used, familiarize yourself with the printed instruction sheet before starting the job. The most common combination consists of a non-adjustable stock, solid dies, and individual guides. You should make sure that the guide and the die are the same size and correspond to the pipe size. Also, attempt to cut threads till the threaded pipe projects about 1/4 inch to 1/2 inch outside the base of your die. (Table 4-2 gives required thread lengths.)

Joining Threaded Pipe

Joining a threaded pipe is a simple affair. It is advisable to screw the fitting on one end of the pipe while it is still clamped in the vise after the operations of cutting, reaming, and threading have been completed. The assembled pipe and fitting should then be removed from the vise, taken to the installation where they are to be fitted, and screwed on with a wrench.

In order to make a perfect joint, the male threads on the pipe and female threads on the fitting should be thoroughly cleaned with a hard brush. The male threads should then be coated with pipe joint compound. Never coat the female threads. Screw the fitting around the pipe for three turns just by the pressure of your hand. Then tighten the joint by using a wrench—Stillson for normal type of work, a strap wrench for a plated or polished pipe, and a chain wrench for

Table 4-5. Allowable Radii of Curvature on Bends of Iron and Steel Pipes.

Diameter of pipe in inches	Minimum recommended radii in inches
1/8	1 1/4
1/4	1 1/4
3/8	1 7/8
1/2	2 1/2
3/4	3 3/4
1	5
1 1/4	6 1/4
1 1/2	7 1/2
2	10
2 1/2	12 1/2
3	15
3 1/2	17 1/2
4	20
5	30
6	42
8	45
10	50
12	60

pipes larger than two inches in diameter. A second wrench may be used to keep in place the pipe that has already been installed. Two or three threads should show outside the completed joint, if threading has been done over the required length of pipe.

Bending Steel Pipe

Smaller size pipes are often bent to provide minor changes in direction, without using additional fittings. Table 4-5 gives the minimum allowable radii of bends for various sizes of pipe. Attempts should be made to use larger radii than these whenever possible.

Smaller size pipes are normally bent without heating, by the use of a simple tool called a *hickey*. It can be prepared in a jiffy if you get a small length of pipe and a T-fitting one or two sizes larger than the pipe to be bent. Insert the piece of pipe into the side inlet of the T and the hickey is ready. Push it over the pipe and apply leverage till the latter bends to the desired extent.

Bench tools and heat are used to bend larger size pipes. A bending block is made by drilling holes in a steel plate (Fig. 4-31) which is then fastened to the bench. Pins are placed in the holes and the pipe is put on the block between the pins so that it goes on the inside of one pin and outside of the other. As leverage is exerted, the pipe bends. Heat is applied to the inside of the bend if necessary and the pipe is continuously shifted forward to make a smooth bend. If required, the pins can be moved to different holes.

DRAINAGE PIPES

The soil and waste pipes in a plumbing system carry the waste water from fixtures (tubs, lavatories, washbasins, washers, etc.) to the house drain. The drain transmits the waste water to the street sewer. Because the waste water contains solids flowing along with water, the drainage lines which carry it should have certain essential features. The changes of direction should be gentle so that the solid particles do not settle because of reduced flow velocity at a sharp bend. The fittings have to be of such a design that they do not cause undue obstruction to the flow inside the pipe. Examples of such obstructions are ridges and pipe shoulders. The insides of fittings are made as smooth as possible, for the same reason. Also, when joining a vertical line with a horizontal one, the latter is given a small, almost imperceptible pitch, like 1/4 inch per linear foot, which maintains a good flow velocity and prevents accumulation of solids. To make joints at such locations, threaded or machined right-angle elbows can be used. These are designed to provide a change of direction just a little over 90°, resulting in the required pitch on the horizontal line.

A drainage pipe does not have to withstand water pressures like in a water pipe, hence it can be made of smaller wall thickness. For instance, when using copper pipe for drainage, a lighter variety with thinner walls is used. This not only keeps the cost down, but also results in ease of handling. When you go to buy a drainage pipe,

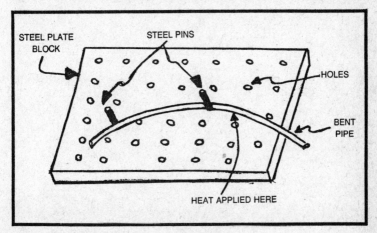

Fig. 4-31. Bending a pipe by leverage and heat.

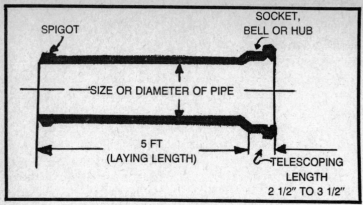

Fig. 4-32. One length of cast-iron pipe.

mention this fact to your supplier and save a few dollars by not buying a water pipe instead. Usual types of drainage pipe are: light copper, cast iron, threaded galvanized steel, clay tile, cement or concrete tile, fiber, and plastic.

CAST-IRON AND THREADED STEEL DRAINAGE PIPES

For drainage lines like sewers, main drains, soil stacks, waste stacks, and underground installations, cast-iron pipe is universally employed because of its durability and resistance to corrosion. The branches between fixture drains and the main drain are generally made of copper tubes of the lighter (DWV) variety. Threaded galvanized steel pipe of 1 1/2 inch and 2 inch sizes is used along with cast iron for making up branch drains and vent lines. It may also be used at times for the secondary stacks. Because it is easily corroded by chemicals, its use is prohibited in underground locations. Usually it comes in 21-foot lengths.

Cast-iron pipe is available in two weights: service and extra heavy. It comes plain or coated with a preservative to resist corrosion. The life of cast-iron pipe is estimated to be more than a hundred years unless installed in a location with a high concentration of chemicals in the soil, or it carries highly corrosive flows. For household plumbing, the service weight pipe is good enough, unless the local plumbing code prohibits its use—which is rather unlikely. The extra-heavy variety is employed when the flow contains corrosive materials or when the pipe has to bear heavy loads, like under roadways with much traffic. Tall stacks in multi-story buildings may also be made of the heavier variety.

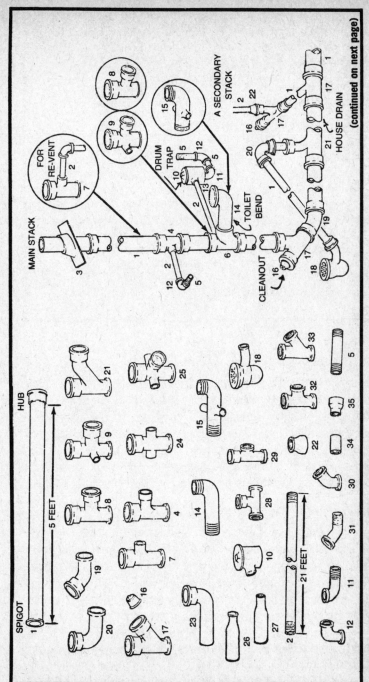

(continued on next page)

Fig. 4-33. Cast-iron and threaded steel pipe fittings.

Parts Lists for Fig. 4-33.

Cast-iron pipe comes in 5-foot lengths, with a socket, hub, or bell at one end and a spigot at the other (Fig. 4-32). When a length shorter than 5 feet is required, it is cut from a special piece having hubs at both ends. Cast-iron pipe sizes range from 2 inches to 8 inches inside diameter. When storing, care should be taken to select a spot protected from weather, otherwise corrosion and pitting may take place. Being brittle, it might crack if carelessly handled, or dropped from a height onto a hard surface like a concrete floor.

Cast-Iron and Threaded Steel Pipe Fittings

A large number of fittings are available, as shown in Fig. 4-33. The illustration shows where some of these are used in the main stack, the secondary stack, the revent pipe, and the house drain. The *sanitary* type fittings must be used to make up all the drainage lines carrying liquid flows. On vent pipes carrying only gases and no liquids the *straight* cast-iron or *ordinary* threaded fittings are used.

It is not necessary to know all the possible fittings but you should at least look at the more common ones illustrated in Fig. 4-33. It will give an idea of what you can get and where to use it in the home plumbing system.

Measuring Cast-Iron Pipe

As illustrated in Fig. 4-32, the total length of a section of pipe is the sum of the *laying length* and the *telescoping length*. The former dimension is usually 5 feet and the latter varies with the pipe size. It is 2 1/2 inch for 2-inch pipe, 2 3/4 inch for 3-inch pipe, and 3 inches for 4-, 5- and 6-inch pipes.

Cutting Cast-Iron Pipe

Cast-iron pipe cannot be cut with a pipe cutter. For cutting the standard service-weight pipe, a 1/16 inch deep groove is made all around with a hacksaw. The pipe is placed over a thick plank of wood with the groove just overhanging it. Then a few blows are carefully applied on top of the overhanging pipe with a hammer till the grooved section breaks off from the rest.

Extra-heavy variety is usually cut by the hammer and chisel method. First make a chalk or file mark (with a triangular file) all around the pipe where a cut is desired. Next place the pipe over a wooden board or mound of earth (Fig. 4-34) and score it around the chalk or file mark with a small, pointed cold chisel. The chisel should not be very sharp, and should be moved along the mark a little at a

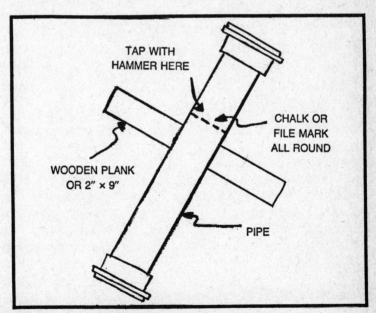

Fig. 4-34. Cutting cast-iron pipe with hammer and chisel.

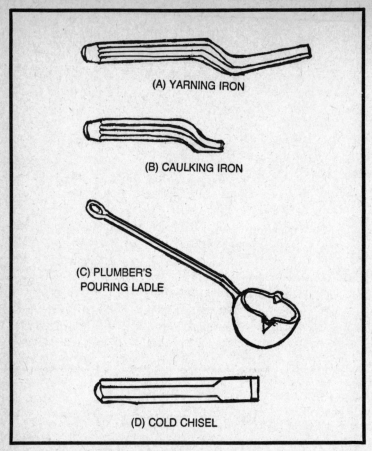

Fig. 4-35. Tools for making cast-iron pipe joints.

time, and tapped with a hammer on its top. Continue this process, turning the pipe round and round and increasing the intensity of blows till the pipe breaks off at the line of cut.

When only a small length of pipe, one or two inches, is to be removed, it can be cut with a hacksaw and an adjustable wrench. The hacksaw is used to cut a deep groove all around to a depth of not less than half the wall thickness of the pipe. Then leverage is applied with the adjustable wrench, and the smaller section of the pipe is broken off.

Jointing Cast-Iron Pipe

Making joints on cast-iron pipe requires a special technique. The spigot end of one length of pipe goes into the bell end of the other and the joint is made by a filling of oakum and poured lead. Several tools are required: a yarning iron, caulking iron, chisel, melting pot, and pouring ladle (Fig. 4-35). Figure 4-36 shows a finished bell-and-spigot joint which, when carefully made, should have an equal thickness of the jointing material all around. The actual procedure consists of the following steps:

1. Remove moisture and foreign matter from the bell and spigot ends of the pipe. Slide the spigot of the upper pipe into the bell or socket of the lower one and make sure that it is properly *centered*. If the upper pipe has a cut end, there will be no spigot.

2. With the help of a yarning or packing iron (shown in Fig. 4-35A), pack the hub with an oakum gasket or a thick layer of loose fibrous oakum: first wrap it loosely around the plain or spigot end, and then pack it firmly with the packing iron, using hammer blows on its top (Fig. 4-37). Take care not to apply very hard blows or you may break the pipe or fitting.

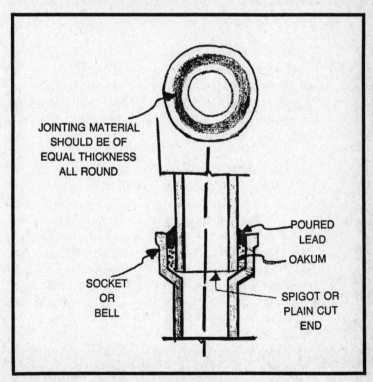

Fig. 4-36. Bell and spigot joint on cast-iron pipe.

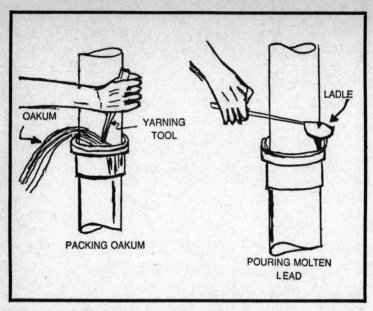

Fig. 4-37. Making a lead joint on cast-iron pipe.

Oakum is a fibrous material that you can obtain from a plumbing store. Pack several layers till the annular space is completely filled, 3/4 inch to 1 inch from the top of the hub. The oakum should be thoroughly compressed and made to have an even top so it can receive the molten lead that will fill the rest of the space.

3. Heat the lead in a melting pot till it melts and gets cherry red. Taking a small amount in a pre-heated ladle, pour it on top of the packed oakum and caulk with a caulking iron using light taps. When this layer of lead has hardened, pour more molten lead into the joint, till it fills completely up to a point a little above the top of the rim. As soon as the lead hardens, which may take a minute or two, start caulking its outer edge with an outside caulking iron. Giving light hammer taps, move gradually around. Next caulk the inside edge with an inside caulking iron. Lead should grip the oakum and be packed tightly against both the pipes. If you crack a fitting or a pipe when making a joint, replace it. Sometimes molten lead is poured all in one shot, and not in two layers. Table 4-6 gives the requirements of jointing materials.

The above method applies to the usual jointing situation, as shown in Fig. 4-36, where the bell is pointing upwards. There may be cases when it is the other way around, and an *upside-down joint* has to be made. In such a case, the initial steps of aligning the socket or plain end inside the hub, and caulking the oakum in the joint, are the same as before. After these steps are taken, a *joint runner* is clamped around the pipe (Fig. 4-38). This joint runner is a fat asbestos rope provided with a clamp. The ends of the runner are raised and clamped tightly; then the runner is slid up the pipe till it rests against the joint tightly. If necessary, it may be tapped a few times with a hammer. Next, using putty, plaster, or fine clay soil, a funnel is made in the raised end. You have to let the funnel dry before pouring molten lead into it; or else hot lead will blow out because of the steam generated. As the lead is poured, it will gradually rise in the joint and fill it. When the joint cools down, remove the runner and the clamp. Then, using a chisel, cut the lump of lead from the space outside the pipe joint. Finally caulk the lead with caulking irons, first on the outside and then on the inside edge.

A *horizontal joint* may be made in a similar manner except that it will not be necessary to form a channel (Fig. 4-39). When poured, the molten lead will just flow down through the opening at the clamp and fill the joint.

If you are working on a pipeline in a spot where molten lead cannot possibly be used, the joint can be made with lead wool or shredded lead that you can buy at any plumbing store. Roll it into several strands, each approximately 1/2 inch in diameter and a

Table 4-6. Lead and Oakum Required to Make Joints on Cast-Iron Soil Pipes.

Pipe Diameter in inches	Amount of Lead per joint in lbs.	Amount of Oakum per joint in lbs.
2	1 - 2	0.20
3	2 - 3	0.30
4	3 - 4	0.45
5	4 - 5	0.55
6	4 1/2 - 6	0.65
7	5 - 7	0.75
8	6 - 8	0.85
10	7 - 10	0.95
12	9 - 12	1.25

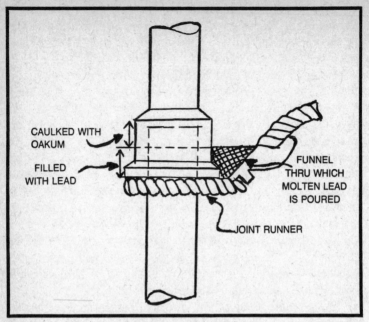

Fig. 4-38. Making an upside-down joint on cast-iron pipe.

couple of feet long. Insert these into the hub and continue caulking till the joint is made to your satisfaction.

There are two more types of joint used for cast-iron pipes: *gasket-type* joint and *no-hub* system. The gasket-type is used when the pipe comes with one plain end and one with a hub. A neoprene gasket is placed inside the bell of one section. The plain end of the second section is pushed in after applying a lubricant. The tight fit gives a waterproof joint.

A much simpler and newer method for making joints is the no-hub system. The ends of all pipes and fittings in this system are manufactured with plain ends. They are joined together by a neoprene sleeve which is kept in place by a shield. The shield, in turn, is screwed down tightly with clamps. The no-hub joint is easy to assemble and disassemble. Some building codes, however, prohibit its use particularly in underground installations. Where permitted, however, this is the easiest and the least expensive joint.

PLASTIC PIPE

For domestic plumbing, plastic pipe is gradually gaining popularity. It's light, easy to work with, resistant to corrosion, and less expensive than other types. It is also self-cleaning; is not subject to rotting, and does not sweat. Many state and local plumbing codes still do not approve of its use, however, except for small size drainage and waste pipes.

Plastic pipe comes in many varieties: polyethylene (flexible variety), polyvinyl chloride (PVC), ABS (acrylonitrile-butadiene-styrene), CPVC (Chlorinated Polyvinyl Chloride), etc. Of these, only CPVC pipe can handle hot water.

The flexible plastic pipe (polyethylene) comes in lengths of up to 1,000 feet and is the best one to work with in a home plumbing system. It has been used in deep wells for quite some time as it can be easily lowered and withdrawn at will. The rigid varieties have been approved by many state and local authorities for use in the wastewater plumbing system.

Fittings that are used on flexible plastic pipes come with threaded ends. To make a pipe joint with these types, slip a metal clamp over the end of the pipe, insert the fitting *into* the pipe, and tighten the clamp after slipping it over the joint.

Rigid plastic pipes come in 10- and 20-foot lengths. Fittings (Fig. 4-40) are joined by the *solvent welding* system. The pipe end is coated with a special plastic cement, and slipped inside the fitting while moving it around to spread the cement evenly. The pipe and fitting are actually fused under the chemical action of the solvent present in the plastic cement—hence the term *solvent welding*.

VITRIFIED CLAY PIPE

The use of vitrified clay pipe inside buildings is prohibited by most plumbing codes. It is brittle and inflexible, and any movements

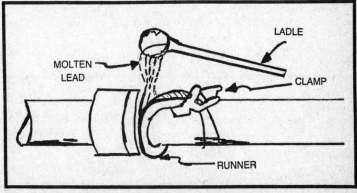

Fig. 4-39. A horizontal caulked joint is made in the same way as an upside-down joint except that it will not be necessary to form a channel.

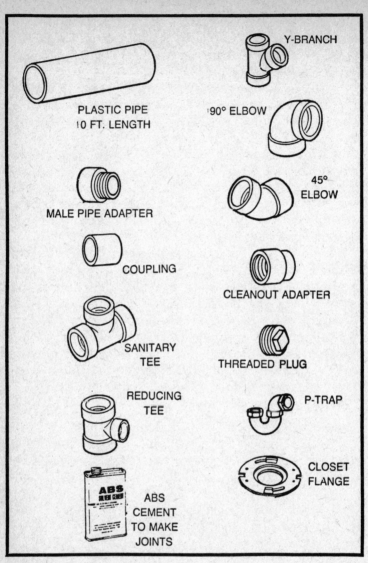

Fig. 4-40. Rigid plastic pipe and fittings.

cause the joints to break open. The only place you may use it in your system is the connection between the house drainage system and the septic tank or the street sewer.

You probably have seen this pipe sometime. It looks dark brown and has a surface glaze. One end is plain and the other usually bell-shaped.

The length is measured in the same manner as for cast-iron pipe. The overall length is its laying length plus the telescoping length which varies from 1 1/2 inches for 4-inch pipe to 4 inches for 36-inch pipe. Cutting is seldom required because it comes in short lengths, up to a maximum of 6 feet. When necessary, it can be cut with a hammer and brick chisel. Because the pipe is brittle, cutting should be done gradually and carefully.

Joints are made with cement mortar or bituminous compounds. The spigot or plain end is inserted into the bell end, and properly aligned (Fig. 4-41). The hub is then packed with oakum to a depth of approximately 3/4 inch. Tamping should be done with a thin, planed-down piece of wood—*not* by a yarning iron which might shatter the pipe. Next the joint is completely filled with mortar or a bituminous compound and tamped to pack it tight. It should be finished with a bevelled edge outside. The mortar used for the joint should have one part of cement and two parts of clean sand. If you are joining only a few feet of pipe, they may be placed in a vertical position; the joint can be made in this position and then moved into the horizontal position or whatever is required according to the plan. When making joints in a horizontal position on the ground spread scrap paper underneath the pipe to prevent loose earth from getting into the pipe joints.

CONCRETE PIPE

Concrete pipe comes with or without steel reinforcement, in sizes from 4 to 108 inches. The ends are bell-and-spigot or tongue-

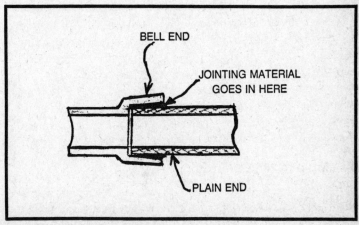

Fig. 4-41. Vitrified clay pipe joint.

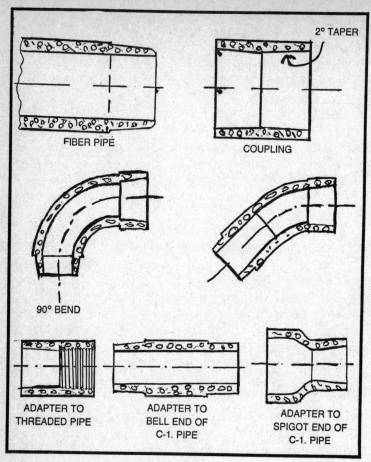

2° TAPER

FIBER PIPE

COUPLING

90° BEND

ADAPTER TO
THREADED PIPE

ADAPTER TO
BELL END OF
C-1. PIPE

ADAPTER TO
SPIGOT END OF
C-1. PIPE

Fig. 4-42. Bituminized fiber pipe and fittings.

and-groove. Cutting is seldom done, specially for reinforced concrete pipe. Joints are made in the same way as for vitrified clay pipe, with cement mortar and oakum. When using any other jointing compounds, the manufacturer's recommendations should be followed. Concrete pipe is largely used for storm sewer and sanitary sewer mains, and also for large water supply mains in the streets.

BITUMINIZED FIBER PIPE

Made of interwoven fibers soaked with bituminous compounds, bituminized fiber pipe resists corrosion, is lightweight, and is easily installed. It comes in sizes from 2 inches to 6 inches and in lengths of

5 feet and 8 feet. Both perforated and plain varieties are available. Like vitrified clay pipe, the plain fiber pipe is used to convey waste water from the building to the septic tank or to the sewer. The perforated pipe is used in the leaching fields to spread the overflow from the septic tank into porous soil for absorption. Usually these leaching pipes are laid at a very small pitch—1/4 inch or even 1/8 inch per foot—and the 8-foot lengths are better suited for precision laying at such small grades than are other types of pipe which come in shorter lengths.

Various fittings are available for fiber pipes: Ys, Ts, bends, reducers, adapter reducers, couplings, etc. (Fig. 4-42). Adapters can be obtained to connect fiber pipe to other types of pipe, like the cast-iron variety.

Fiber pipe has tapered or *tooled* ends. It can be cut to the required length by a cross-cut or rip hacksaw. Cuts produce plain ends which have to be tapered by a fiber-pipe tapering tool before the pieces can be attached to fittings or other pipe lengths.

You can make the joints easily (Fig. 4-43). After clearing any grease or burrs from the tapers on both the pipe and the fitting, attach them to each other. Normally the fitting will readily slide up to within 1/4 to 1/3 inch of the shoulder on the taper. Now put a wooden block against the fitting if you are joining it to an installed

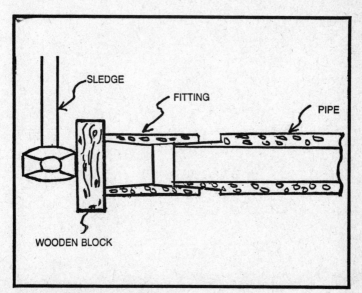

Fig. 4-43. Making a fiber pipe joint.

pipe, or against the end of the pipe if you are joining it to an already installed fitting on the line. Keeping the block in place with one hand and the line braced by your helper, apply light taps on the block with a sledge. This will gradually bring the pipe and the fitting together; finally, the fitting will rest against the taper shoulder. The heat produced during the driving process fuses the skin materials of the pipe and the fitting to produce a watertight joint.

Common Pipeline Problems and How To Fix Them

Common Pipeline Problems and How To Fix Them

A properly designed and installed plumbing system gives very good service; despite its large number of components, there are usually few malfunctions and breakdowns. When something does go wrong, you can easily put things right, with a minimum number of tools and supplies, by following the simple procedures explained in this book. This chapter deals with problems related to water supply and drainage lines, while subsequent chapters are devoted to sinks, traps, toilets, faucets, tubs, showers, and electric appliances like garbage disposers, and dishwashers.

The following problems usually occur on pipelines:

1. Leaks at water supply pipes and joints.
2. Leaks at drainage pipes and joints.
3. Condensation drips from pipes.
4. Freezing of exposed pipes.
5. Noises in pipelines.
6. Water hammer (a banging noise heard in a water pipe following an abrupt change in flow and pressure).
7. Low water pressures.
8. Clogs in pipelines.

This chapter is devoted to a discussion of ways to troubleshoot all these problems except for the cloggings which will be discussed in the next chapter along with similar situations at sinks, lavatories, and traps.

LEAKING WATER SUPPLY LINES

There are many types of leaks. Some cause a little inconvenience while others can flood your basement or one of the floors. The measures taken to stop a leak have to be compatible with the seriousness of the situation.

Water invariably contains some dissolved chemicals which corrode and gradually weaken the pipe that carries the flow. Pipe so weakened may crack under vibrations or when hit by some object. Internal water pressure or *water hammer* may also trigger a leak. (Water hammer, as mentioned before, is a bang heard in a water pipe, following an abrupt change of flow and a resultant surge in pressure.)

Very often leakage starts at the threaded joints of a pipe and you will find that either the joint has come loose or the pipe has fractured. The drip will probably stop with a little tightening of the joint. However, take care that you do not loosen an adjoining fitting. If you can't stop the leak by tightening the joint, remove the fitting and replace it with a new one. This should be satisfactory unless the pipe is highly corroded and completely breaks under the force of the tools when you try to install the new fitting. If this happens, there is no alternative except to replace the entire length or a complete run of the pipeline, including the corroded fittings. Small leaks at a threaded fitting can be repaired by opening the joints and re-making them with some good jointing material.

Flexible copper tubing enlarges every time it freezes; ultimately, the hardening and the strain will break it down. Plastic pipe, however, is unaffected by freezing.

Complete replacement is the most satisfactory way to deal with leaking joints or pipes. But very often, leaks develop at a time when you do not have the necessary tools and materials or are otherwise not ready to do a complete job. If so, you have to be content with stop-gap repairs.

Figure 5-1 illustrates various types of emergency repair. Very small leaks may be stopped by a triple wrapping of waterproof tape. The pipe should be wiped dry with a rag and the taping started about three inches from one side of the hole and carried the same distance

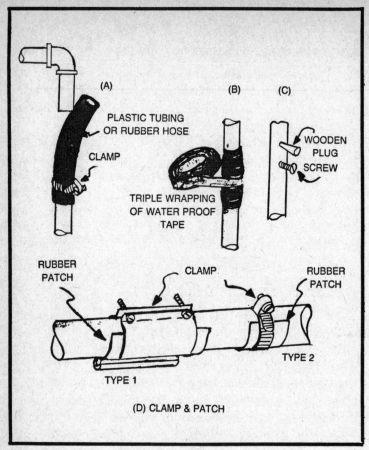

(A)

PLASTIC TUBING
OR RUBBER HOSE

CLAMP

(B)

TRIPLE WRAPPING
OF WATER PROOF
TAPE

(C)

WOODEN
PLUG
SCREW

RUBBER
PATCH

CLAMP

RUBBER
PATCH

TYPE 1

TYPE 2

(D) CLAMP & PATCH

Fig. 5-1. Emergency repairs to leaky pipes.

on the other side. Three wrappings should be enough. Very tiny leaks can be sealed by compound sticks like Krak-Stik which you can get at any plumbing or hardware store. As you rub the stick over the hole—even when water is running in the pipe—the leakage stops.

Self-tapping wooden plugs or screws are also used to stop leaks, but their use is confined to large diameter pipes or tanks. On smaller pipes, these plugs reduce the flow. The right size of screw, when properly tightened, provides sufficient pressure to close the leak (Fig. 5-1C).

A very common and easy way to repair leaks on a pipe having cracks and holes is the *clamp and patch* method shown in Fig. 5-1D. You need a clamp and a patch made from sheet plastic or inner tube.

The latter should be cut about 3 inches longer than the damaged section of the pipe and slightly less wide than the outer circumference of the pipe. Clamps come in commercial sizes and you may buy one according to the pipe size. For covering a large area, use a type I clamp with two screws. For smaller lengths, a type II clamp will suffice. If it is not a large pipe, a patch can be quickly made by splitting a small length of common garden hose and slipping it over the pipe leak after applying plumber's cement on the pipe surface. Clamps may then be fitted at both ends.

Another method for making temporary repairs to a pipe length that has several leaks and areas of deterioration is to cut out the affected length with a hacksaw and slip a length of rubber hose or flexible tubing over the ends. Then tighten the tubing with clamps, as shown in Fig. 5-1A. Before you start to cut the pipe, *don't forget to shut off the water supply*, otherwise you will flood the whole area. The inside diameter of the hose should be equal to the outer diameter of your pipe. You will find that a 3/4-inch garden hose will fit over a 1/2-inch pipe and a 1-inch hose will fit over a 3/4-inch pipe.

The best way to repair a leak in a pipe is to replace the entire section with proper fittings, as Fig. 5-2 illustrates for a threaded pipe. After the supply is shut off, cut the pipe with a hacksaw and unscrew the two portions from the line. The cut should be at least 4 inches away from fittings on either side. (If a union happens to be on this line, you are lucky and can just unscrew the lengths on either

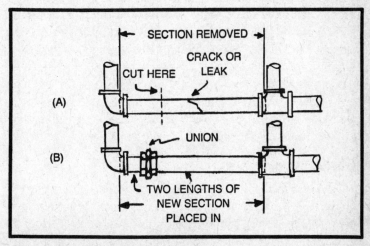

Fig. 5-2. Replacing a leaky section of pipe.

side without having to cut the line.) Now make a new section with two lengths of pipe and a union (Fig. 5-2B) so that it is exactly of the same length as the old pipe. Replace this section in the line, first tightening at one end and then at the other.

Often leaks develop on pipes located inside partitions or under floors. In such cases it will be necessary to dismantle a part of the floor or to remove plaster or sheetrock from the walls before repairs can be done. Sometimes the leaky pipe can be uncovered at two accessible points near the fittings. It can then be cut at these points and the leaky portion can be abandoned. In its place, flexible copper tubing is installed by the use of adapters. Because it is flexible, this tubing can be put inside partitions and floors, through the two openings, with the help of a chain. If there is no danger from rodents, plastic pipe may be used.

Joints in copper pipes may sometimes leak if damaged. The repair is simple. First remove all water from the pipe and then heat the joint to melting temperature. Touch the wire solder at the leaking part of the joint and fill it with molten solder. When you are working close to other fittings, the solder in these other joints is likely to flow out. Avoid this by wrapping these joints with a wet cloth.

Sometimes a section of exposed copper pipeline may get hit by an object, as in a tool shed or garage, and get cracked or crushed. The damaged section should be cut out and replaced with a new section, which can be attached to the line by means of *slip couplings*. The procedure is illustrated later in Fig. 12-5 except that in the present case the new section will be made of a plain length of copper pipe with no T-fitting. Slip couplings are small lengths of tubing with an internal diameter slightly larger than the outer diameter of the copper pipe on which they are to be used. These are slipped on the ends A and B (Fig. 12-5) and, after the new section of pipe is put in place, are centrally spaced over the joints. Solder is melted with a propane torch and the joint is made as usual by welding.

LEAKING DRAINAGE PIPES

All the methods described for water pipes can be used on drainage pipes too; however, since drainage lines do not run under pressure, repairs can be made much more easily. Simply clean the leaking area with some soapy water, dry it thoroughly, and wrap it around with electrician's tape. This is very effective on small and medium size drains and will stop leakages even at the joints. If the drainage pipe happens to be made of cast iron with leaded joints, the leakage will generally be at the joint itself, and can be stopped by caulking the joint with a caulking tool. Additional lead yarn may be added if necessary. If a caulking tool is not readily available, use a hammer and chisel. Don't cut too deeply into the lead. Place the chisel inside the lead and give light blows with the hammer. As the lead spreads out, the leakage will stop.

LEAKS CAUSED BY DISASTERS

Disaster leaks may be caused by the bursting of a water line or the opening up of a joint. These leaks may flood an entire floor and result in considerable damage. In such emergencies you don't have time to call a plumber and await his arrival. You should familiarize yourself with the elements of your plumbing long before such an event occurs. For instance, as has been mentioned, every member of your household should know where the main shut-off valve is located, and how to turn it off. Since the electric appliances are likely to get short-circuited when they get wet, the electric supply should also be shut off; you should know beforehand where the electric master switch is located and how to shut it off as well.

In most cases you will find the water shut-off valve on the main water line just outside your house. It is either a gate valve which can be turned round by hand, or an L-shaped rod that may need a wrench. A few clockwise turns will shut off the supply. Since these valves are seldom used, they get corroded by moisture. It is a good idea to check them once or twice a year and to operate them by turning them off and on. A little lubrication will also keep them in good working order. It will be helpful if you make a little sketch to show the direction in which to turn the valve to shut off the supply. You may want to hang the sketch by the valve. Sometimes the shut-off valve is located in your basement, along with the water meter (Fig. 5-3).

After the water and electric supplies are shut off, you should examine the pipeline that has burst and assess the damage. Many times you will find that either the pipe has sprung a few good-sized leaks or a joint has burst open. Repairs can be made as described before for ordinary leaks. In a few cases, however, a section of the

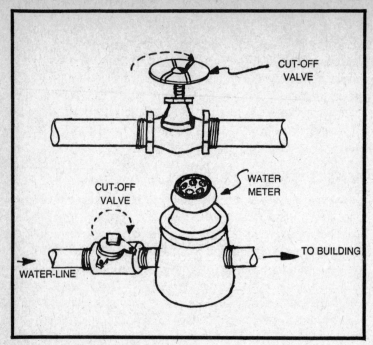

Fig. 5-3. Cut-off valves and water meter.

line may be corroded and deteriorated so badly that there is no alternative but to replace it with new pipe.

A similar but much less serious situation is caused when a waste water drain clogs and overflows. Since a drain does not run under pressure, the emergency can be countered just by making sure that no additional water is allowed to flow into it until you examine the situation and make the necessary repairs. Baths, toilets, sinks, washers, etc., which flow into the drain, should not be used during this period.

CONDENSATION DRIPS FROM PIPES

These drips may damage plaster, wallpaper, structural members like studs and sills, floor coverings, and articles or tools lying under a cold-water line. The phenomenon, generally called *sweating of pipes*, is caused by condensation of the moisture in the air as it comes in contact with the cold surface of the water line. Beads of moisture collect and drip off continuously. Because the cold water in the pipe is not stationary, but flows to the fixtures, it does not have time to get heated to the room temperature; more cold water continually comes from the street main. As such, the condensation and dripping continue. This problem, which may be experienced in the basements during summer months, can be eliminated by the use of dehumidifiers. These devices also help stop condensation on the cool surfaces of walls and floors. A crude method for dealing with sweating pipes is to keep a few collecting pans under the areas of drips.

A very effective method for dealing with the problem is the use of anti-drip insulation tape, which comes in self-sticking rolls. Both the pipe and the fittings should be fully covered with this tape. Alternatively, the pipe may be coated with a special paint containing cork granules. The self-sticking tape itself may contain cork granules. Another type of tape to use is asbestos tape (non-self-sticking), which is attached to the pipe by asbestos cement. You will find patented varieties of no-drip compounds at a plumbing store. These compounds can be applied like a paint, with the help of a brush. These may not be very durable, however, and you may have to apply several coats to achieve a satisfactory effect.

If considerable amount of condensation develops at a toilet tank and keeps dripping on the floor, you may attach a tray directly under the tank. The tray should be a little larger than the underside of the tank and should either have a drain in the center leading to the bowl, or be provided with absorbent pads.

FREEZING OF EXPOSED COLD-WATER LINES

Where temperatures during the winters go down below freezing, exposed pipes should be properly insulated at the time of installation. All pipes running underground should be laid well below the frost level. The depth of frostline below the ground varies from locality to locality; you may have to contact your local U. S. weather bureau to find the average frost depth in your area. Install the pipes accordingly.

Figure 5-4 illustrates a method for insulating exposed pipes. The pipes are first wrapped with tar paper and then covered with an insulation which generally consists of a 1 1/4 inch to 2 inch thick felt layer running continuously so as not to leave any air gaps between adjacent lengths. Finally the felt layer is covered with spirally wrapped canvas until its edges are overlapped and its outer surface is painted.

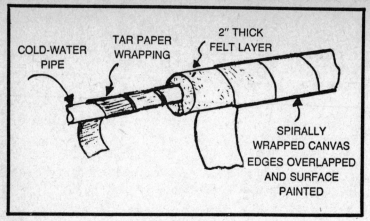

Fig. 5-4. One method of insulating cold water pipes to prevent freezing.

An exposed pipeline that has already been installed without any insulation may be insulated by enclosing it in a rectangular wooden box which is then tightly packed with sawdust, mineral wool, ground cork, or similar material. The thickness of the insulation should not be less than two inches. Figure 5-5 illustrates how a riser pipe can be insulated by enclosing it inside an earth tile. The pipe is wrapped with a layer of felt and placed inside the tile, leaving an annular space or air gap which also helps insulation. The top portion of the pipe just below the floor is enclosed in a wooden boxing with an insulating material like sawdust packed in between.

In new constructions, it is important to insulate water supply pipes properly. Attempts should be made to install as many pipes as possible along the inner walls; however, you will always have pipes on the outside walls connecting to the outdoor faucets. The outside pipes should be of the frost-free variety. As the low winter temperatures start to prevail, shut off the supply to these outside faucets and drain off the line by opening the tap.

Another way to insulate exposed pipes is to wrap them with heat cable or heat tape which has an automatic thermostat that kicks in the heating system as soom as the temperature drops down to 35° or 36° F.

Pipes that freeze due to low temperatures are likely to burst. Water expands as it turns into ice and if there is no space for expansion, the pipe is subjected to severe stresses. Depending on the pipe's strength, it may burst. This bursting does not always occur at the point where freezing starts. For instance, ice may start forming at an exposed section of the pipe and progress towards the inside until it meets an obstruction like a bend, a rough spot, or a valve. As the movement is stopped, the pipe at that spot is subjected to high stresses, and it may burst. This is why a pipe may mysteriously burst inside a kitchen which is normally quite warm.

What do you do to thaw a pipe found frozen on a chilly morning? Several alternatives are available—some good, some bad. Each one uses a source of external heat.

A quick and inexpensive way is to use electric heating by attaching the terminals of a welding machine or a pipe-thawing transformer to the frozen ends and let the heating continue until the ice melts and the flow of water resumes (Fig. 5-6). You have to be very careful with this method because if done without proper precaution, it may prove hazardous.

If the pipe is accessible, heat can be applied by wrapping the pipe with cloth, heavy towels, or burlap bags, and pouring scalding water over it. Place a bucket under the pipe to catch the overflow and be very careful lest you burn yourself. Thawing should always be

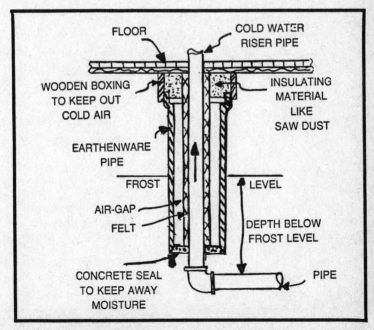

Fig. 5-5. Protecting vertical cold water riser pipes from frost.

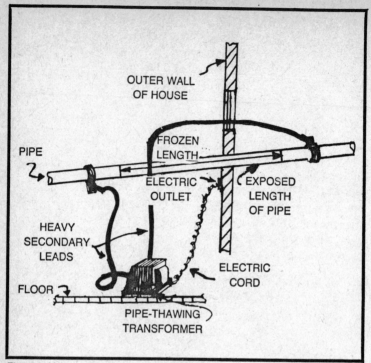

Fig. 5-6. Using a pipe-thawing transformer.

started at one end of the pipe, never from the middle; otherwise the formation of steam inside the pipe, or even the expansion of heated water entrapped by ice, may lead to a burst. Start from the faucet side of the frozen section and work toward the supply end, keeping the faucet open for the escape of steam or water. This will also serve to indicate when the ice has melted. In any case, be prepared to shut off the water supply if the pipe has ruptured.

Other ways to apply heat are: to play a jet of steam on the frozen section to inject steam into the pipe, or to heat it with an open flame or with charcoal fire. An open flame can be provided by a propane torch, which again should be used very carefully; a fire can start if you happen to ignite combustible material like wood, cloth, or paper lying close by, or if a wooden wall is running behind the pipe. Asbestos siding may be used as a protective shield. The flame should not play at one spot too long—keep it moving back and forth. Also do not apply too much heat at the joints or else they will open up and create additional poblems. Sometimes slower methods like holding an electric iron against the pipe or using an electric heater are preferred because they are safer.

Another very good method often used to thaw drain pipes as well is to run boiling water into the pipe if a section of it can be removed. This operation can also be started from the outlet. A small pipe or a garden hose may be used for a horizontal pipe. For a vertical pipe or for the end of a drainage pipe, either a garden hose or a rubber tubing will have to be used (Fig. 5-7). The tubing is inserted into the pipe until it strikes against the ice deposit. On the drain pipe, you will have to remove the trap. Attach a funnel to the other end of the hose and, after raising it, start pouring hot water (almost boiling) through the funnel. A bucket should be placed under the end of the

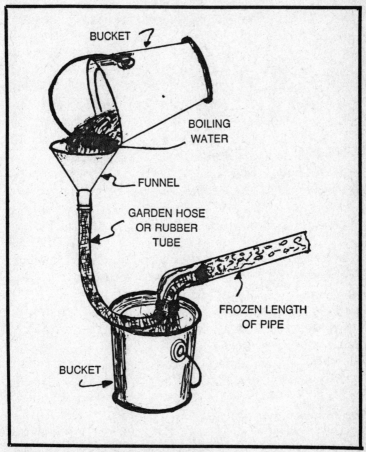

Fig. 5-7. Thawing a frozen pipe with hot water.

pipe to collect backflow. Be careful not to get scalded by hot water backing out of the pipe and splashing onto your body. Gradually the ice will start melting; the hose will have to be pushed further and further until the whole blockage has been removed.

NOISES IN PIPELINES

There are a variety of noises you may hear inside your plumbing system from time to time. Each one has a different cause. Generally people tend to attribute every noise to *water hammer*, but this is not always correct. One of the most common noises is the whistling and chattering at faucets, which may be caused by a loose or worn-out washer or poor hydraulic design, especially if the faucet is a cheap one. You should open the faucet, take out the spindle assembly and check the washer and its seat. If necessary, change the washer. More detailed instructions on faucets will be found in Chapter 8. In poorly designed faucets the water passage area is insufficient—a condition which causes a high velocity of flow. When this high velocity water changes direction near the faucet outlet, it generates air bubbles which subsequently collapse, creating vibrations and noise. Depending on the frequency of vibration, the noise is of the chattering, pounding, or whistling variety. In old plumbing systems, where Fuller-type faucets may still be found, such noises are the result of either a loose ball inside or a worn-out ball shaft and spindle eccentric, which make the assembly rattle.

Squeaking and banging noises are often caused by pipes striking against walls, brackets, and hangers or some other solid objects. You have first to locate the exact area of trouble by turning the water off and on, and looking for any movements on the pipeline. If the noise comes from a length of pipe located behind the wall or below the floor, it is not necessary to tear the walls or floor apart. Stops placed at each end of the line where it comes out of the walls or floors will effectively eliminate the noise.

When the noise is coming from the vicinity of a tube strap or U-clamp you will probably find that the pipe is loose and is banging against the wall. A patch of rubber or a small piece of garden hose slit lengthwise and inserted around the pipe will silence the noise. If the pipe is banging against a masonry wall, place a wooden block between the pipe and the wall and secure it to the wall with masonry nails. Use a pipe strap to attach the pipe to the block. Figure 5-8 illustrates methods for eliminating noises on pipelines. Lengthwise movements of long horizontal pipes can be reduced by providing firm supports in the shape of pipe straps, hangers, or shelf brackets (brackets attached to the underside of a shelf and supporting a pipe running underneath). Care should be taken that pipes are not fixed rigidly. Temperature changes cause expansion and contraction, and the pipe should be free to move to some extent. When securing a pipe with an anchor or a bracket, always place a rubber piece between the pipe and the clip. Sometimes a water pipe and a drainpipe running next to each other vibrate and rattle. Probably it may be a good idea to solder them to each other.

Pipe that is inadequate in size or has collected deposits on its inside surface during a long period of use, may present noise problems due to high velocity of water flowing through its restricted area. You should either replace the pipe or insulate the outside to cut down the noise. Several types of sound-dampening insulation can be purchased.

Drainpipes do not have noise problems similar to those on water pipes. But if the vent pipe gets clogged, you will hear a sort of

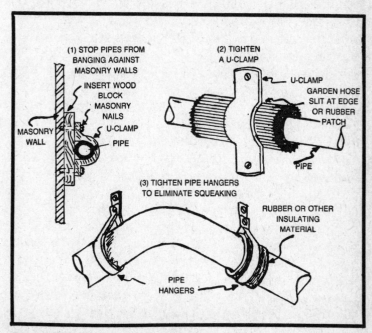

Fig. 5-8. Eliminating noises in pipelines.

sucking sound when waste water goes down from a sink or washbasin into the drain. Sometimes there may be no vent at all. In addition to the noise problem, the absence of a vent pipe may result in the water-seal of the fixtures being broken by the back pressure of gases in the house drain and sewer. This condition may lead to sewer gases entering your home. If that is the case, buy an antisyphonage trap from your plumbing store and install it on the drain. This will take care of both the noise and the sewer gases. A clogged drain, on the other hand, can easily be cleaned with a plumber's snake.

WATER HAMMER

And then there are the water hammer noises on water lines. These are pretty common. When a faucet or valve is closed abruptly, the flowing water is brought to a sudden rest. The momentum of water is converted into shock waves which travel back and forth between the valve or faucet and the point where the pipe connects to a larger pipe or tank, or changes its direction. In addition to causing a hammer noise, which can be heard almost all over the house, the energy of the wave also vibrates or shakes the pipe violently; this vibration may rupture the pipe at its fittings, or crack the fittings themselves. This is why the use of malleable iron fittings is recommended on water pipes. In hard rigid pipes made of steel, brass, or iron, the water hammer noise and stresses are much more pronounced than in flexible pipes like plastic, copper, or lead, which tend to dampen and absorb the waves or pressures.

Although the problem of water hammer is sometimes tackled by installing pressure-reducing valves or regulators, or by bracing the pipelines, the real cure is the provision of a device called *air chamber* which is a small length of vertical pipe (a foot and a half or more) capped at the top and atached to the line near the valve or faucet (Fig. 5-9). These air chambers are generally provided inside the walls and you seldom see them. They contain air which gets compressed when the water hammer wave hits it, and they thus provide a sort of cushion which considerably reduces the impact and noise, and prevents pipes from shaking and banging. An air chamber may be the continuation of the riser pipe (Fig. 5-9A) or it may be offset as in Fig. 5-9B. The minimum chamber length is 18 inches and the minimum capacity is equal to one percent of the capacity of the pipeline on which the water hammer problem exists. The size of the

142

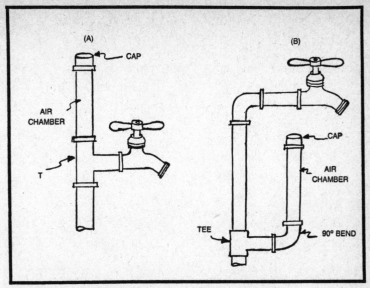

Fig. 5-9. Air chambers to absorb water hammer shocks.

air chamber pipe should be one or two sizes larger than that of the pipeline.

Sometimes, when the water pressure of your supply is high, and the flow velocity in the pipes is more than normal, air may be sucked out of the air chambers by the drag of fast moving water, thereby resulting in a vacuum. In such an event, the air chambers get fully or partly filled with water and lose their effectiveness. When water hammer noises start on a system which was quiet in the past, you may suspect that one or more air chambers have failed because they have become filled with water. Cut off the supply from the main valve and let the lines drain out completely through the faucets. The air chambers will fill once again with air and become effective. Open the supply to restore service. Over a period of time an air chamber is likely to get clogged with impurities or chemicals in the water. Cleaning should be done after removing the cap from the top. The air chamber pipe is always a little larger in size than the pipeline so it can accommodate some clogging until it is cleaned out.

When no air chambers exist on the system, you may install substitute devices which provide an air cushion to prevent water hammer noises. Figure 5-10 shows one such device in the shape of a coil which can be fitted at the faucet or the valve.

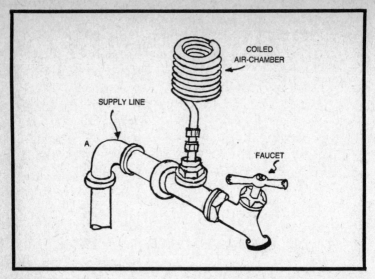

Fig. 5-10. Coiled air chambers can be fitted on existing lines to control water hammer.

You may also make an air chamber. Replace the bend (Fig. 5-10A) with a T and at its top attach an 18-inch length of pipe of the same size as the water line or somewhat larger. Close this pipe with a cap, and the air chamber is ready. Take care that when you attach the pipe and put in the cap, there is no water in the pipeline. After the cap is put in, resume the supply.

If you get water hammer noise even after an air chamber is installed, the chamber is probably full of water and has no air at top. Drain the line completely by shutting off the supply and opening all the faucets so that air enters the entire system. Then close all faucets and resume the water supply by opening the shut-off valve.

In new additions to your plumbing system, the pipe sizes should be made large enough so as not to develop high velocities in the lines. Also, the faucets should be of good design and should not unduly restrict the flow.

WATER PRESSURE PROBLEMS

A very common problem facing homeowners is that of low water pressure or a variation in pressure during different times of the day or year. If the public water supply is not delivered at adequate pressure and the trouble is more or less permanent, there is no alternative except to install a booster pump in your house to improve the pressures. Other reasons for low pressure are: a clogged service pipe, inadequate sizes of water lines in your house, or a clog or obstruction on any line inside or outside. To determine where the fault lies, you have to get hold of a water pressure gauge.

Place the gauge on the service pipe a little upstream from the meter (i.e., towards the curb). Shut off the supply to the house by closing the shut-off valve. If the gauge shows adequate pressure (50 pounds per square inch), then the public water supply is not at fault and either the service pipe or your own plumbing system is the culprit. Open all the faucets in the house, as well as the shut-off valve, and let them run. If the pressure at the gauge drops down quite a bit, the service pipe is either clogged or inadequate in size. If, however, the pressure does not drop appreciably and yet the pressures at the fixtures are not enough, then the water pipes inside the house are either clogged or too small. Next take the gauge inside the house. Attach it to the main line and observe the pressure first without any water running through fixtures and then with all of them open. Note the drop in pressure. If the drop is insignificant, move the gauge further along the line towards the faucets and other fixtures. Finally you will find a spot on the main or branch lines where the pressure drop is appreciable. This indicates that the line between this point and the fixtures is either inadequate in size or is clogged. You may find several such spots on different lines when you run this pressure test in succession on the various lines. The affected supply pipes should either be cleaned (which will be difficult in most cases), or replaced with pipes of larger sizes.

If you find that the mixture of hot and cold water at your shower suddenly changes in temperature or volume when some other outlet nearby is opened, and this happens very often, it indicates that the pipes in the system were installed with inadequate sizes or have been reduced in their discharging capacity by corrosion or scaling. Another reason may be too many additions of fixtures and outlets as years have gone by without increasing the sizes of pipes. A large number of fixtures and many bends in the pipelines result in excessive friction loss which leads to low pressures. Maybe you have added a new bathroom or have installed a dishwasher and laundry washer. In all these cases, the best remedy is the replacement of pipes with those of adequate size. A temporary measure to rectify the low pressure problem at the bath and shower outlets when other outlets are open is the installation of an automatic mixing valve. This, of course, is a local cure and in no way increases the water flow from the under-sized pipes.

In some low-lying areas, or in areas where the public water supply comes from a high overhead tank with no pressure-reducing valve in the line, high water pressures at the fixtures may cause problems. Whistling noises and water hammer may be very common. This condition can be remedied by using a pressure-reducing valve on the service line.

Drains, Sinks, and Lavatories

Drains, Sinks, and Lavatories

Stoppages can occur in any part of the drainage system. They are caused by the gradual accumulation of grease, dirt, and similar material in the lines, or by indiscriminate disposal of food, coffee grounds, rags, paper, hair, fruits, vegetables, etc., into sinks, toilets, and other fixtures. Methods used to remove the blockage depend on whether it is the main drain or one of the fixture drains that is blocked.

So first you have to determine the location of the blockage. Open all the outlets at the showers, bathtubs, and sinks and observe if the drains are working at each one of these (Fig. 6-1). Do not flush the toilets for this test, or else you might cause an overflow from the large quantity of water released. If all the fixture drains are working except one, then that particular fixture drain is clogged. If, however, two or more fixtures are not draining off their water, this indicates that the main house drain has the stoppage.

CLEARING THE MAIN DRAIN BLOCKAGE

The main drain may have one or more *cleanouts* through which it can be cleaned. When there is only one cleanout, it will be located at the highest point of the main drain and cleaning should be done through it. If there is more than one cleanout, you have to determine which portion of the drain is blocked. Remove the plug of the

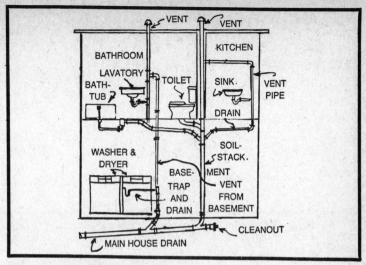

Fig. 6-1. A typical drainage system.

cleanout nearest to the house sewer, and place an empty bucket under it. If water starts dripping into the bucket, it indicates that the drain between this cleanout and the soil stack is clean and the blockage is located towards the sewer side. If no water drips from the cleanout, open up the next cleanout towards the soil stack and repeat the procedure. In this manner you will be able to determine which length of the drain is blocked. (The soil stack itself practically never clogs.)

After you have determined which cleanout is to be used for cleaning, place a bucket under it and open up the cleanout plug (Fig. 6-2) so that all the water drains out. Three types of equipment can be used:

- a water hose without a nozzle
- a hand auger
- an electric auger

First try the water hose. Push it through the cleanout into the drain until you feel that it has struck the blockage. Now seal the opening by placing wet cloth all around the hose. Keeping the hose firmly pressed against the blockage, let a little water flow into it. Increase the water pressure as the material starts to move on. Once it is broken up, move the hose forward and backward to clean up the drain completely. Then turn off the water and withdraw the hose.

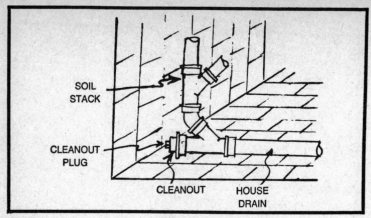

Fig. 6-2. Soil stack connects to the house drain through a cleanout Y. If house drain gets blocked, take out the plug and remove the blockage by an auger or snake.

If you don't succeed with the hose method, try the hand auger. As before, remove the plug from the cleanout after you have placed a bucket under it. Go on pushing the auger into the drain, same as you did with the hose, until you feel the blockage (Fig. 6-3). Continuing to turn the handle of the auger (always in the same direction), move it in and out until the obstruction is broken and the auger starts moving freely. Take it out, insert the water hose, and turn the water on. If water flows freely into the cleanout and the drain, you have removed the blockage. If it does not, then use the hand auger once again for a few minutes more. In most cases you will succeed.

Note: The hose and the auger should always be cleaned before use, so as not to cause any contamination or spread any disease bacteria. If the blockage persists, it is probably caused by roots of trees having entered the drain through its joints or through the house sewer. Such difficult blockages require the use of an electric auger which you can rent from an equipment renting store. It has the same type of flexible cable as a hand auger but, in addition, has a flexible blade with very sharp teeth which when turned round and round can cut the strongest stoppages including those caused by tree roots. These electric augers come in different designs, so be sure to get the operating instructions from the renting dealer and read them very carefully before starting the job.

After you remove the blockage, wash the inside of the drain thoroughly with the water hose so that all dislodged material is removed. Replace the cleanout plug and remove the bucket. To check that the job has been done satisfactorily, test the flow by flushing one of the toilets several times and running water through other fixtures, too. If, however, you have not succeeded in getting rid of the stoppage, call your plumber.

CLEARING FIXTURE DRAIN BLOCKAGE

Each fixture is connected to the soil stack or to the main drain through what is called the fixture drain system. There is always a trap in the line and a connection to the vent pipe. Any part of the drain system can develop a blockage although you will find that in most cases it will not happen far from the fixture itself. It will almost always be on the horizontal portions of a drain and seldom on the risers.

Sometimes the stoppage at a sink may occur when merely the strainer or stopper has collected dirt. If it is a strainer, you may remove it by unscrewing the two nuts by which it is attached to the basin. Or there may be no screws at all and a little prying with a knife

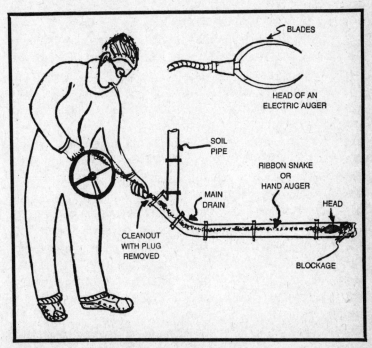

Fig. 6-3. Cleaning blockage on main drain by hand auger (plumber's snake).

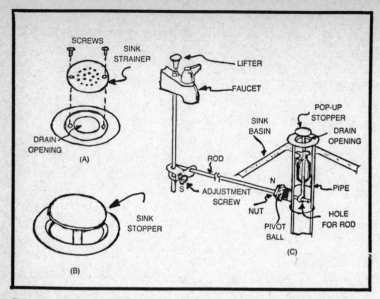

Fig. 6-4. (A) Sink strainer, (B) sink stopper, (C) stopper operating system.

or screwdriver will take it out. Clean the drain opening as far down as you can reach. Clean the strainer and screw it back.

A stopper can usually be removed by turning it counterclockwise and lifting up. Clean the drain opening and replace the stopper by turning it clockwise. In some designs, the stopper cannot be removed just by turning it around, however. Figure 6-4C illustrates the working of such a stopper. By raising the lifter, the rod turns about the pivot ball and lowers the stopper to close the drain opening. When the lifter is pressed down, the stopper pops up. To clear the drainpipe, you have to take this mechanism apart. First place a bucket under the pipe to collect any drip and to prevent a mess. Loosen the adjustment screw S, and remove the nut N from the pipe. This will enable you to take out the rod, thus freeing the stopper and its vertical rod. Just lift out the stopper and clean it. Also clean the drainpipe as far down as you can reach. Replace the stopper, and install the rod by inserting it properly at both ends. Replace the nut and tighten the screw. The bucket may now be removed. Test the drain by turning the faucet on. Chances are good that the blockage has been removed.

If the above procedure does not succeed, the next thing to use is the plumber's friend, the plunger. There are two types of plungers—flat and molded (Fig. 6-5). The molded one is suitable for rounded surfaces like those in toilet bowls, while the flat type is most efficient for comparatively flat surfaces like sinks and shower drains.

To use a plunger, first remove the stopper or the strainer. If the stopper cannot be taken out easily, just raise it to its full open position by pressing the lifter at the faucet. Lubricate the base of the plunger with a thick coating of petroleum jelly. Open the faucet and let the sink fill with water until it is 2 to 3 inches above the drain opening. Plug the overflow opening with damp cloth. This prevents leakage of pressure when the plunger is being worked. If the sink is a double one, the plunger will be used over one drain opening at a time; the opening not in use, and the overflow hole, should be tightly plugged.

Now cover the drain opening with the plunger and press its handle swiftly up and down several times. Lift the plunger after a few strokes and see if the drain is clearing. Repeat the process a number of times (it can take quite some time to remove the blockage with a plunger). Finally, when you feel that the drain has been cleared, open the faucet and let water run. If the drain runs freely, shut off the faucet and replace the strainer or the stopper.

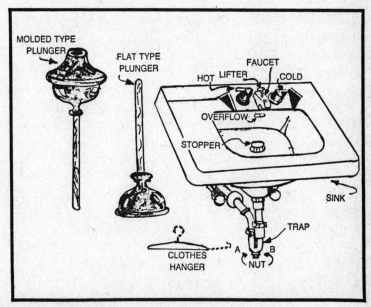

Fig. 6-5. Using plungers.

If you have been able to clear the blockage only partially, the use of a *chemical drain cleaner* can probably complete the job. However, this should not be used on a drain which is completely clogged. The chemical drain cleaner comes either as a liquid or in crystal form. To use either one, remove the stopper or the strainer, and place a plastic funnel over the drain opening. Drop the required amount of cleaner as indicated in the instructions on the container label. Remove the funnel and let the chemicals ferment for a few minutes before turning the faucet on. If the drain is now clear, replace the strainer or the stopper. Rinse the funnel and store it away to be used for drain cleaning only.

The foregoing procedures apply in general to blockages on toilets, sink, and bathtub drains, as well as on shower and floor drains. If you do not succeed in clearing the drain, there are other measures that can be taken.

Difficult Blockages on Sinks

When the plunger fails to remove the blockage in a sink, you have to open up the trap (Fig. 6-5) and clean it. Dirt, grease, hair, paper, and any other articles which accidentally fall into the sink get caught in the trap and ultimately result in a blockage. In most cases you will find a nut at the bottom of the trap (see Fig. 6-5). Place a bucket under the trap, and remove the nut by turning it in the direction of arrow A.

If you have previously tried to clear the blockage by using a chemical cleaner, it will be advisable to protect your hands by wearing rubber gloves. The waste water in the line will drip into the bucket. Take a wire clothes hanger, cut off the hook and straighten it up. Bend one end into a hook of a size that can be inserted into the trap opening. (Or, you may use any other small size wire of suitable strength and bend one of its ends into a small hook.) Insert the hook into the opening and move it back and forth. The collected material will start falling down into the bucket. Repeat several times by inserting the hook and working with it until the blockage has been cleared. Now use a small piece of wet cloth or brush to clean and wipe the trap opening. The plug can now be replaced and water can be turned on.

If you find that there is no nut at the bottom of the trap, the trap assembly has to be dismantled. Using a wrench or a pair of pliers,

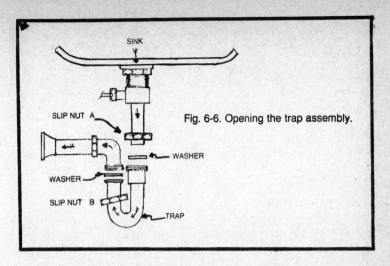

Fig. 6-6. Opening the trap assembly.

loosen the slip nuts A and B (Fig. 6-6), and take out the trap. Two layers of adhesive tape should be wrapped on the chrome pipes and fixtures before using any tools. This will maintain their finish.

Remove the deposits inside the pipes with a piece of wire and thoroughly clean the inside with a piece of rag or a brush. If the washers are worn out, get new ones from the store. Reposition the trap correctly, insert the two new washers, and tighten the slip nuts. Turn the water on, and remove the layers of adhesive tape from the pipes and fixtures.

Chances are very good that the blockage has now been removed. If not, the final and the most effective remedy is the use of a hand auger.

Using a Hand Auger to Open Blockages

If the blockage has not been removed by using the above methods, circumstances indicate that not only the trap but the sink drainpipes—the vertical or horizontal portions or both—are blocked. To correct this, you need a hand auger. The vertical portion of the drain can be tackled by inserting the auger through the stopper opening; but for cleaning the horizontal portion beyond the trap, you will have to dismantle the trap as described before and illustrated in Fig. 6-6.

Two types of augers are shown in Fig. 6-7. One is a short, flexible hand auger which is very convenient for toilets and sinks. The other one is a coiled-spring snake or flexible drain auger. It has a

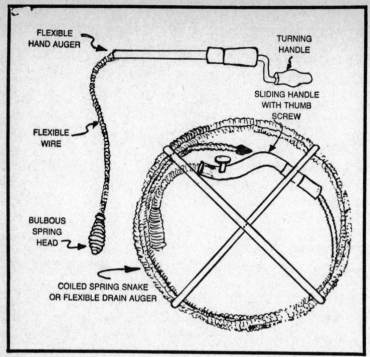

FLEXIBLE
HAND AUGER

TURNING
HANDLE

SLIDING HANDLE
WITH THUMB
SCREW

FLEXIBLE
WIRE

BULBOUS
SPRING
HEAD

COILED SPRING SNAKE
OR FLEXIBLE DRAIN AUGER

Fig. 6-7. Two types of augers.

long length of flexible wire terminating in a bulbous spring head. If you insert it into a drain and turn the handle round, you will be able to clean up difficult blockages formed inside a large length of the pipe. Even hard blockages like ones caused by tree roots can be removed this way.

To clear the blockage in the vertical portion of the sink drain, remove the strainer or the stopper. Insert the hand auger and push it down until it strikes against the obstruction (Fig. 6-8). Press it hard, turning the handle around in one direction only, and then suddenly release it by pulling it back. Press and release it several times until the obstruction is removed and the auger moves freely back and forth inside the drain. Now test by opening the faucet. If water has started flowing normally, the blockage has been removed. Withdraw the auger, clean it, and put it away for future use.

Run the hot water faucet for a few minutes to clean the drain of all sticking matter, grease, etc. Finally replace the strainer or stopper in the sink opening.

If the above treatment does not clear the blockage, it indicates the problem is located on the horizontal length of the drain, beyond the trap.

Open the trap assembly as described before (see Fig. 6-6), taking care to wear rubber gloves if chemical drain cleaner has been used. Insert a hand auger inside the drain (Fig. 6-9). Turning the handle in one direction only, push it in until the obstruction is felt. Press it forward and pull back several times until it moves freely. Make a note of the exact length of the auger that has gone into the drain, and withdraw it. Replace the trap and fully tighten the nuts. Open the faucet and let it run full. If it flows freely, the stoppage has been cleared. If not, open the trap once again and insert the hand auger deeper than before. If you feel the blockage, remove it by manipulating the hand auger as before. If you do not feel the obstruction, it is probably further on, and a flexible drain auger is needed to remove it (Fig. 6-7). If you don't want to use this or if you do not succeed when you do use it, it will be advisable to call a plumber.

REPLACING A LAVATORY OR SINK

There are times when you will want to replace a sink or lavatory, either because of extensive damage and malfunction, or

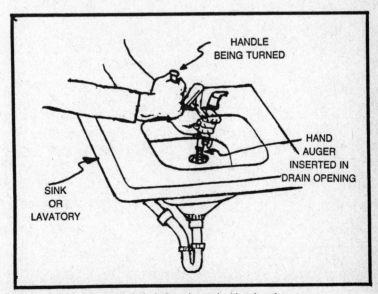

Fig. 6-8. Sink of lavatory drain being cleaned with a hand auger.

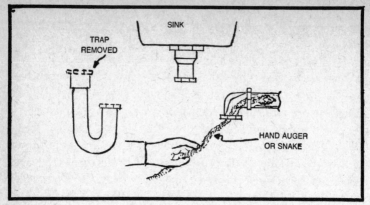

Fig. 6-9. Cleaning sink drain with hand auger—trap removed.

just for a change of style. When buying a sink, make sure that the installation instruction booklet is contained in the package. These instructions vary considerably for different types and models of sinks available in the market.

Basically there are two types of sinks or lavatories, depending on the method of mounting (Fig. 6-10): wall-mounted and cabinet-mounted. The wall-mounted sinks are normally used in bathrooms, while the cabinet-mounted ones will be found both in the bathrooms and kitchens. The replacement procedures described here cover both types. The sink that you choose to buy may not be exactly like those in the illustrations here, but the guidelines for replacement will still apply because the basic connections for the hot and cold water lines, the stopper linkage, and the drain lines remain the same.

Before removing the old sink, you have to study how it is attached to the wall or cabinet at its back and underside. A hanger assembly (Fig. 6-10) is used to attach a wall-mounted sink to the wall. The sink rests on the horizontal portion of the assembly which is secured to the wall by means of studs on the back.

A cabinet-mounted sink may either be an integral part of the countertop itself, or it may be a separate piece which is dropped in or dropped out of the cabinet opening.

Having ascertained the method of mounting, you have now to figure out which of the water supply and drainage lines are to be disconnected and how. If the faucet is not attached to the sink, as in some types of cabinet-mounted fittings, the water lines do not have to be disconnected. In the wall-mounted types, the hot and cold

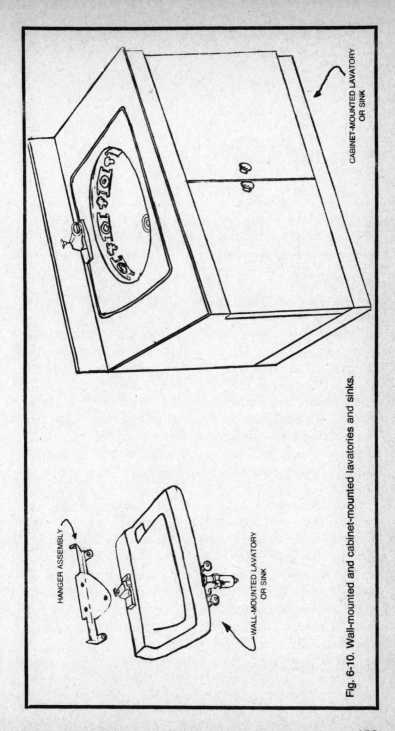

HANGER ASSEMBLY

WALL-MOUNTED LAVATORY OR SINK

CABINET-MOUNTED LAVATORY OR SINK

Fig. 6-10. Wall-mounted and cabinet-mounted lavatories and sinks.

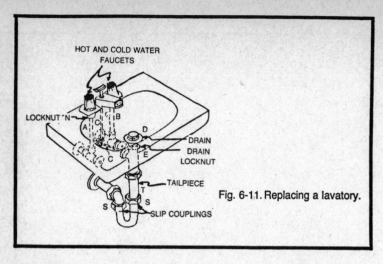

water lines (A and B, in Fig. 6-11) should be disconnected by unscrewing the nuts (N, in Fig. 6-11). Be sure to shut off the water supply first, or you will flood the floor.

The drain line should be disconnected by unscrewing the slip couplings (S, in Fig. 6-11). The stopper linkage C will also need disconnecting. If a garbage disposer exists under the sink, disconnect it at the sink drain. Figure 6-12 illustrates a double kitchen sink with an attached garbage disposer. The two drain lines come together at the trap and then a single line carries away the drainage flow to the back of the cabinet. If such a fixture has sinks which lower out of the cabinet, then you have to dismantle the trap as well as the drain line including the garbage disposal before the sinks can be removed.

Having disconnected or removed all the required water supply and drainage lines and fixtures, you are ready to take out the sink. If it is a heavy one, like those mounted in cabinets, you might secure the help of some other person.

In many cases it will be possible to re-use the old faucet and the drain. You may take the faucet off the old sink by opening the two locknuts and the washers under the hot and cold water controls (Fig. 6-11, locknut N). The drain D can be taken off by removing the locknut and washer under the stopper.

Steps for installing the new sink are exactly the same as those for the removal, except in reverse: lift the sink out of its container, clean it, and place it in the position that was occupied by the old sink (over the wall hanger, or inside the cabinet openings, as the case may be). The drain opening should be properly aligned over the drainpipe, the faucet openings over the hot and cold water supply lines. Apply a layer of plumber's putty on the bottom of the faucet, place the locknuts and new washers in position, and tighten them. Next insert the drain D into the drain opening, place the washer and the drain locknut E below the underside of the sink, and tighten up. A little plumber's putty should be applied on the top of the washer so that it grips the surface of the sink.

If someone holds the sink in place while you are attaching it to the cabinet or wall-hanger assembly, the job will be easier. The manufacturer's instructions should be followed.

After the faucet and drain are attached and the sink securely mounted, connect the water supply lines and the drain line. Water

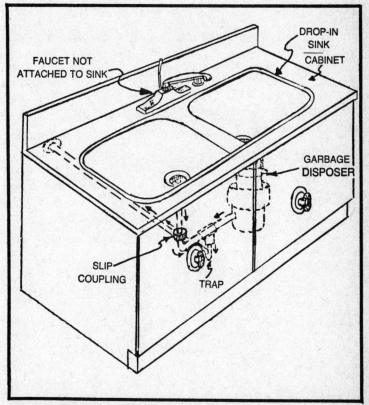

Fig. 6-12. Cabinet-mounted drop-in sinks with garbage disposer. (Faucet is not attached to sinks.)

Fig. 6-13. The trieste sink from Kohler has three compartments. The garbage disposer is attached under the middle one. The faucet can be moved to any side. Courtesy: Kohler Co.

Fig. 6-14. Boutique lavatory from Kohler is ideal for bathrooms and powder rooms that are cramped for space. A narrow-width lavatory with stylish, delta-shaped basin, the compact Boutique measures only 21 by 13 inches, and can be installed in a counter top as narrow as 15 inches from front to back. Courtesy: Kohler Co.

Fig. 6-15. This lavatory with sleek design and modern trim is put out by Kohler Co.

Fig. 6-16. A sink in the basement bar is easy to install if the drainage can flow to the street sewer or the septic tank under gravity; otherwise a small pump can be put in. Courtesy: Kohler Co.

lines will be connected by tightening up the locknuts N. New washers should be inserted. Now connect all the drain lines which were disconnected at the time of removing the old sink. These include the garbage disposer line, the stopper assembly, and of course the drain lines down from the drain stopper. Use new washers.

Very often, minor modifications on the existing pipes will be needed before the new sink fits correctly in place. It may be necessary to cut or lengthen the tailpiece T for an exact fit to the trap. The traps may have to be re-aligned by tightening or loosening the slip couplings. After the entire job is completed, turn the faucet on. If some connection is leaking, tighten it up, using a plumber's tape if necessary.

Figures 6-13, 6-14, 6-15, and 6-16 illustrate some of the more unique sink designs available.

Toilets: Selection, Installation, and Repairs

Toilets: Selection, Installation, and Repairs

Though the selection of plumbing fixtures is often dictated by economic considerations, one does not buy them every day, and it is worthwhile to consider other factors as well. You will find displays of a multitude of designs, from the economy lines of various brands up to the most sophisticated and expensive ones. Those with lower price tags are generally well-built to give long, trouble-free service; but the investment of a few additional dollars for the more expensive ones can often provide extra comfort, convenience, and eye-appeal. You have to decide what you prefer.

After you receive any new fixtures from your store or the manufacturers, take good care of them until they are installed. During unpacking and handling, the surfaces should not get scratched. Careless handling may cause chipping or cracking. When storing temporarily, use foundation pads and wooden blocks. The fixtures should not be subjected to loads caused by someone standing or walking over them or by material stored on top.

The average life of a good plumbing fixture is pretty long, but ultimately it might get damaged or cracked, or it may simply begin to look old or out of style to you. If at any time you wish to remodel your bathroom to modernize it, or to add a new one due to the increased size of the family, fixtures will need to be replaced or added.

Work of this sort is simple if you have a home under construction, or if a new bath is being added. The water supply and drainage lines are easily put in through the walls and the floor when the framing is not yet covered with sheetrock. The tub is installed at this stage before the floor is finished. The backing for toilets and sinks is also attached to the wall studs and then the floor tiles and wall coverings are put in. Finally, the lavatory sink and the toilet are installed.

During remodellings, however, you will have to uncover the floor and the walls if the tubs and lavatories are to be replaced, or if a new wall-hung toilet is to be installed either as an additional facility or as replacement for an old floor-type model. It will be smart to find out the roughing-in dimensions of the inlets and outlets of the new fixtures before you buy; it will save you a considerable amount of work if these are more or less the same as those of your old units.

TYPES OF TOILETS

A domestic toilet consists of a flush tank and a bowl with cover. The flush tank obtains its water supply from the water main (Fig. 7-1). The flush mechanism will be discussed later in this chapter. The function of a toilet is to receive and remove waste; its efficiency is measured by its quiet operation and the extent to which the amount of contamination and nuisance it generates is kept to a

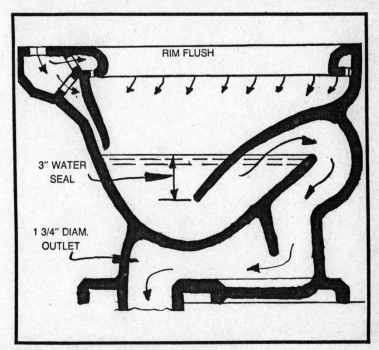

RIM FLUSH

3" WATER SEAL

1 3/4" DIAM. OUTLET

Fig. 7-1. A washdown closet bowl.

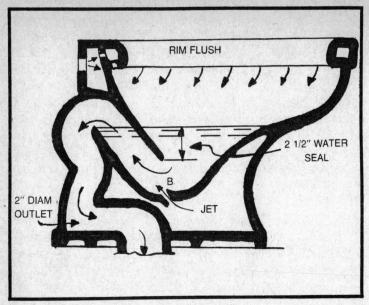

Fig. 7-2. A reverse-trap closet bowl.

minimum. The larger the water surface area a bowl provides, the better the sanitary conditions. There are four kinds of domestic toilets based on flushing action:

1. washdown toilets
2. reverse-trap toilets
3. siphon-jet toilets
4. siphon-vortex toilets

Figures 7-1, 7-2, and 7-3 illustrate the washdown, reverse-trap, and siphon-jet closet bowls. Figure 7-4 illustrates the three types of toilet flushing actions: siphon vortex, siphon jet, and washdown. Siphon vortex is the most efficient in cleaning and flushing.

Washdown toilets are the oldest type, with noisier and much less efficient operation than the other types. Flushing consists of a direct wash-out action without the presence of jets or vortices. This results in more frequent cloggings. Also a large surface area of the bowl stays out of water causing contamination and nuisance. These continue to be sold because of their lower price range, however.

Reverse-trap toilets have an opening at the inlet to the trapway (see point B in Fig. 7-2) through which a jet of water streams out with a force. This helps the siphonic action in cleaning out the solid wastes much more efficiently than in a washdown toilet. There is much less contamination and fouling, too, because a larger surface area of the bowl stays covered with water. Due to the jet action, clogging is less likely to occur. Through somewhat noisy, this type is the least expensive among siphon-type toilets.

Siphon-jet toilets are essentially the same as the reverse-trap toilets, except for a larger and more efficient jet (see Fig. 7-3). There is less fouling because a much larger surface area of the bowl remains under water. The outlet or the trapway passage is larger in diameter than in other types. This makes the operation quieter and the toilet less likely to clog.

Siphon-vortex toilets are the most efficient, attractive, and expensive of all. The flushing action is almost silent and fouling is at a minimum; most of the bowl surface stays covered with water. The flushing action, and the direction of the vortex that forms, are both illustrated in Fig. 7-4A. Figures 7-4B and C show flushing action in siphon-jet and washdown toilets.

Toilet bowls come in two shapes: round rim and elongated rim. Many people feel the elongated rim bowl looks somewhat more elegant and is more comfortable to use than the round shape. It stays clean with little effort because the water surface area is much larger and most of the bowl surface remains submerged.

If you are fascinated by the appearance of an off-the-floor toilet or if you find the floor area under it easier to clean, do install it by all means. Its installation in new construction or as an addition will present no problems; but in existing baths, you will have to open up the wall-facing and attach special metal-carriers within the wall to support the weight.

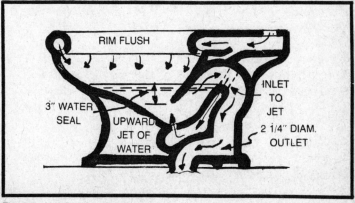

Fig. 7-3. A siphon-jet closet bowl.

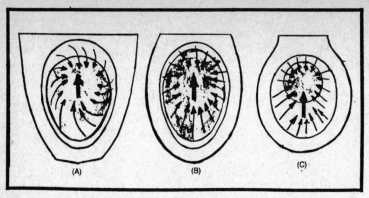

Fig. 7-4. Toilet flushing actions: (A) siphon vortex, (B) siphon jet, (C) washdown.

Toilets also come in special designs to suit unique situations. (Several are illustrated at the end of this chapter.) If, due to space limitation, a toilet can go only in the corner, you can buy one with a triangular flush tank.

THE WORKING OF A TOILET

If you open the top cover of a toilet flush tank, the small tubes, pipes, valves, etc., may look somewhat confusing. Actually, the mechanism is not that complicated. Once you get familiar with it, problems can easily be identified and necessary repairs easily done.

Figure 7-5 shows the workings of the various parts of a toilet flush tank. The *trip handle*, also called the *flush handle*, is the small metallic part that you operate whenever the toilet is to be flushed. When pushed down, it raises the *trip lever* which in turn lifts a chain (the *upper lift wire*) and the lower lift arm, which works through a guide arm attached to the overflow tube, and ultimately lifts the *flush ball*.

The flush ball is made of soft rubber and normally rests on the *flush-valve seat* at the bottom of the tank. As the flush ball lifts up, water suddenly flows out through the outlet to the toilet bowl. Due to the big size of the opening, a large volume of water surges out, cleaning the toilet bowl and washing away its contents. Consequently, the water level in the flush tank rapidly drops. The rubber flush ball stays floating till the water level falls to the level of the opening. You don't have to keep the trip lever pressed; just press it and release. The flush starts and continues till the tank is emptied, and the flush ball gets back to its seat, stopping the flush. In Fig. 7-5 you will also observe a round *float* made of rubber or thin metal. It normally stays floating at the water surface, and is attached through a metallic *float* made of rubber or thin metal. It normally stays floating at the water surface, and is attached through a metallic *float arm* to the *float valve assembly* at the top of the *supply pipe*. The float valve remains closed when the tank is completely full of water and the float is at its topmost position.

As the flush starts, the float gradually falls down with water, thus opening the float valve. When the float gets to the lowest position near the bottom of the tank, the float valve is fully open and is admitting water from the supply main into the flush tank through the tank refill tube. As the tank starts filling up, the float also goes up with the rising water level and starts closing the float valve, which gets completely shut when the float reaches its topmost position. No more water then enters the tank. This process repeats itself every time you operate the trip handle.

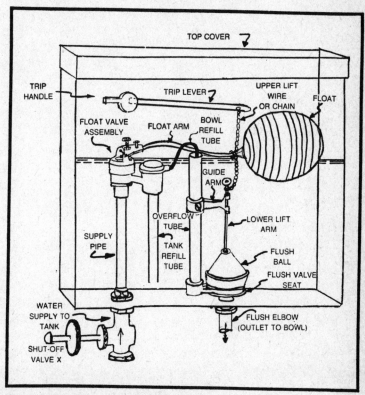

Fig. 7-5. Mechanism of a toilet flush tank.

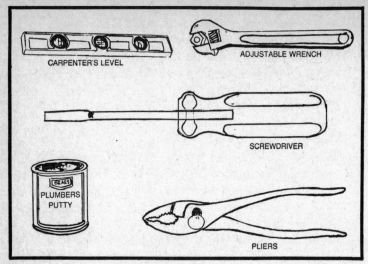

Fig. 7-6. Tools for toilet repairs.

The flush tank has a supply pipe connected to the water supply line. When the float valve opens, water rushes from the supply pipe into the tank refill tube and fills up the tank. There is also a flexible *bowl refill tube* through which a small quantity of water flows down to the overflow tube and on to the toilet bowl. This flow, which takes place towards the end of the flush, restores the water seal of the toilet. There is another advantage of the overflow tube; if, due to some defect in the mechanism, the float valve does not close fully even after the tank is full, the incoming water simply flows down the overflow tube to the toilet and on to the house drain without flooding your bathroom.

COMMON PROBLEMS AT TOILETS

Some of the problems common to toilets are as follows:

1. Toilet running continuously
2. Toilet not flushing, or slow in its function
3. Leaking toilet tank
4. Sweating toilet tank
5. Cracked toilet tank or bowl

For most jobs , whether involving repairs or installation of new units, you will seldom need any more tools than these: a pair of pliers, an adjustable wrench, a screwdriver, a putty knife, and a carpenter's level (Fig. 7-6).

A Continuously Running Toilet

A toilet may run continuously for two reasons: a defective float or a defective flush ball. Remove the top cover of the tank and note the water level. If the top of the overflow tube is under water, this is why water is continuously flowing down into the toilet bowl. The float needs to be repaired. On the other hand, if the water level is 3/4 inch or more below the top of the overflow tube, the defect lies with the flush ball. Ideally the water level should be about 1/2 inch below the top of the overflow tube after the tank gets full and the inflow stops.

Repairs to the Float. Lift the top cover of the tank and put it away where it will not be damaged. Now hold the float arm and lift it up slowly till it won't go up any further; apply only a little pressure or else you will damage it (Fig. 7-7). If the water entering the tank shuts off, either the float or the float arm has the defect. Probably the float is touching the upper lift wire or the side of the tank. If so, apply a little lateral pressure to the float arm till the float gets freed and stays a reasonable distance away. Unscrew the float from the arm by turning it in a counter-clockwise direction. Shake it to check if there is any water inside; if there is, the float is no good. Repairs are inadvisable. Just discard it and get a new one. Screw the new one on to the float arm by turning it in a clockwise direction. If it now stays immersed about 1/2 inch in water, good. If not, bend the float arm till

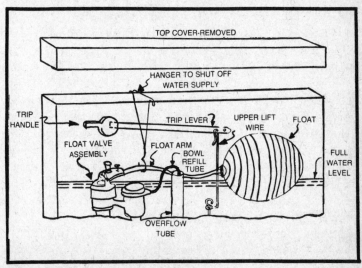

Fig. 7-7. Float repairs at a running toilet.

173

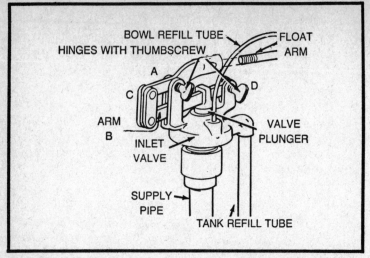

Fig. 7-8. As the flush proceeds, the float goes down with dropping water level and the float arm is depressed. Piece C turns around hinge A, lifting arm B and with it the valve plunger. This opens the inlet valve and the tank starts re-filling.

it does. Now flush the toilet by turning the trip-arm. If the water shuts off when the tank level is about 3/4 inch below the top of the overflow tube, you have removed the malfunction. If not, bend the float arm further in the required direction until the desired result is obtained. Replace the cover of the tank.

If, when you raised the float arm, the water did *not* shut off, the defect probably lies with the float valve assembly.

Figure 7-8 illustrates the normal working of this mechanism. There are many variations in design and the one inside your flush tank may not be exactly as shown in this figure, but the general working principle is the same. In some cases the assembly comes as a sealed unit which has a long life, but once it develops a defect, repairs are not possible. Just buy a new unit and install it after taking out the old one. A new type of inexpensive unit called *plastic flush control* has a self-contained, sealed mechanism which provides quiet working and more precise water level control. You may be much better off installing it when replacing your defective unit.

To repair the non-sealed valve assembly, close the valve on the supply line under the tank (see shut-off valve in Fig. 7-5). Turn the trip lever to flush and empty the tank. Now remove the thumbscrews and take out the arm B (Fig. 7-8). This will release the valve plunger, which should be taken out. If the washers are damaged or worn out, get exact replacements from the hardware store and put them in the correct position. Install the valve plunger and, after replacing the arm B and the float arm, tighten the thumbscrews. Open the shut-off valve and flush the toilet to make sure that the defect has been removed.

Repairs to Flush-Ball System. If normal water level in the flush tank is 3/4 inch or more below the top of the overflow tube, and you have a running toilet, the defect lies with the flush-ball system, which should be repaired. Several problems are possible: the flush ball may be damaged or worn out, the ball seat may be uneven and ill-fitting, or the lift arm may not be properly screwed on to the flush ball.

Before anything can be done, the flush tank should be emptied of water and kept empty. If the tank has a shut-off valve (x in Fig. 7-5), the supply can be stopped by closing this valve, after which the tank should be flushed out by turning the trip lever. If, however, there is no shut-off valve, tie a string to the trip lever and weight it down at the end hanging outside the tank. Another alternative, illustrated in Fig. 7-7, is to place the hook of a metallic clothes hanger around the trip lever, and bend its ends on both sides of the tank so that the trip lever stays in its topmost position, keeping the inlet valve closed.

After the tank is empty, inspect the flush ball assembly (Fig. 7-9). If the lift arm is loose, try to tighten it by turning the flush ball counterclockwise. If it does not stay tight, the flush ball needs replacement. Also check the lower surface of the flush ball that sits on the ball seat. If it is worn or damaged, water must be leaking through the opening between the flush ball and the seat; this would be the reason for a running toilet. The flush ball must be replaced. Unscrew it from the lower liftarm and get an exact replacement. Hold the new flush ball above the seat and screw it on to the lift arm by turning it counterclockwise. Now you should make sure that the new flush ball sits evenly over the ball seat. Operate the trip lever several times and observe whether the flush ball falls down and grips the ball seat evenly. If it does not, the flush-ball guide arm should be adjusted. If the lift arm is simply a chain, adjust its length until the flush ball starts to sit evenly on its seat. If the lift arm is attached to the overflow tube through a guide arm, as in Fig. 7-5, unscrew the tightening screw and turn the guide arm up and down or sideways until the flush ball starts to sit on its seat evenly. Re-tighten the screw.

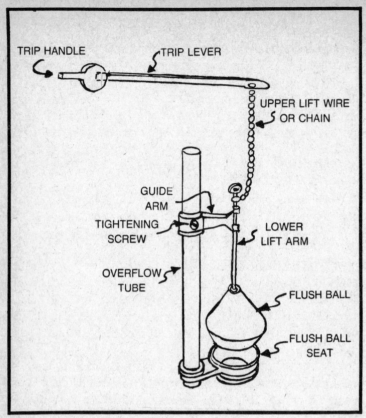

Fig. 7-9. Flush-ball system repairs.

Raise the flush ball up by pressing down the trip lever, then clean the flush ball seat with steel wool or emery cloth. Both the inner surface and the top rim should be cleaned until smooth.

Since all the working parts of the flush-ball assembly have been checked and repaired as necessary, it is fairly certain that the defect has been removed.

Remove the string or the coat hanger, or turn on the shut-off valve (whichever case applies), and flush the toilet by turning the trip lever. Check to see that the toilet flushes properly and does not run continuously. Replace the top of the tank.

Toilet Not Flushing or Slow

You will need a pair of pliers and an adjustable wrench to fix this problem. As before, take off the top cover of the flush tank and store it in a safe place. Look inside the tank. The refill tube might have fallen out of the overflow tube (Fig. 7-10). If so, put it back in place; you may have to bend it a little so that it stays inside the overflow tube.

Another possibility is that the flush handle may have become loose, and stopped gripping the trip lever. Check it. If loose, tighten the nut on the inside of the tank with the adjustable wrench, holding the trip handle firmly in place.

The most common reasons for a no-flush toilet are: a broken upper lift wire or chain, and a loose or unscrewed lower lift arm.

In the case of a broken upper lift wire or chain, get a new one. Unscrew the lower lift arm from the flush ball by turning it counterclockwise. Slide it out of the guide arm, and then remove the pieces of broken chain or wire both from the lower lift arm and the trip lever. Keeping the new connecting wire or chain in place (see Fig. 7-10), insert the lower lift arm through its hook and through the guide arm until it reaches the top of the flush ball. Attach the upper end of the new connecting wire to the trip lever. Finally, turn the flush ball counterclockwise around the lower end of the lift arm and screw it on tightly.

The length of the upper lift wire should be adjusted so that the hook at its lower end stays about 1/4 inch below the hook at the top

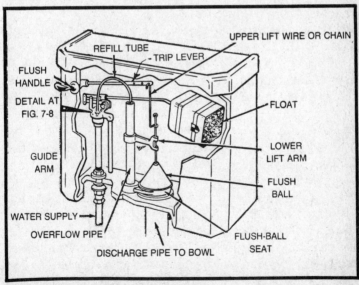

Fig. 7-10. A slow or no-flush toilet may have a broken upper lift wire or a loose or unscrewed lower lift arm.

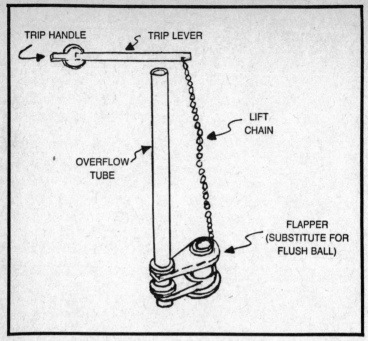

Fig. 7-11. Flapper with lift chain.

of the lower lift arm. Flush the toilet to see if the defect has been removed and then replace the top of the tank.

If the no-flush condition is being caused by a loose or unscrewed lower lift arm, try to tighten it by turning the flush ball counterclockwise. If it stays loose, replace both the flush ball and the lift arm. After performing this operation, it will be necessary to adjust the length of the upper lift wire or chain as explained previously. Now flush the toilet. If the flush ball drops after the tank is fully emptied, the defect has been corrected.

Sometimes you may find that the flush ball drops before the tank has been completely emptied. If so, adjust the length of the upper lift wire as explained earlier. If, however, it is not a wire but a chain as in Fig. 7-9, disconnect it from the trip lever and reduce its length so that when you put it back between the trip lever and the flush ball, there is very little slack. Check by flushing the toilet. If it still does not flush properly, readjust the length of the chain until the defect is removed. It may be advantageous to substitute a *flapper* for a flush ball, as in Fig. 7-11. Read the manufacturer's instructions if you do so. Finally, replace the top of the tank and open the supply.

Leaking Toilet Tank

If water collects on the floor directly under the flush tank, there must be a leak either from around the base screws at the tank bottom which connect it to the toilet bowl, or through wornout washers at the inlet pipe (Fig. 7-12). To identify the actual location, wipe the underside of the tank with a dry cloth or sponge, and watch for the water to start leaking again.

If the inlet pipe is leaking, it should be opened and the two washers changed. You will need only an adjustable wrench to do this. First shut off the water supply by closing the shut-off valve near the inlet pipe if there is one, or close the one on the branch line or the main supply line. As before, remove the tank top and put it away safely. Turn the trip lever to flush out and empty the tank, and then wipe the bottom dry. Place a bucket under the inlet pipe and, with an adjustable wrench, loosen the nuts #2 and #3, shown in Fig. 7-12A. Take out the inlet pipe. Holding the ball-cock assembly in place, loosen nut #1 and take it out, along with the washer #2 above it. Then remove the spud washer #1 from the top and lift up the ball-cock assembly.

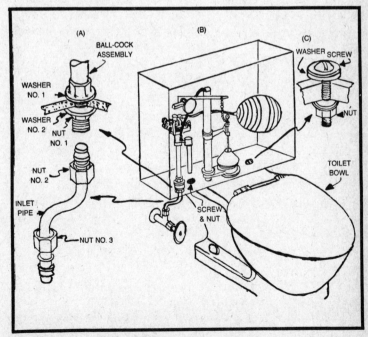

Fig. 7-12. Repairing a leaky toilet.

After getting new washers, place the new spud washer #1 in place and insert the ball-cock assembly through it. Now you can install the new washer #2 and nut #1. Again holding the ball-cock assembly in place, tighten this nut without applying too much pressure or else the tank bottom may crack. Replace the inlet pipe in its original position and tighten nuts #2 and #3. Replace the tank top and open the shut-off valve. If the job has been neatly done, the leak will have been removed. Otherwise, the whole thing will have to be done again.

If the leakage appears around the connecting screws of the tank at its bottom, either the washer or the nut and screws may have been corroded by the chemicals in the water. As before, remove the top of the tank. Hold the bottom nut (Fig. 7-12C) in place with an adjustable wrench, and tighten the screw at the tank bottom with a screwdriver. Wipe the area around the nut with a cloth or sponge and check to see if the leak has been eliminated.

If leakage continues, you have to replace the nut, washer, and the screw. Stop the water supply and empty the tank by flushing it. Wipe dry the bottom and take out the screw, washer, and the nut with the help of your screwdriver and wrench. Get new ones of the same size from your plumbing or hardware store and install them in the original order. Do not overtighten them, otherwise the tank material may crack. Replace the top of the tank and open the shut-off valve.

A Sweating Tank

The temperature of water inside a toilet tank is much lower than that of the heated air in the building. Usually this air is moist as well, and when it comes in contact with the cool outside of the tank, its moisture condenses, causing the sweating. This can be prevented by lining the inside walls of the tank with 1/2 inch thick foam rubber padding or similar insulation material (Fig. 7-13). To do this, remove the top of the tank after shutting off the water supply at the branch or main line. Mark the full water level on an inside wall of the tank. Flush the toilet and completely dry up the inside tank walls and bottom by wiping with a piece of cloth or sponge. Wait for a few minutes before proceeding further.

Measure foam rubber padding (1/2-inch thick) so it will cover the four walls of the tank up to a height of 1 inch to 2 inches above the water line marked. Apply resin glue to the four walls, avoiding the bottom (read the glue manufacturer's instructions for the correct

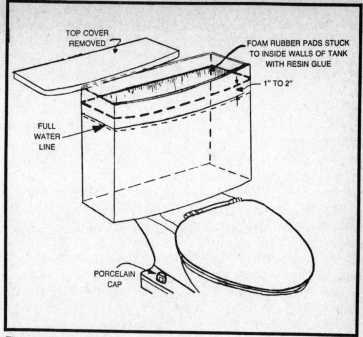

Fig. 7-13. Repairing a sweating tank.

way to apply). The padding should now be placed over the resin glue so that it completely covers all the four walls. Press the padding with your hands to insure that the glue grips the padding and there are no loose spots. Let the glue dry for a couple of hours or so, as dictated by the manufacturer's instructions. Finally, replace the top of the tank and open up the water supply.

Cracked Toilet Tank or Bowl

If a toilet tank has developed cracks and water is leaking through, temporary repairs can be done by using a *silicone tub caulk* which can be bought at any hardware store. Manufacturer's instructions should be followed. Shut off the water and, with a piece of cloth or sponge, clean the area all around the crack(s). Then apply the sealant.

Repairs will be needed both on the outside and inside faces of the fixture if a through-break has occurred or if sizeable pieces of the material have come loose. First apply the tub caulk to the outside and let it harden for the length of time prescribed in the instructions. After this, apply pieces of reinforcing tape to cover the cracks and the area around them. Finally apply the tub caulk to the inside of the crack. If the crack is located in the toilet tank, the tank should be flushed and emptied befcre the repairs are done. Water should be turned on again after the sealant has set fully.

REMOVING AND INSTALLING A TOILET

You don't take apart or replace a toilet every day; there has to be some good reason for doing this. The bowl or the tank may have been damaged due to careless use or an accident; the bowl may be leaking at the floor; or the facility may have grown too old and you may wish to improve the appearance of the bathroom by doing a remodelling and modernizing job. In any case, the old toilet will first have to be removed and then reinstalled after repairs, or replaced with a new one.

If you have such simple tools as a screwdriver, an adjustable wrench, a carpenter's level, and a putty knife, and can obtain the following supplies from the store, you can do the job: wax gasket or putty seal, rubber spud washer, supply pipe washer, and shims of different thicknesses (wooden shims or metallic washers will do).

The actual procedure for removing an old toilet and installing a new one in its place depends on whether it is floor-mounted or wall-mounted. Let us first start with the floor-mounted type, which is the most common.

Removing and Installing a Floor-Mounted Toilet

The first thing to do is to shut off the water supply by turning the shut-off valve to its off position. If there is no individual valve for the toilet, this may be a good time to install one. This will allow you in the future to stop the supply to the toilet while water continues to run in the rest of the house.

Remove the top of the toilet tank and store it in a safe place. Trip the flush handle to empty the tank and, with a sponge or piece of cloth, soak up the remaining water. Remove as much water as possible from the bowl by bailing it out with a mug or similar container. Disconnect the water supply pipe at the bottom of the flush tank.

If you only wish to remove the bowl, without disturbing the tank if possible, check to see if the connection between the two parts is through a large-diameter pipe called a *spud* (Fig. 7-14). Most older installations have spuds with slip nuts at both ends. To disconnect the bowl from the tank, just loosen the two slip nuts and slide them

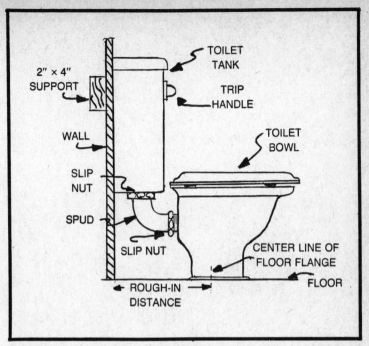

Fig. 7-14. Spud connection between tank and bowl in older installations.

onto the spud itself. To do this you will need a special wrench called a spud-wrench because the nuts are much larger than those you find on a common sink. The spud can now be taken out, leaving the tank attached to the wall with the bowl free to be removed. In case you want to take off the tank too, remove the hanger bolts from inside the tank and lift the tank from the wall bracket. Newer tanks generally rest over the bowl with no connection to the wall.

Figure 7-15A illustrates a floor-mounted toilet with the tank attached to the bowl through two screws at the bottom. There are also two wall screw holes, indicating that the tank is attached to a wall bracket; however, the following description will hold true whether or not the tank is wall-mounted: having removed the wall bracket screws A (see Fig. 7-15A) from inside the toilet tank, loosen and remove the two nuts and washers from the holes B at the bottom of the tank. You will need a screwdriver and an adjustable wrench to do this. Carefully lift up the tank and store it in a place of safety. The spud washer C can now be removed.

The bowl is attached to the floor by a pair of nuts and bolts on both sides. The bolts are held in place by a metallic floor flange which

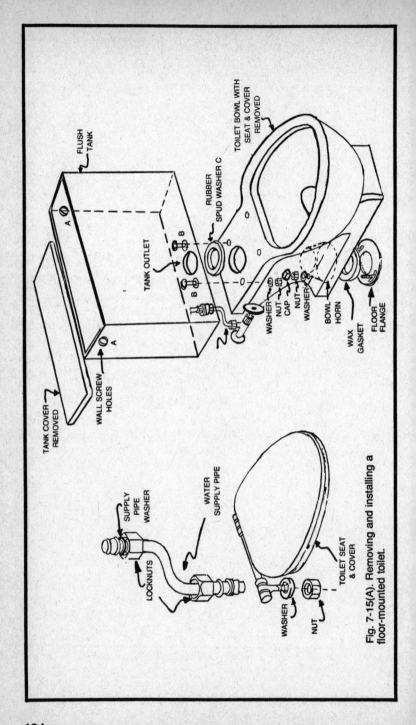

FLUSH TANK

TANK OUTLET

TANK COVER REMOVED

WALL SCREW HOLES

RUBBER SPUD WASHER C

TOILET BOWL WITH SEAT & COVER REMOVED

WASHER

NUT CAP

NUT

WASHER

BOWL HORN

WAX GASKET

FLOOR FLANGE

SUPPLY PIPE WASHER

WATER SUPPLY PIPE

LOCKNUTS

TOILET SEAT & COVER

WASHER

NUT

Fig. 7-15(A). Removing and installing a floor-mounted toilet.

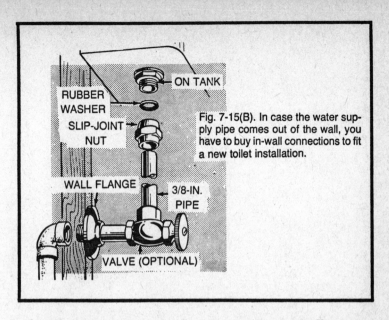

Fig. 7-15(B). In case the water supply pipe comes out of the wall, you have to buy in-wall connections to fit a new toilet installation.

ON TANK

RUBBER WASHER

SLIP-JOINT NUT

WALL FLANGE

3/8-IN. PIPE

VALVE (OPTIONAL)

sits around the soil pipe (see Fig. 7-15A and Fig. 7-16). To remove the bowl, unscrew the nuts with a wrench and remove them along with the washers. These nuts usually have ceramic caps at their top, set in place by a chemical compound. To remove the caps, you will have to pry off the compound with a putty knife. Sometimes the caps have threads inside them and can be screwed on and off. First try to

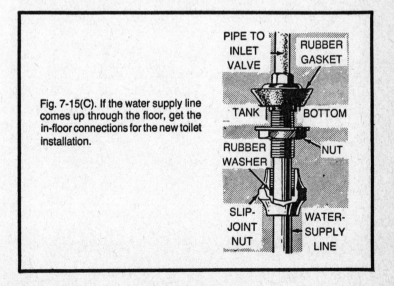

Fig. 7-15(C). If the water supply line comes up through the floor, get the in-floor connections for the new toilet installation.

PIPE TO INLET VALVE

RUBBER GASKET

TANK BOTTOM

RUBBER WASHER

NUT

SLIP-JOINT NUT

WATER-SUPPLY LINE

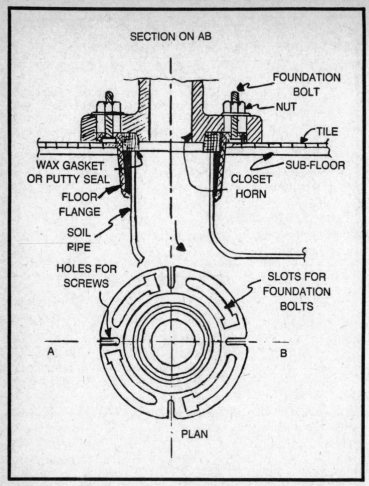

SECTION ON AB

FOUNDATION BOLT

NUT

TILE

SUB-FLOOR

CLOSET HORN

WAX GASKET OR PUTTY SEAL

FLOOR FLANGE

SOIL PIPE

HOLES FOR SCREWS

SLOTS FOR FOUNDATION BOLTS

A

B

PLAN

Fig. 7-16. Toilet installation. Toilet flange is slipped around the soil pipe and screwed to the floor after inserting foundation bolts to receive closet bowl.

unscrew them. If you don't succeed, it means you should pry them off.

The bowl is now ready to be lifted up. Tap its top gently a couple of times or twist it round slightly so that it comes free. Lift the bowl straight up without tilting it backward or else you may spill out some water still remaining inside. Store it away in an upside down position in a place of safety.

As mentioned earlier, the new bowl should have the same rough-in dimension as the old one if it is a wall-mounted tank. The rough-in dimension is the horizontal distance between the finished wall and the center of the floor flange (Fig. 7-14). The dimension of the new tank can be smaller than the old if the tank is not attached to the wall but is merely resting on the bowl. Before setting the bowl in place, clean up the floor flange by removing the old putty seal or wax gasket from it. If you are re-setting the old bowl, clean up the inside of its *horn* (Fig. 7-16). Next, install a new putty seal or wax gasket inside the bowl horn. Press it down firmly till it sticks and stays in place. Now lift the bowl up and, holding it just above the floor flange, align it with the two bolts of the flange. Gently lower the bowl into place. It may be necessary to twist the bowl backward and forward in a horizontal direction so that it sits correctly in position over the bolts and the floor flange. Apply some pressure with your hands on the top of the bowl so that the gasket grips the flange tightly and forms a waterproof seal.

At this point, check if the bowl has a level top. Place a carpenter's level over the bowl and slide it in different positions to see that the bowl is truly level. If not, insert metallic or wooden shims under the bowl (letting the carpenter's level stay at top), till you are satisfied that it is truly level. You will have to move the shims about quite a bit till a satisfactory result is obtained.

After placing a new rubber spud washer over the bowl opening just under the tank outlet, lower the toilet tank gently so that the openings align. With an adjustable wrench install the bolts and nuts that you had removed earlier from the openings, B. Check the alignments of the tank and the bowl with respect to the wall. Finally tighten the bowl over the floor flange bolts by replacing the nuts and new washers. Be careful not to overtighten the nuts or you may crack the fixture. Replace the caps over the nuts after applying the sealing compound. If the caps have threads inside them, just screw them down.

Next insert the screws through holes A inside the tank wall and secure the tank to the wall mounting. Replace the tank top.

At the start of this operation, you had taken out the water supply pipe when dismantling the tank. This should now be re-installed. After inserting a new washer, hold the supply pipe at its correct position between the tank bottom and the water supply main and tighten the two locknuts with a wrench.

Finally, install the bowl cover and the seat by replacing the washers and nuts and tightening them with your hands—not a wrench. Open up the water supply. If you have followed all instructions correctly, your toilet troubles should be over.

Removing and Installing a Wall-Mounted Toilet

Figure 7-17 shows a wall-mounted toilet with the tank resting over it. The procedure for removing the bowl and installing a new one is basically the same as that for the floor-mounted model, only it is simpler. You will need the following tools and supplies: an adjustable wrench, a closet flange gasket, a putty knife, washers, a screwdriver, and a pair of pliers.

As before, shut off the water at the main, the branch main, or at the fixture shut-off valve if one exists. Remove the cover of the tank and store it a safe place. Turn the trip handle to flush the tank. Remove all water remaining in the tank by soaking it up with a piece of cloth or sponge. The supply pipe to the tank should now be disconnected and removed after unscrewing the two locknuts, as explained in the previous section (Fig. 7-15). Also, by removing the

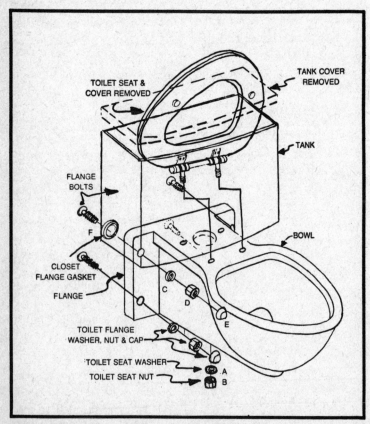

Fig. 7-17. Removing and installing a wall mounted toilet.

nuts and washers A and B (Fig. 7-17), you will be able to take off the toilet seat and its cover. Store these safely.

The toilet bowl is attached to the wall by means of four flange bolts which have their heads fixed inside the wall; the washers, nuts, and caps, C, D, and E, are on the bowl side of the flange. To detach the bowl, first remove the caps by prying them off or unscrewing them, as the case may be, and then unscrew and remove the nuts from the bolts along with the washers. You will have to use a wrench for this purpose and during this operation will have to support the toilet bowl or it will fall down on the floor. You may need someone to help you.

The toilet bowl should be removed to a safe spot and its flange scraped with a putty knife till the old gasket F comes off completely. (If you are discarding this old toilet and installing a new one, this step is unnecessary.)

Begin the installation by placing a new gasket F in its proper place on the back of the toilet flange at the toilet opening. If necessary, press it firmly till it stays in place. Lift the toilet bowl and carefully pin it on to the four bolts in the wall. With the help of the adjustable wrench install the four nuts and new washers. Screw on the caps or secure them by applying a sufficient quantity of the sealing compound.

The water supply to the tank can now be restored by reinstalling the supply pipe which was taken off in the beginning, and opening the shut-off valve. The toilet seat and cover should be placed back in position with the bolts going down through the proper holes in the bowl, and they should be securely installed by tightening the nuts B after the washers A are inserted. Replace the cover at the top of the tank. This completes the job.

A note of warning: By now you must have realized that there is nothing complicated or difficult in removing and installing a toilet; yet it will be a good idea to check your local plumbing code. Some communities still require a licensed plumber to be hired for doing this job even though a handyman can do it quite efficiently and with very little bother.

Fixing a Loose Toilet Bowl

A toilet bowl may come loose from misuse or careless initial installation. If you look down on both sides of the bowl bottom where it rests on the flange, you will notice two porcelain caps (Fig. 7-13). The bolts by which the bowl is secured to the floor are located under

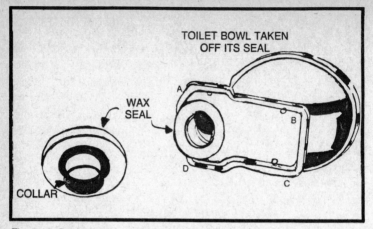

Fig. 7-18. Replacing the seal of a leaking toilet bowl.

these caps. The caps are usually attached to the bowl by plaster of Paris or by a caulking compound. Sometimes they are screwed on.

If the problem is only a loose bowl with no seepage of water noticeable at the floor, the defect can be remedied by removing the caps and tightening the nuts. The caps can be taken off by working with a knife to scrape out the filling compound, and tapping with a small hammer. Tighten the nuts, using very little pressure. If you overtighten them, the bowl is likely to crack; so be very careful.

In case there is leakage of water at the base it will be necessary to change the seal. Shut off the water supply, flush the toilet and sponge out the remaining water. Now disconnect the tank from the incoming water line, unscrew the foundation nuts, and remove them. Carefully lift the toilet bowl straight up (see Fig. 7-18) and remove the old and worn-out seal; you will probably have to scrape it off. Get an exactly matching seal from the store. A putty ring should be applied along A, B, C, D (in Fig. 7-18 the rim of the toilet base). The new wax or rubber ring should be placed inside the discharge opening. Lower the toilet carefully over the floor flange. It should come down straight and very slowly; don't let it slide down. After it settles in place, press down firmly and give a slight twisting motion back and forth. If you have done it right, the floor flange bolts will go through the holes in the base of the toilet. It will be advisable to get a little help from someone during this operation. Now slip the nuts on to the bolts and tighten them lightly; the flange may crack if you use too much force. Replace the caps after applying the setting compound.

If a new tile floor has been installed recently in the bathroom the bowl may not fit properly over the floor flange. In such a case, two wax seals should be used, one over the other, to get a tightly fitting joint. After the toilet has been installed, open the water supply.

If the leak is at the base of a toilet in which there is a *spud* connection between the tank and the bowl, first remove this spud pipe by unscrewing the slip nuts. This will disconnect the flush tank. Lift the toilet straight up without tilting it and put it upside down on thick paper padding. Remove the old seal by scraping it with the putty knife. Also scrape off the setting compound from the rim of the flange. Check the level of the floor and the floor flange with a carpenter's level. It is possible that the floor has settled in places and is not truly level. Place small pieces of wood shingles near the flange bolts to serve as shims, and put back the toilet over the floor flange. Check the level and adjust the shims till the bowl top is almost truly level. Without disturbiing the shims, very carefully lift the toilet and store it away. Apply a thin bead of plaster of Paris along the rim of the

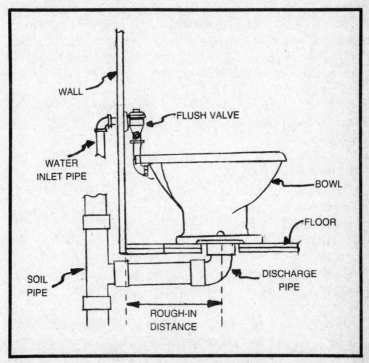

Fig. 7-19. A tankless flush-valve installation can be used when the water supply main for the building is 1 1/4″ in diameter or larger.

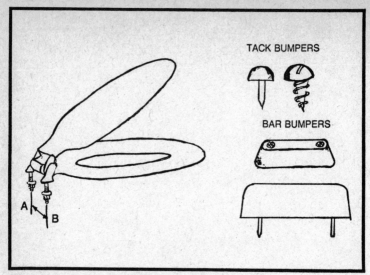

Fig. 7-20. Toilet seat & cover, and bumpers.

bowl and a little thicker bead along the shims. Put in a new toilet seal. Install the toilet by lowering it down over the floor bolts and the wax seal. Check the level again. If it is all right, tighten the nuts lightly; do not use too much pressure. Wipe off excess plaster of Paris from around the toilet, and wipe the edge of the rim with a piece of wet cloth or sponge.

A tankless flush-valve installation can be used when the water supply main for the building is 1 1/4 inches in diameter or larger. See Fig. 7-19.

Replacing a Toilet Seat

The most pertinent dimension of a toilet seat is the distance between the seat bolts (distance A-B in Fig. 7-20). Measure it carefully and obtain a replacement that fits in the same position. In some models, the seat bolts go through the toilet tank. If this is the case, the replacement you buy should fit this type of installation. If your toilet is of special design, it will be preferable to get an exact replacement made by the same manufacturer. Even though you don't have to shut off water or flush the toilet while changing the seat and the cover, it will be a good idea to do so. You might drop a washer, nut, or your wrench, and getting it back will be easier in a dry bowl. If you find that the nuts and bolts have rusted, apply lubricating oil and wait for some time before using the wrench.

Tapping the nut lightly will help. Do not apply too much force when using the wrench; if it slips off, you may crack the tank or bowl. When a regular wrench does not reach far enough, try a deep-throated socket wrench. If the nut still does not come off, your last resort is to get a hack-saw, put it under the hinge, and saw through the two bolts. Here, also, be very careful not to apply unnecessary force. If the saw jumps off, it might crack your bowl or tank the same as a flying wrench would.

Having removed the old seat and cover, install the new one by inserting its bolts into the holes and tightening the nuts. Don't apply too much pressure or the rubber washers may get crushed and their life span will be shortened.

If the toilet seat is merely a little loose, the reason may be a crushed rubber washer or worn rubber bumpers. The rubber washers can be replaced after removing the seat from its foundation. The bumpers, which are made with screws or nails, can be unscrewed or pulled out with a pair of pliers. New ones should be put in new holes made close to the old ones. Bumpers are of two types: tack bumpers and bar bumpers (see Fig. 7-20).

CLEARING TOILET CLOGS

Clogs occur when objects get caught in the toilet trap. Sometimes toilet paper and grease, together with articles accidentally dropped into the toilet, form such a tenacious deposit that it really takes a lot of effort to clean it out. If this condition combines with another defect like a running toilet (due to a non-fitting flush ball in the toilet tank) you are in real trouble. However, the *plumber's friend*, or plunger, which you should always keep handy for such emergencies, will get rid of the clog in most cases. If it does not help, use a toilet auger or a drain auger. If this too fails, you will have to take out the toilet bowl completely and then clean it. However, this procedure is not very easy to execute and should be tried only as a last resort.

Before you use the plumber's friend or plunger, see that there is sufficient water in the toilet to cover its rubber suction cup. If not, bring a pan of water from the faucet and pour it into the bowl until there is enough water to cover the rubber cup. In fact, the plunger will function much better if you can manage to pour water in the bowl till its level is just below the rim. *Do not flush the toilet*, or the bowl will overflow and soil everything on the floor including any carpeting you may have. After applying a thick coat of petroleum jelly all

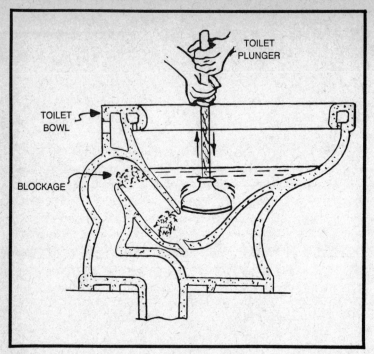

Fig. 7-21. Clearing toilet blockage with a plunger.

around the base of the suction cup, place it over the bowl opening, while keeping the handle as vertical as possible. Work the plunger up and down vigorously until the water drains out, indicating that the stoppage has been cleared (Fig. 7-21). You will usually succeed with this procedure unless the clogging is real tough.

If the plumber's friend fails, you should use an auger. A toilet auger is preferable but a drain auger will do. The drain auger is likely to scratch the surface of the bowl, though, so use it very carefully. Insert the auger into the trap and start turning the handle, at the same time pushing the auger further and further till you feel the obstruction (Fig. 7-22). The handle should always be turned in one direction only. After you hit the blockage, pull the auger in and out, turning the handle constantly, until the obstruction is removed and the auger starts moving freely. At this stage, *never* flush the toilet to check if the blockage has been removed. Bring a pan of water from the faucet and pour it into the bowl. If it flows freely into the trap, the blockage has been removed. If water stays in the bowl without flowing into the trap, repeat the above procedure until you succeed in removing the blockage. Take out the auger and check your progress by pouring water into the bowl. If the water flows into the trap satisfactorily, flush the toilet two or three times to wash away all the remnants of the blockage. Clean the auger very thoroughly before storing it away; you don't want the germs from the bowl to spread all over the house next time you use the auger. A regular plumber's auger may be used in cases when the clogging is very severe.

If everything fails and the clogging still persists, the bowl has to be removed from the floor. This can be done as described earlier under the heading: *Fixing a Loose Toilet Bowl.* After the bowl has been lifted off the floor flange, it should be placed upside down on a padding made of old newspapers. The obstruction can now be worked on directly through the discharge opening. In case your

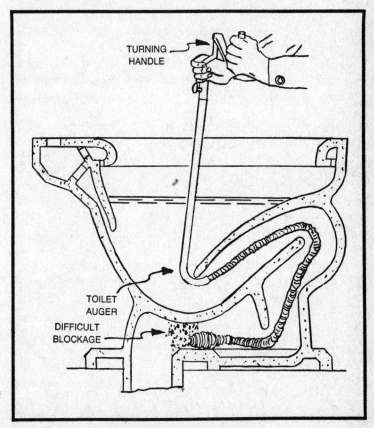

Fig. 7-22. Clearing difficult blockage with a toilet auger.

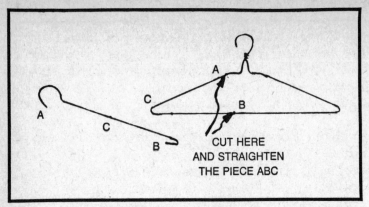

CUT HERE
AND STRAIGHTEN
THE PIECE ABC

Fig. 7-23. A substitute cleanout tool can be made from a wire coat hanger.

earlier efforts have caused the blockage to pass on to the waste line, clean it up by working with a snake through the soil pipe opening that is now exposed.

If during an emergency you are unable to obtain a closet or sink auger, here is a way to prepare a substitute from an ordinary wire coat hanger: cut the hanger at the two spots shown in Fig. 7-23 and

Fig. 7-24. A floor-mounted, one-piece toilet occupies less space than other types. Courtesy: Kohler Co.

Fig. 7-25. A wall-mounted toilet is usually liked by the housewife because the space underneath can be easily cleaned. Courtesy: Kohler Co.

Fig. 7-26. Some modern toilets come in unique desgins to complement modern decors.

197

straighten out the portion A-C-B. Bend one end to form a hook about 1 1/2 inches to 2 inches wide, and bend the other end into a hook about 3/4 inch wide. Insert the narrow hook into the trap area and work it around to remove the blockage. Although not as effective as the toilet auger, it will work in most cases.

Figures 7-24, 7-25, and 7-26 illustrate some toilet designs currently on the market.

Faucets: Types, Repairs, and Replacements

Chapter 8

Faucets: Types, Repairs, and Replacements

Faucets come in two types: compression faucets and non-compression faucets. You can easily distinguish one from the other because a compression faucet has separate hot and cold handles with washers. As either handle is turned toward *off*, its washers compress a *seat* that closes the water supply; when turned in the other direction, water is allowed to flow from the supply pipe to the faucet. In the noncompression type of faucet there is a single knob or lever connected to both the hot and cold water supply lines. The knob or lever regulates the proportion of hot and cold water that flows, as well as its volume. Figures 8-1 and 8-2 illustrate the two types of faucets.

The compression-type faucet is in some ways the more complicated of the two. Figure 8-3 shows an exploded view of one compression faucet. The various parts contained in each handle, listing from the top, are:

- metal cap
- handle screw
- turning handle
- packing nut
- packing material (not found in some designs)
- washer
- valve stem with ribbed upper end and a plastic O-ring at bottom

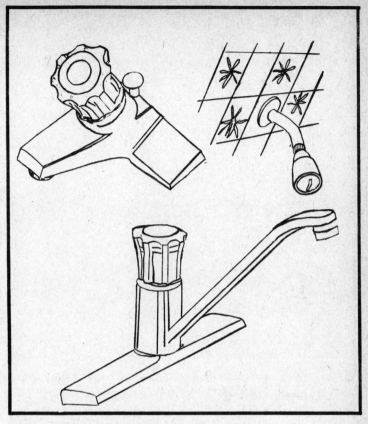

Fig. 8-1. Typical non-compression type single faucets.

- seat washer
- screw
- nylon washer
- valve seat assembly

This may look complicated, but it is easy to open up and repair, when necessary.

FAUCET PROBLEMS

Usual maintenance problems with all types of faucets are:

1. Clogged or dirty aerator
2. Spout drip
3. Stem and base leaks
4. Faucet handle out of alignment

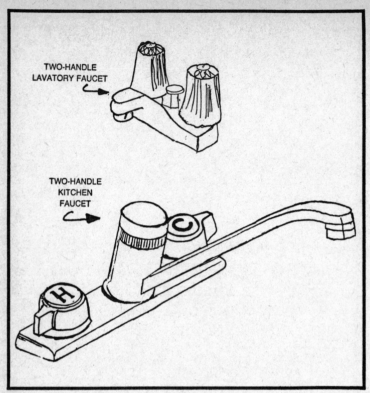

Fig. 8-2. Typical compression-type faucets.

You do not need much know-how, or a large number of wrenches and tools, to deal with these malfunctions. A screwdriver, a pair of long-handled pliers, and an adjustable wrench will do almost all faucet repair jobs. If you already have a set of open-end wrenches, they will help you get a better grip on the nuts than will an adjustable wrench. A basin wrench is also very handy. When working in tight spots, like those under a sink or a lavatory basin, the basin wrench gets a grip on different-sized nuts; as its jaws flip over to the opposite side, you can continue working on a nut without taking out the wrench after every half turn or so.

Fixing a Clogged or Dirty Aerator

A clogged or dirty aerator will reduce the quantity of water flowing out of a faucet and may make the flow turbulent and uneven. As time goes on, fine particles suspended in the water will deposit

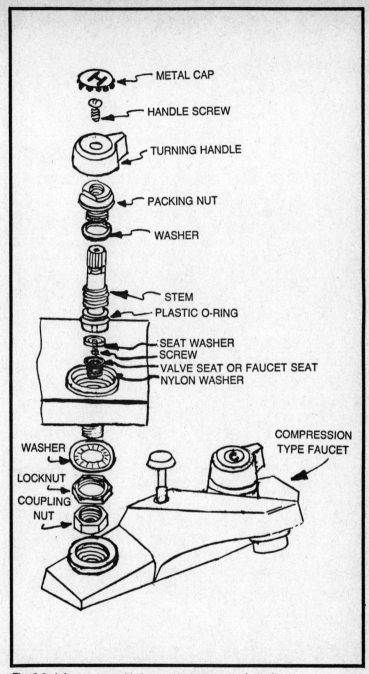

METAL CAP

HANDLE SCREW

TURNING HANDLE

PACKING NUT

WASHER

STEM

PLASTIC O-RING

SEAT WASHER
SCREW
VALVE SEAT OR FAUCET SEAT
NYLON WASHER

WASHER

LOCKNUT

COUPLING
NUT

COMPRESSION
TYPE FAUCET

Fig. 8-3. A faucet assembly is easy to open up and repair.

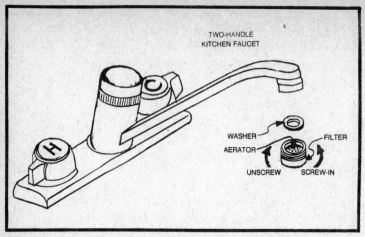

Fig. 8-4. A clogged or dirty aerator and/or filter reduces the supply. Take them out by turning clockwise. Hold the aerator, under running water. The debris inside the filter should be removed by a toothpick or brush.

inside the small openings of the aerator and the filter and clog them. Before taking out the aerator, water should be shut off by turning the faucet handle(s) to *off*. Try to remove the aerator by turning it in a clockwise direction (Fig. 8-4) with your fingers. If you can't do it, use a pair of pliers; but first cover the outer surface of the aerator with two layers of adhesive tape to protect the finish.

If the washer is worn out, get an exact replacement. You may have to take the aerator assembly to the plumbing store. After you have taken out the aerator, clean the fine screen by holding it about 9 inches below the faucet opening and letting water run with full force for a couple of minutes. If necessary, clean it further with a toothbrush. Take out the filter from the other end of the assembly and clean it, too, with a toothbrush or toothpick. Be sure to remove all the debris. Replace the aerator and the filter and install them back on the faucet by turning in a counterclockwise direction. Remove the adhesive tape layers after making sure that the faucet is working properly.

Fixing Drips and Leaks

A dripping or leaking faucet, in addition to being a constant nuisance, also wastes water and, therefore, money. The dripping water can stain sinks and bath floors, and ultimately destroys their finish and elegance.

Differentiation should be made between *drips* and *leaks*. A drip occurs when the faucet handle is turned off, yet some water is still flowing out at the spout. A leak is in effect if you observe water oozing from the stem or the base of the faucet when it is running. The malfunction is called *stem leak* or *base leak*, as the case may be.

A defective washer or a worn-out valve seat can cause a drip. Water in the supply line is always under pressure; that is why it comes out with a force at the fixtures. If the washer and valve seat do not maintain a watertight seal , some water under pressure will pass through them and keep dripping out the faucet. The drip can be stopped simply by putting in a new washer or repairing the valve seat so that a watertight shut-off is provided when the handle is turned off.

Repairing Spout Drip

For a single faucet, the water supply should be shut off at the individual shut-off valve or at the branch or main supply line, before the faucet is dismantled for inspection. On a double faucet with separate hot and cold water controls and a common spout, you'll have to determine which faucet is causing the leakage to go to the spout. The test is simple if there are separate shut-off valves for each faucet. Close one of the valves and see if the drip has stopped. If it has, then that particular faucet is leaking. Try the other one also; both may be leaking. You cannot identify and isolate the problem in cases where no individual shut-off valves exist. In these cases you will have no alternative except to repair both the hot and cold water faucets.

Shut off the supply at the individual valves or at the branch or main line, as the case may be. Remove the faucet handle. The top screws are often hidden under the round plastic or metal caps which are marked H or C (Fig. 8-5). If the caps are of the screw-on type, unscrew them. Otherwise, pull them off. The handle screw can now be removed with a screwdriver, and the turning handle can be pulled off (see Fig. 8-3). Remove the packing nut by turning it in a counterclockwise direction. Also remove the stem along with the washer. Take out the seat washer by opening the bottom screw with a screwdriver.

Examine the washer and the screw. If they are worn out, obtain and install exact replacements. Thoroughly examine the valve seat

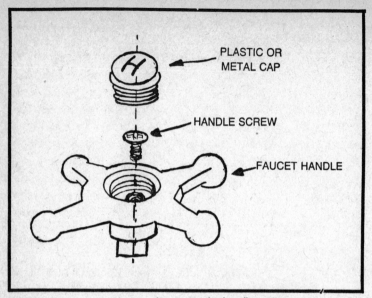

Fig. 8-5. Plastic or metal caps often cover the handle screws.

because worn-out valve seats result in drips too. Refacing the valve seat so that it fits the washer evenly will be explained shortly. Reinstall the stem after the new washer has been fitted to it. Some stems simply screw onto the faucets. Replace the washer, the packing nut, and the screw on the turning handle. Snap on or screw on the metal cap, as the case may be. Open the shut-off valve and turn the faucet handle. Examine for drips. The entire procedure should be followed for the other faucet, too, if necessary.

If a faucet drips even after a new washer has been put in, the fault probably lies with the valve seat. When a worn-out washer is not changed in time, the spindle rubs against the faucet seat every time it is turned, resulting in damage to the seat. Another cause for a worn-out seat is corrosion of the metallic faucet seat by the chemicals present in water, or the physical accumulation of such chemicals around the seat, preventing the washer from sitting tightly over it in the closed position.

An uneven and defective faucet seat can be aligned and repaired with a *reseating tool* (Fig. 8-6), which does not cost too much. The faucet assembly should be dismantled as described earlier, and the packing nut of the faucet should be slipped over the tool's stem and screwed back over the top of the faucet. Tighten the nut until the cutting edge of the tool touches the valve seat. By turning the handle of the tool back and forth several times, you will *grind* the faucet seat. Do not overdo it or else you will completely *destroy* the valve seat which does not have too much material. The grindings should be flushed away.

If the faucet seat is irreparable, if it has been destroyed by too much grinding, or if you don't have the reseating tool, the seat can be taken out and replaced with a new one. A seat-removing tool will be required for this. After replacements and repairs, the faucet should be reassembled and the water supply should be turned on. If the job has been done carefully, there should be no drip from the faucet.

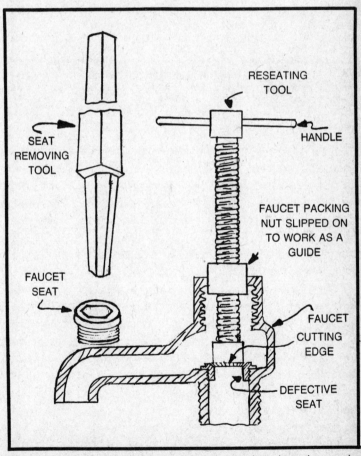

Fig. 8-6. An uneven faucet seat can be brought into shape by an inexpensive grinding or reseating tool. Do not grind away too much material.

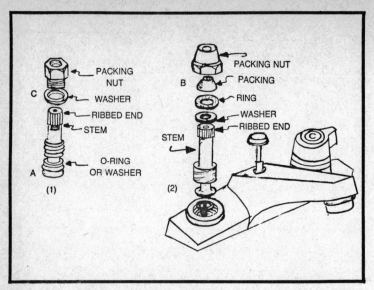

Fig. 8-7. Stem leak is caused by worn-out washer "A" or packing material "B". Base leak results from worn-out washer C. Obtain exact replacements. Two different types of assembly are shown above.

Correcting Stem and Base Leaks

When a faucet is turned on, water flows out from the spout; if you observe some flow around the faucet handle, it is called a *faucet leak*. A worn-out washer at the bottom of the stem or damaged packing in a packing nut on top of the stem cause *stem leak*. A *base leak* is caused by a worn-out washer at the base of the packing nut (Fig. 8-7). There are two types of packing nuts: one has a washer (C in Fig. 8-7) at its base while the other type is stuffed with packing material (B in Fig. 8-7).

To remove these leaks, shut off the water supply at the individual shut-off valves or at the branch or main supply line. Use two layers of adhesive tape to cover those surfaces of the faucets which will come in contact with the wrenches. Open up the faucet assembly as explained under *Repairing Spout Drip*. (See Fig. 8-3). Remove the turning handle and take out the packing nut by turning it counterclockwise. If the stem also comes out with the packing nut, separate the two with a wrench.

If the packing nut has the packing material inside, as in Fig. 8-7 (2), remove the packing. If it is the other type, as shown in Fig. 8-7 (1), there will be no packing under the packing nut. Take out the washer or O-ring from the bottom of the stem. Get exact replacements and install them in place of the worn-out parts. A small quantity of heat-resistant grease may be applied to the washer. Assemble the stem and the packing nut. The stem should be inserted inside the packing nut if it is not already inside the faucet. Tighten the packing nut with a wrench. Mount the turning handle and install the handle screw. Snap on the caps or screw them on, as the case may be.

Place the faucet handle in the off position and turn the water supply on. Now open the faucet and see if you find a leak.

The *base leak* results from a worn-out washer (C in Fig. 8-7). When doing the previously explained repairs for stem leak, the faucet assembly will be open; always check the washer. If wornout, it should be replaced. If, after having done these repairs, the faucet is still leaking, there must be a spout drip. Repair this as explained under *Repairing Spout Drip*.

Aligning Faucet Handles

If the turning handles of the faucet are not in proper alignment, they will give a bad appearance; it will be a good idea to align them properly whenever you can spare the time.

Bring the handles to the off position, thereby turning off the faucet. Remove the caps and the screws from the tops of the faucets. Take out the handles and put them back so that they look symmetrical. Install the screws, and snap on or screw on the caps as necessary. Test by turning the two handles so that they are in positions which permit freedom of movement for maximum flow through the spout.

NON-COMPRESSION TYPE FAUCETS

The modern non-compression type faucet has no washers. A rubber diaphragm or metal-to-metal contact serves to control the flow of hot and cold water. You will find only one spout or faucet as compared with the two faucets in the compression type described before (Fig. 8-8). These one-spout faucets give less trouble, and repairs are easily done on them. Depending on the control mechanism, the single-handle faucets can be classified into three categories: ball faucets, valve faucets, and cartridge faucets.

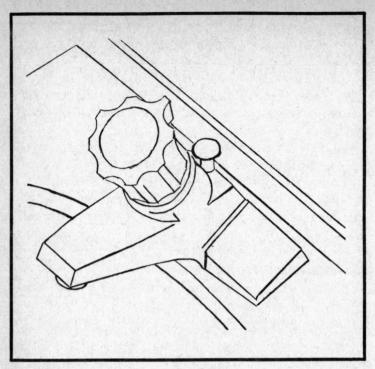

Fig. 8-8. A typical single-control lavatory faucet.

You cannot tell definitely which type a faucet is just by looking at it. You have to open up the mechanism to find out its type. Although there are wide variations in the looks and construction details of faucets put on the market by various manufacturing companies, the basic principles remain the same. When proceeding with repairs, it will help to have the manufacturer's instructions handy; however, the following descriptions will furnish sufficient guidance for you to do the repairs if manufacturer's instructions are not available.

Ball Faucets

Ball faucet assembly details are shown in Fig. 8-9. When the handle is turned, it rotates a ball within the faucet which controls the flow of hot and cold water. If the faucet has developed a drip or leak, or is otherwise defective, you can easily dismantle the assembly.

First shut off the water at the individual shut-off valve or at the branch or main supply line. Wrap two layers of adhesive tape around the cap of the faucet to protect its finish. Snap off the cap from the top or unscrew it as the case may be. You will then notice the handle button. Unscrew it and remove the handle. In some designs, there are no caps; the handle has a screw around its base which should be opened. The handle can then be removed. Next remove the lower cap by rotating it counterclockwise. The cam assembly and the ball will now be exposed and should be lifted out along with the seat assemblies (the seats and springs). In some models, there is a swing spout (see Fig. 8-1, bottom sketch), which should be pulled out after moving it back and forth (sideways). Normally there will be an O-ring at its base which should also be removed.

Examine the following parts and see if they are worn out or corroded by chemicals contained in water: the ball, the seat assemblies (seats and springs), the cam, the cam packing, and the O-ring (in case of a swing spout).

Get replacements for defective parts and start reassembling. If your faucet has a swing spout, start by installing the O-ring: apply a

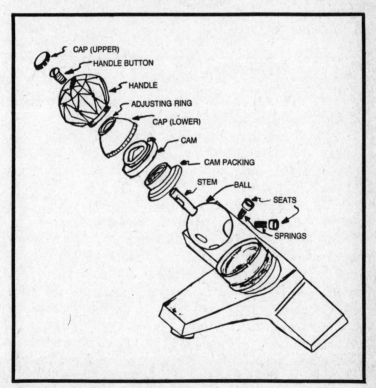

Fig. 8-9. A dismantled ball-type faucet.

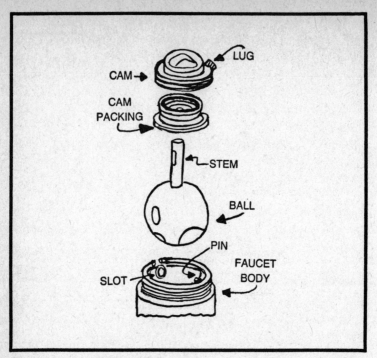

Fig. 8-10. Reassembling a ball faucet.

small amount of grease to the O-ring and then push down the swing spout. Rotate it until it sits over the slip ring.

The two seat assemblies should now be placed inide the faucet body in their correct location. The slot on the ball should go over the pin in the faucet body and the lug on the side of the cam should go into the slot body (Fig. 8-10).

Having installed the ball, the cam packing, and the cam, place the lower cap on top and tighten it by turning in a clockwise direction first with your hands and then with a pair of pliers. The handle should now be placed over the stem, the water should be turned on, and an inspection should be made of the area around the stem to see if there are any leaks. Do not place the upper cap in position yet. If there is no leak, take off the handle and position the cap on it. Tighten it and remove the protective adhesive tape which was attached in the beginning to protect the finish. Finally place the handle or knob over the lower cap again and tighten the handle screw or button. You have now gotten rid of the drip or leak.

Valve Faucets

Figure 8-11 illustrates a valve faucet. There are no washers inside. The flow of hot and cold water is controlled by water pressures and by the rigidity of a spring contained in the valve assembly. Figure 8-12 shows the integral parts of the system. The *mesh screens*, or *strainers*, protect the valve assembly from being damaged or clogged by the fine, suspended matter which is often present in water. For this reason, the screens should be checked occasionally and any deposits should be removed by flushing them out under running water or by using a fine toothbrush.

When you have a problem like a leak or drip in a valve faucet the first thing to do, as usual, is to shut off water by closing the individual fixture valve, if one exists, or by closing a shut-off valve at the branch or main water supply line. Open the faucet and allow all the water in it to drain out. Cover the *connecting ring* (Fig. 8-11) with two layers of adhesive tape to prevent its surface from being damaged, and loosen it with an adjustable wrench which should be turned in a coun-

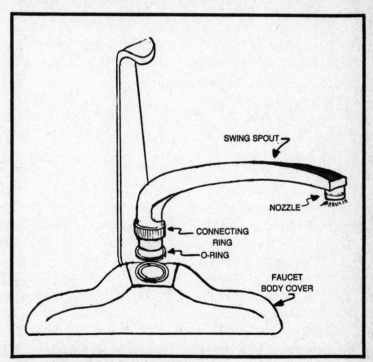

SWING SPOUT

NOZZLE

CONNECTING RING

O-RING

FAUCET BODY COVER

Fig. 8-11. Valve-type faucet (no washer).

terclockwise direction. The swing spout can now be lifted up. Take out the O-ring and remove the faucet body cover. You will see plugs on either side. Again using your adjustable wrench, unscrew the plugs, one at a time, and take out the *gasket*, the *strainer*, and the *valve assembly*. Next, take out the valve seat with the help of a valve seat removal tool or an Allen wrench.

Examine the strainer and clean it up by holding it under a stream of water and then cleaning with a fine toothbrush. If you find that the strainer is damaged, get an exact replacement. Also examine the following parts to see if they are worn out, damaged, or corroded by the chemicals present in water: the gasket, the valve assembly, the valve seat, and the O-ring.

Get replacements for defective parts from the plumbing or hardware store and start reassembling. First install the new valve seat using your valve seat removal tool, and then the valve assembly and the strainer. Finally, place the gasket in proper position and screw in the plug. After all this is done satisfactorily, replace the faucet body cover.

The only thing left now is to install the swing spout. To do this, apply a small quantity of heat-resistant grease to the O-ring, and slip it on the spout (see Fig. 8-12). Drop the spout carefully into the opening at the faucet body and tighten the connecting ring with an adjustable wrench, working in a clockwise direction. The protective tape can now be removed. Open the water supply shut-off valves, turn the faucet on, see if the leaks and drips have disappeared.

Cartridge Faucets

Cartridge faucets have a cartridge assembly which has ports or holes that control the flow of hot and cold water. The advantage of a cartridge is that you can take out a defective one and obtain a replacement without the bother of opening it up. Some cartridges can be repaired by your plumbing or hardware dealer, but repairs are not really worthwhile because the replacement is generally inexpensive. Also, the life of a new part is normally much longer than that of an old one which has been repaired.

Cartridges come in various designs, but they have one common feature: they are held in position by a retaining clip. This clip may be either one of two types: an *external* retaining clip, (Fig. 8-13A), or an *internal* retaining clip (Fig. 8-13B).

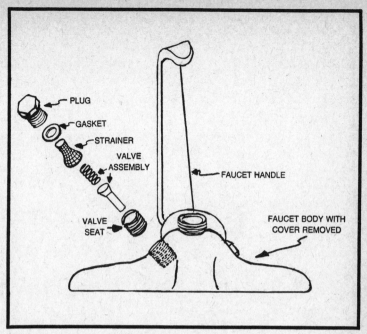

Fig. 8-12. Valve-type single faucet with cover opened and valve assembly removed.

Once this retaining clip is removed, the cartridge assembly can simply be lifted out. You have to be very sure to get an exact replacement—take the old one to the store to match it.

Cartridge Faucet with External Retaining Clip. To open a defective, leaking, or dripping faucet of this type you will merely need a screwdriver. Shut off the water supply at the shut-off valve and open the faucet to let the water inside it drain out. After removing the external retaining clip, lift out the cartridge assembly (Fig. 8-13A). Get an exact replacement from the plumbing or hardware store and install the new one in the place of the old. Snap on the retaining clip, open the shut-off valve and turn the faucet on. The drip or leak will have stopped if the correct cartridge has been put in.

Cartridge Faucet with Internal Retaining Clip. To repair a defective faucet of this type, shut off the water supply at the individual shut-off or at the branch or main water line. Open the faucet to drain off water contained in it. If there is a cap at the top of the handle, remove it by snapping it off or unscrewing, as necessary,

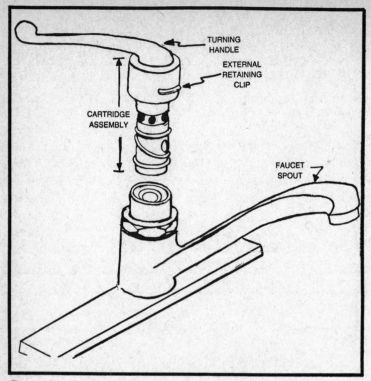

Fig. 8-13(A). Cartridge-type faucet with external retaining clip.

and take out the gasket under it. Remove the handle screw with a screwdriver and lift up the handle. The retaining clip is under the clip retainer ring. Remove the ring and you will see the clip. The cartridge assembly will be free as soon as you remove this clip. Take out the assembly and get an exact replacement from your plumbing or hardware store.

Put back the new cartridge assembly and replace the retaining clip. The clip retainer ring can now be slipped in position and the handle installed by tightening the screw. Replace the gasket and cap if they were removed. Turn the water on and check for drip. Also check for any leaks after turning the faucet on. If the job has been done carefully, you will find no problems.

REPLACING KITCHEN FAUCETS

Fittings like faucets have a long life, but ultimately they develop defects which cannot be easily corrected. That is the time to install replacements. If your house is comparatively old, you may at some time or other, want to modernize your kitchen or bathroom by putting in new cabinets, countertops, bathtubs, toilets, etc., along with new paint on the walls and tiles or wall-to-wall carpeting on the floors. Along with such a project, you may also want to replace old faucets in the bathroom and kitchen with new, sleek, elegant-looking models. Some examples are provided at the end of this Chapter.

When buying the replacements, be sure you will be able to use them. Sometimes due to space restrictions or the odd dimensions of the old fixtures, you will have to make special efforts to get the correct size. It will always be advisable to have the old fittings handy when you are selecting the new ones from your plumber. If you don't want to carry them along, at least measure out the pertinent dimensions, like the sizes of the water lines underneath the faucets and the center-to-center distance between the shanks of a two-handle

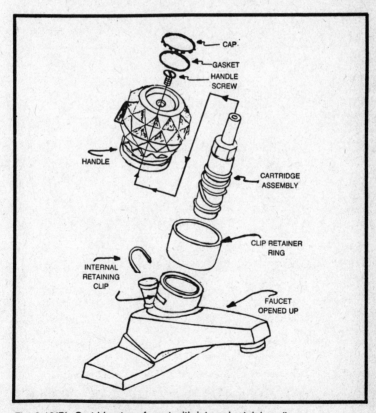

Fig. 8-13(B). Cartridge-type faucet with internal retaining clip.

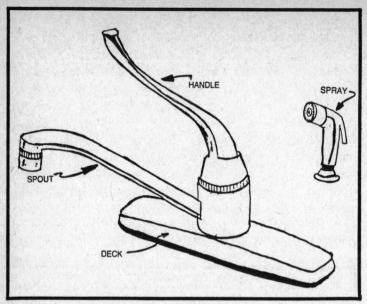

Fig. 8-14. Kitchen faucet with handle.

faucet. If you are replacing a single-sink faucet, make a note of whether it has male threads or female threads.

Replacing Single-Handle Kitchen Faucets

Single-handle kitchen faucets come with or without a separate spray assembly connected to the spout through a flexible hose (Fig. 8-14). Single-handle faucets do not have washers. Instead they have a cartridge, ball, or valve assembly to control the flow of hot and cold water. Their life span is much longer than that of the washer-type faucets. When you buy a new faucet unit, it comes with simple instructions. There is nothing complicated at all in installing the unit.

If you are getting a new single-handle faucet as a replacement for an old double-handle faucet, select one which will cover the old holes in the sink. With a flashlight, examine the underside of the sink and measure the center-to-center horizontal distance between the studs. Is it 6 inches or 8 inches? Also measure how far removed the water supply line is from the studs. These are the two most important dimensions you will need when selecting a new faucet assembly.

Perhaps you would prefer to have a spray assembly, too. It may come attached to the faucet deck or it may be separate. If your sink has three holes, you need a faucet with the spray attached to the deck itself (Fig. 8-15). If there are four holes, you need a separate spray to cover up the fourth hole (Fig. 8-16). If you don't need a spray and your sink has only three holes, buy a faucet without a spray. It will be less expensive.

To do the replacement job, the following tools and supplies will be required: an adjustable wrench or channel-lock pliers, a basin wrench for work in tight spots, and plumber's putty.

Shut off the water by closing the shut-off valve. Turn the faucet on, to drain off the water held inside it. Unscrew the nuts from under the faucet deck and remove them along with the washers. If there is a spray hose connection, detach it from the faucet and remove the nut and washer from under the spray hose so that it can be taken off. Disconnect the copper supply tubes from the supply line and, if necessary, bend them to the position shown in Fig. 8-15. The faucet assembly can now be lifted out. It will probably have to be loosened by tapping gently or by moving it back and forth. Remove the gasket from under the deck.

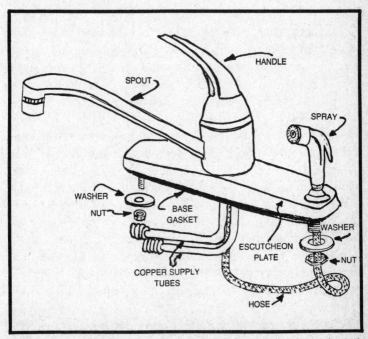

Fig. 8-15. A sink with three holes will take a faucet with spray attached to the deck itself.

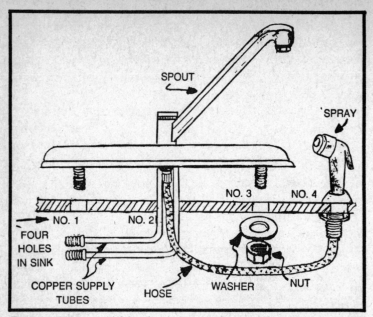

Fig. 8-16. When your sink has four holes get a faucet with separate spray which will go in the fourth hole.

When installing a new faucet assembly, first place the gasket over the deck. Remove the nut and washer from the spray hose assembly, and lower the hose through the sink hole on the extreme right. Take the hose up through the middle hole and connect it to the faucet. If the spray hose is separate from the faucet deck, it can be installed at this stage over sink hole #4 (Fig. 8-16). The hose can be lowered down through this hole, raised through hole #2, and connected to the faucet. The faucet assembly can then be lowered over the sink so that it rests squarely on the gasket. If there is no provision for a gasket, apply a layer of plumber's putty over the sink before lowering the faucet deck. Particular caution should be exercised to avoid kinking the copper supply tubes when lowering the assembly and passing these tubes down through the sink hole.

Install the faucet to the sink by positioning and tightening the mounting nuts and washers. Next you have to bend the copper supply tubes and align them to meet the supply lines. The water supply lines in your home always run in such a way that when you stand facing the mounted faucet, the hot water line is on your left. The bending of the copper tubes is necessary because the single-handle faucets are manufactured in such a way that the right-hand side copper tube is for hot water, and left-hand side is for cold water. The tubes have to be connected within the faucet so that you actually do get hot water by turning the faucet towards the left and cold water by turning it towards the right, which is the normal way. This is why the copper supply tubes have to be bent in a criss-cross pattern (Fig. 8-17).

There is a technique for bending them which will prevent damage to the tubing: grip the tube firmly at the bend with your right hand (Fig. 8-18) and slowly pull it with your left hand towards the right side, applying pressure with the thumb and the palm.

The only thing left now is to connect these copper tubes to the hot and cold water supply lines. Apply pipe joint compound and use two wrenches, one to hold the shank of the fitting on the copper supply tube and the other to turn the nut on the water supply line in a counterclockwise direction. Care should be taken not to twist and damage the tubes.

In case the supply lines are not long enough, or the connecting fittings do not match exactly, you may get adapter tubes and fittings from the store where you got the replacement faucet unit. The

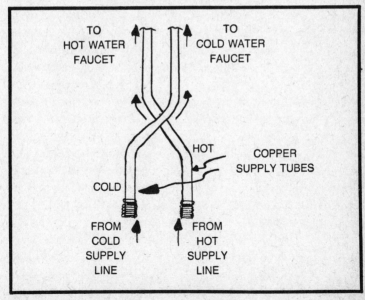

Fig. 8-17. The hot and cold supply tubes will have to be bent in a criss-cross pattern.

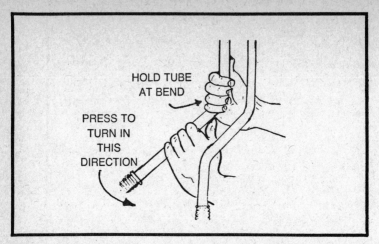

Fig. 8-18. There is a special technique for bending the copper supply tubes of a faucet. Grip the tube firmly with the right hand and slowly pull with the left hand to the right, applying pressure with thumb and palm. Take care not to damage the tubes by applying sudden pressure.

water supply can now be turned on by opening the shut-off valve. Check for any leaks and drips. Also check to see if the hose spray is working properly. At this time it would be a good idea to clean the filter and aerator at the spout head, too.

Replacing Double-Handle Kitchen Faucets

Like the single-handle faucets, the double-handled ones are also available with or without a separate spray attachment. The procedure for replacement is practically the same as for the single-handle faucet described previously. As before, you will have to measure the distance between the studs, and the distance from the studs to the supply lines, in order to get a suitable replacement. If there are three holes in the sink top, you will not be able to attach a spray hose unless you drill another hole. The method of installing the spray hose will be the same as that for single-handled faucets. The free end of the hose will be connected to the underside of the spout after running it through the middle hole.

There will be no need to bend any copper supply tubes because there are none in this type of faucet. The connections between the supply lines and the hot and cold faucets are made through straight pieces of copper tubing (see Fig. 8-19). Be sure to place the black base gasket under the faucet deck before installing it. In case there

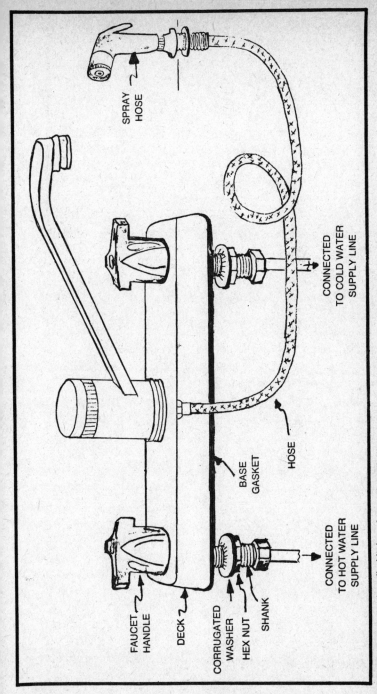

SPRAY HOSE

CONNECTED TO COLD WATER SUPPLY LINE

HOSE

BASE GASKET

FAUCET HANDLE

DECK

CORRUGATED WASHER

HEX NUT

SHANK

CONNECTED TO HOT WATER SUPPLY LINE

Fig. 8-19. Double-handle kitchen faucet installation.

are no shut-off valves on the supply lines, this would be a good time to install them.

A different design of a double-handle kitchen faucet features a concealed deck. The deck goes under the sink top, and only the two handles and the spray hose can be seen. Installation is done by holding the deck under the sink after removing the handles and then placing the handles in position and screwing them down.

You will find, in some older installations, faucets that are attached in the backsplash against the wall. The hot and cold supply pipes in such a case will most probably be coming through the wall directly. If you want to replace the faucet assembly, first close the shut-off valve, and open the faucet by removing the slip nuts behind the backsplash. Install the new faucet by dropping it in position and tightening the nuts and washers.

SINK STRAINERS

Unless your kitchen sink has a garbage disposal attached to it, the sink will have a strainer in the bottom to prevent waste material from entering the drainage line and blocking it. The strainer opening can be blocked with a plug if you want to fill the sink with water, as when cleaning the dishes. Replacement may sometimes be necessary if the strainer gets damaged. Often the open-close mechanism will start malfunctioning. Figure 8-20A shows a newly installed strainer. Figure 8-20B shows the parts that go into making up the connection.

To take out the damaged strainer, first disconnect it from the drainage line. You will have to work under the countertop. Open the slip nut with a wrench and take out the small size washers. Next, remove the larger slip nut and the set of washers; this will free the strainer. Lift it out and get a suitable replacement from the store, along with new washers for the drain-line connection. You will also need Teflon tape and plumber's putty.

Steps for installation are just the reverse of those for dismantling. First apply plumber's putty all round the strainer opening in the bottom of the sink. Unscrew the slip nut from the new strainer and take out the washers. Place the strainer in position over the putty layer and, working from under the sink, install the larger washers and the large slip nut. You may want to ask someone to hold the strainer inside the sink while you tighten the slip nut with the help of a screwdriver and hammer. Tightening should be done with light

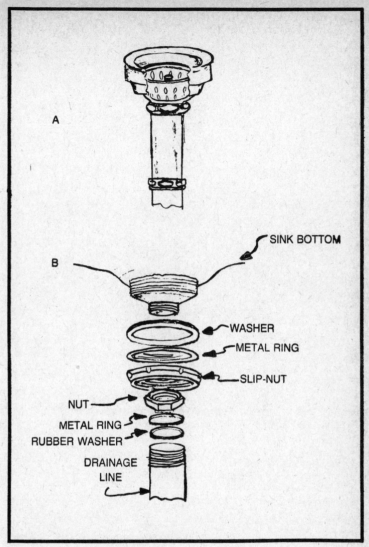

A

B

SINK BOTTOM

WASHER

METAL RING

SLIP-NUT

NUT

METAL RING

RUBBER WASHER

DRAINAGE
LINE

Fig. 8-20. Sink strainer and its parts.

hammer taps only. You are now ready to make the connection to the drainage line. Using the new set of washers and the smaller slip nut, wrap the threads with Teflon tape and make the connection. Turn the faucet on and check for leaks. Close the strainer opening with the plug, fill up the sink with water almost to the top, and again check for possible leaks.

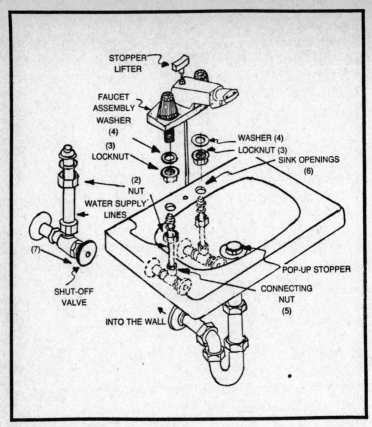

Fig. 8-21. Replacing a lavatory faucet.

REPLACING LAVATORY FAUCETS

Lavatory faucet assemblies come with either double-handle or single-handle controls. The method of removal and replacement is more or less the same for both types, and very much similar to that for kitchen sink faucet assemblies described earlier in this Chapter. One main point of difference is the pop-up drain which most lavatory units have; these are operated by a lifter at the faucet deck.

Figure 8-21 illustrates how the faucets for hot and cold water are connected to the supply lines. For each one, there is a shut-off valve (7) to stop the supply during repairs.

To open the faucet assembly, you will need an adjustable wrench or a channel-lock pliers and a basin wrench for work in tight spots. A small quantity of plumber's putty will also be needed.

First stop the flow of water by closing the shut-off valves, and open the faucet to let the inside water drain off. By loosening the adjustment screw at the bottom, screw (1) in Fig. 8-22, disconnect the stopper lifter from the linkage and pull it out. Now loosen the nut (nut (2) back in Fig. 8-21) on the supply lines below the sink. You may have to use a basin wrench if the space underneath is limited. Disconnect the supply lines after slipping the nuts and washers on them. Next open the locknuts and washers (3) and (4) in Fig. 8-21, under the faucet assembly, which will now be free to be taken out. If necessary, apply a few gentle taps or move the assembly back and forth so that it comes loose and can be lifted up.

When you get a replacement, make sure that the distance between its inlet pipes is the same as that in the old assembly, or the sink openings will have to be modified. Remove the washers (4) and locknuts (3) from the new assembly. (Numbers refer to Fig. 8-21). Clean the area of the sink around openings (6) and apply a layer of putty around the bottom edge of the faucet assembly. If the faucet assembly comes with a gasket, install it and place the assembly over the sink so that the shanks go down through the two holes (6). With a wrench, install washers (4) and nuts (3).

The supply lines have now been connected to the gasket assembly through nuts (2), which should be fully tightened with a wrench to prevent leakage. Install the stopper lifter by threading the lifter rod (2) through the linkage and tightening the screw (1) in Fig. 8-22. The installation is now complete. Turn the water on and check for any defects, leakages, or drips.

Installing A Pop-Drain in a Sink

When you buy a new pop-drain unit (Fig. 8-22), it comes complete with the following parts:

- pop-drain body (7) with flange (8)
- operating lever (3) with nut, ball rod, and seal (4, 5, 6)
- strip rod (10) with clip
- operating rod or lifter rod (2)

The following steps should be followed for installation (numbers refer to Fig. 8-22):

1. Remove tailpiece (9) by unscrewing it.
2. Unscrew nut (4) and mount the gasket and seat on the ball rod (5). Tighten the nut after making sure that the ball

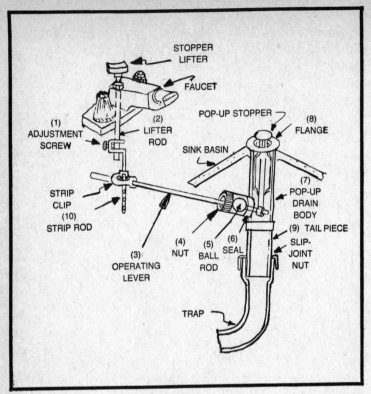

Fig. 8-22. Details of stopper linkage assembly.

slides into the correct position to make the proper connection.

3. Remove flange (8) by unscrewing it. Apply plumber's putty around the sink drain hole, and place the flange over it. Holding the pop-up drain body (7) under the sink, align it below the sink hole and tighten the flange over it. The ball rod should again be checked to see that it is in the correct position. The locknut and washer should now be installed; this will make the pop-up drain body hold firmly to the underside of the sink.

4. Align the tailpiece (9) on the trap, and screw the tail into the body. Tighten the locknut on the trap after inserting a new washer.

5. Lower the lifter rod (2) through the hole in the spout. Attach it to the strip rod (10).

6. Attach the operating lever (3) to the strip rod (10) through a strip clip which should be adjusted so that it opens and closes the pop-up drain properly.

The installation is now complete. Insert the stopper in the sink hole and try the arrangement a couple of times to see if it works properly. If any adjustment is needed, particularly at the junction of strip rod and the operating lever, it should be done as required.

Installing a New Single Faucet

Sometimes you wish you could add a new water outlet where there is none, like in a newly-constructed bar in the basement; or maybe you would like to have a water fountain at a pipe which runs along an outside wall. These are easy to install if you can get hold of a drill with a 1/4-inch metal bit and buy the following items (see Fig. 8-23): a saddle-type faucet (illustration A), and a drill guide (6).

The saddle-type faucet should be of a size that can be suitably installed on the pipe. First turn off the water and clean the surface of the pipe where the faucet is to be installed. Use light sandpaper. Next remove nuts and bolts from the saddle strap, and install the faucet at the required spot by tightening the strap around the pipe

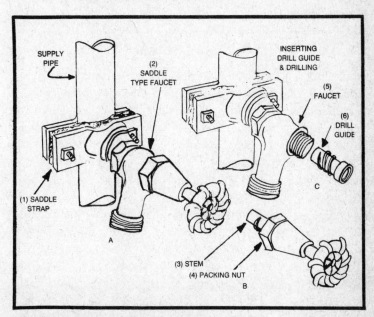

Fig. 8-23. Installing a new single faucet.

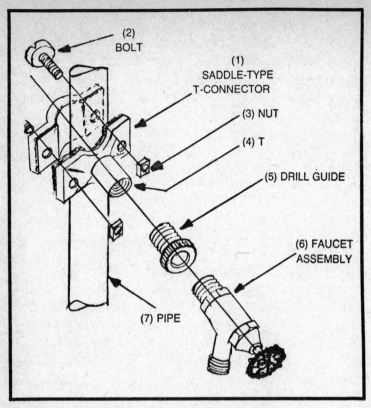

Fig. 8-24. Attaching a faucet through a saddle-type T connector.

with nuts and bolts (Fig. 8-23A). Unscrew the packing nut and take it out along with the faucet handle (Fig. 8-23B). Insert the drill guide into the faucet opening and, with the 1/4-inch metal drill, make a hole in the pipe. Remove the drill and the drill guide. Clean the faucet and remove the metal drillings. Put back the stem and packing nut in the faucet hole and tighten up. Water can now be turned on. Open the faucet. You have a new fixture now. Wash away any remaining metal drillings.

Another type of faucet connection uses a saddle-type T connector, illustrated in Fig. 8-24. This is actually suitable for installing any type of threaded pipe fitting including a faucet. The procedure for installation is similar to the one described above. The saddle T is first installed at the pipe by placing it around the pipe and tightening with nuts and bolts. A drill guide is then inserted into the T and a hole is drilled in the pipe with a drill and 1/4-inch metal bit, as before. After cleaning the pipe and removing any drillings, the faucet assembly is screwed on to the T. Water is then turned on and any drillings lying about are flushed off.

Replacing a Hose Connection Faucet

It is a very simple job to replace a hose connection faucet (Fig. 8-25). Shut off the water at a valve on the supply line and open the faucet so that any water contained inside its body drains out. While clamping the pipe firmly with a pipe wrench, turn the faucet counterclockwise, with an adjustable wrench, until it comes off the line. Get a suitable replacement according to the size of the pipeline. Place it on the line and tighten it with your hand as much as possible. Then, holding the pipe firmly with a pipe wrench, turn it clockwise with an adjustable wrench until fully tightened. It will be a good idea to wrap Teflon tape over the threads of the pipe before the new faucet is installed over it. Turn the water on and check for any leaks.

ADDING A NEW OUTDOOR FAUCET AND AN EXTENSION PIPELINE

Pipe can be extended, as explained in Chapter 4, by using a copper or galvanized pipe to match the existing plumbing.

A stop-and-waste valve should be installed on the line in the basement. It has a drain hole through which water from the line can

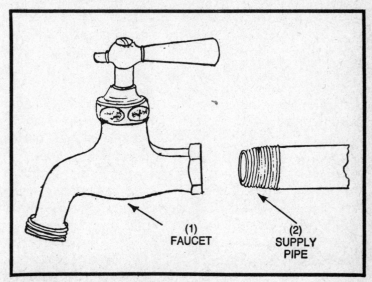

(1)
FAUCET

(2)
SUPPLY
PIPE

Fig. 8-25. Hose connection faucet.

be drained out. The hole normally stays capped. A turning handle at the top is used to open and close the valve. After you close the valve by turning the handle, remove the cap from the drain hole, thus draining out the water from the line. This will keep the outdoor faucet from freezing during the winter. This arrangement will work whether the new pipeline is laid flat or has a downward or upward pitch. The cap of the drain hole should be put back after the drained water has been collected in a bucket.

The faucet on the outside wall of a heated building can also be made freeze-proof. The faucet handle stays outside the wall while the main body is inside the basement. Every time the faucet is shut off, it drains along with the pipe section running through the wall.

Figure 8-26 shows the arrangement for a non-heated outside building or a garage. Year-round service can be maintained without danger of freezing if the vertical pipe is wrapped with electric tape up to a point just below the frostline, to keep it warm. In addition, the exposed length should be covered with insulating tape. A thermostat installed above the ground line will control the heating and keep it at the desired level. In addition, a stop-and-waste valve should be provided on the line inside the main heated building.

Faucets inside a heated garage attached to the main building are also likely to freeze if the door is left open by mistake. The same precautions should be taken as for an outdoor faucet—i.e., use freeze-proof faucets, or a stop valve arrangement within the heated building.

INSTALLING A CUT-OFF VALVE

When a new fixture like a sink or lavatory is installed, it is usual to place a new cut-off valve on the line to stop the supply in case the fixture ever needs repairs. You won't want to run to the shut-off valve on the main water supply line every time there is a problem on a fixture. The cost of adding a shut-off valve on an existing fixture is not much, and the method of installation is pretty simple.

Just remove the section of pipe leading from the fixture into the wall or the floor, install a cut-off valve on the *stub-out* at the pipeline (Fig. 8-27), and join the fixture to the valve with flexible copper tubing. This tubing generally goes by the name of Speedee.

If the supply pipe is coming up from the floor, you will need a straight cut-off, but if it is projecting out from inside the wall, a

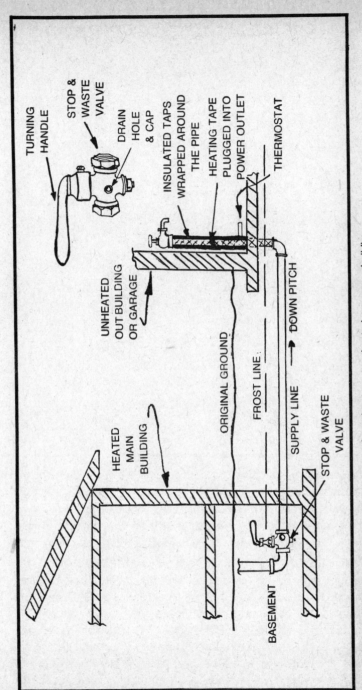

TURNING HANDLE

STOP & WASTE VALVE

DRAIN HOLE & CAP

INSULATED TAPS WRAPPED AROUND THE PIPE

HEATING TAPE PLUGGED INTO POWER OUTLET

THERMOSTAT

UNHEATED OUT BUILDING OR GARAGE

HEATED MAIN BUILDING

ORIGINAL GROUND

FROST LINE

SUPPLY LINE   DOWN PITCH

STOP & WASTE VALVE

BASEMENT

Fig. 8-26. Arrangement for year round freeze-proof service to a non-heated garage or building.

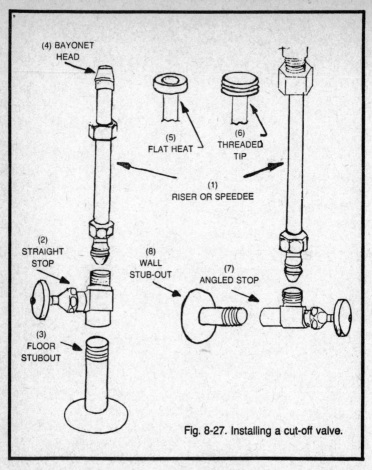

(4) BAYONET HEAD

(5) FLAT HEAT

(6) THREADED TIP

(1) RISER OR SPEEDEE

(2) STRAIGHT STOP

(8) WALL STUB-OUT

(7) ANGLED STOP

(3) FLOOR STUBOUT

Fig. 8-27. Installing a cut-off valve.

right-angled cut-off will be required. Also, a threaded supply pipe will take a threaded cut-off, but for a copper stub-out you will have to get an adapter which will be sweat-soldered at one end, and screwed on to the cut-off at the other end. After having connected the cut-off to the supply line, make the connection between the cut-off and the fixture. If you don't want to go to the bother of cutting and piecing together pipes, buy a Speedee kit. There are three different designs of Speedees, each serving a different purpose. For a kitchen sink, a threaded-end Speedee is used; for a toilet-tank connection, a Speedee with flat flange end is used; and for a lavatory, one with a boyonet-end is used. Some kits contain a cut-off already joined to the Speedee. If the kit you get has them separate you will have to join them with either a compression fitting or a flared connection. The kit contains full instructions to complete the job and provides necessary parts like rings and connectors.

For household purposes, cut-off valves are of the globe type which can shut off the supply either fully or partially. Before you start installation of a cut-off, make sure that the supply is shut off at a valve on the branch or main line. When making a threaded joint connection, always clean the threads and apply new joint compound or tape. When making a flared joint, make sure that the flaring is perfectly round before you install the cut-off. Sometimes it may be necessary to reflare the supply line using a flaring tool.

REPLACING FIXTURE SUPPLY TUBES

Fixture supply tubes, generally made of flexible copper, convey water from the water supply line to the fixture. One tube is for hot water and the other for cold water. If you are replacing a fixture, like a faucet, it will be a good idea to replace the fixture tubes too. Of course, replacement is necessary any time the tubes get damaged or develop a leak.

Fig. 8-28. If you have an antique decor in your home, these 24-carat gold electroplated finish faucets will blend perfectly. Courtesy: Kohler Co.

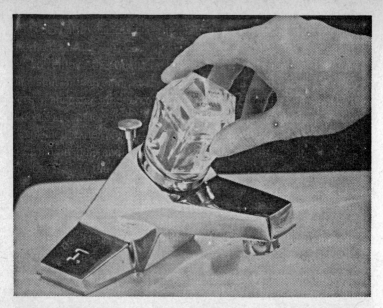

Fig. 8-29. 'Centura' single control faucets. Courtesy: Kohler Co.

Shut off the water at the stop valves at the lower ends of the tubes or at the supply lines. Unscrew the nuts at the upper and lower ends of one of the tubes, place an empty bucket underneath to collect any water, and take out the tube. Cut a new piece of copper tubing of the required size and length, as explained in Chapter 4.

The connections will be of the compression type using a nosepiece compression ring, and a flange nut at each end. Slip a compression ring over one end of the tube and hold it vertically in position so that the upper end with the ring fits into the fixture connection. Place a flange nut around the tube at the lower end and slide it up to the top. Tighten the nut with your fingers. Slip another nut and sleeve at the lower end of the tube. Align the tube; bend it smoothly, if necessary, until it is in line with the lower connections. Tighten the nut again with your fingers.

If the connections appear all right, gently tighten them with a wrench. Connect the other tube in the same manner, and open up the water supply. Check for any leaks from the joints.

Figures 8-28 and 8-29 show some modern faucet designs.

Bathtubs and Showers

Bathtubs and Showers

You can find a variety of bathtubs and showers on the market, offering a wide range of conveniences. One leading manufacturer, The American Standard, offers in addition to the rectangular, corner, and recess baths, a complete triwall system with grab bars, ceiling, and lights, as well as an ultra bath whirlpool equipped with an automatic timer to provide a stimulating message. Of course the prices go up with the extent of conveniences provided.

Many shapes of tubs and showers are available: rectangular, oval, square, etc. Usual construction materials include fiberglass, cast iron, and formed steel with porcelain enamel surface. Cast iron bathtubs are heavy and durable. They come in widths ranging from 30 inches to 48 inches, and lengths from 4 feet to 6 feet. Steel bathtubs are lighter in weight than those of cast iron, and come in widths ranging from 30 inches to 36 inches, and in lengths of 4 1/2 feet and 5 feet. Water falling from the shower to the tub causes a considerable amount of noise which can be reduced by a sound-dampening undercoating provided as an option.

The fiberglass bathtubs with or without shower arrangement are the most common today. They come in one piece and include three side walls running about 6 feet above the bathroom floor. They have a decided advantage over the conventional designs because the latter types have to be connected to the bathroom walls through joints that neither look very neat nor stay watertight.

INSTALLING A MODERN BATHTUB

If the tub you select fits exactly in the space occupied by an old one, installation will involve only the hookup of plumbing connections and fixtures; but more often, the new tub of modern design will occupy larger floor space and its installation will necessitate moving one or two walls partly or completely.

Study the manufacturer's instructions to get the exact roughing-in dimensions. The framing has to be built before placing the tub in position and connecting the water supply pipes and the drains. This will protect the finish of the new tub.

In essence, the replacement job will consist of: disconnecting and removing the old tub, building the framing for wall(s), cutting a hole in the floor, running new pipe, installing the tub, making water and drain connections, and finishing the walls and the facing.

If you are installing a new tub and shower combination in place of an old tub with high legs and without an enclosure, a framing enclosure, illustrated in Fig. 9-1, will be required. Most probably

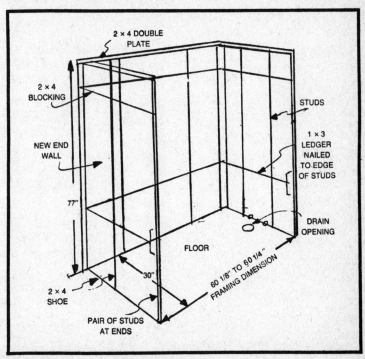

Fig. 9-1. Fig. 9-1. A new bathtub will need an enclosure with minimum framing dimensions of 77" × 60 1/8" × 30".

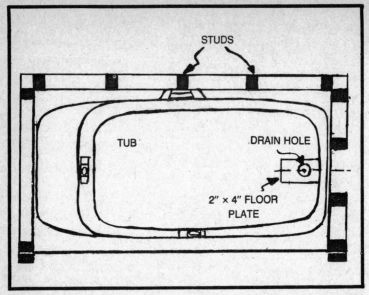

Fig. 9-2. Plan of a bathtub and its enclosure. The drain hole should be covered with a removable 2″ × 4″ floor plate.

you will have to build a new end wall and strip the other end wall and the back wall completely of all its tiles or other covering. The tub will sit on the subfloor, so remove the tiles or other floor covering from the top of the subfloor and clean it up; remove all dirt, sticking matter, protruding nails, etc., from its surface.

Now you come to the most important part of the project: the plumbing. There will be connections for a drain line, two water lines, and the shower pipe. If necessary, change the location of the drain hole in the floor to match the requirement of the new tub. Installation of a 2 × 4-inch floor plate will facilitate future repairs (Fig. 9-2). Examine the hot and cold water lines and fit new extensions, offsets, or adapters so that they come up exactly to the point where connections have to be made to the new tub and shower unit inside the wall. Install the vertical pipe for the shower outlet. It will need at least one cross brace in the framing, and a few U-clips, to hold it rigidly in a vertical position.

The drainpipe should be modified or changed so that it can be connected to both the drain and the overflow opening of the new fixture. You may refer to the rough-in dimensions given by the manufacturer or you may want to actually measure these dimensions out. In order to install the faucet unit and its stub-out securely in position, it will be necessary to notch a cross-piece. After these details are attended to, take out the tub from the crate and position it on its supports inside the enclosure. Be careful not to strike it against the floor or the bare walls. You will need some help at this point. Go through the manufacturer's recommendations and secure the tub to its foundation accordingly.

After the tub is placed in position, check the level at the top of the rim in both directions, with the help of a plumber's level. A very small pitch towards the drain hole maybe allowed. If the tub slopes in the other direction, place a 3/8-inch padding on the subfloor to correct it. Shims are prohibited because they provide only point supports and the tub bottom may crack under the load of the water and the bather. The unit should now be secured to the studs with flathead brass screws. Holes for the screws should be drilled through the lip of the tub, and the screws should be countersunk into them.

To facilitate access to supply pipes for future repairs, it will be desirable to install a removable access panel in the new wall at the head of the tub. The walls can now be finished according to your taste. They should, of course, be waterproof. The usual method of waterproofing is to install furring strips on the studs right up to the ceiling and cover them with nailing wallboard. A coat of water-resistant sealer should be applied to the face of the nailing flange and the wallboards should completely cover it. Paint the wallboard with a color that matches the decor of the bathroom.

If you are installing a prefabricated bathtub and enclosure unit, the prefab walls should be installed after the tub has been secured in position. Manufacturers include special clips for attaching these walls to the studs. Dow's interior sealout or a similar substitute should be used to completely seal the joint between the plastic walls and the tub.

Next, the actual supply and drainage fixtures should be installed. Working from the rear and underside of the tub, make the drain and overflow connections. (See Fig. 9-3). The supply system consists of two valves with operating handles, a diverter valve at the spout, one connecting pipe leading to the spout stub-out, and another running upward to the elbow to which the shower spout is connected. Figure 9-4 shows the arrangement of faucet handles, the

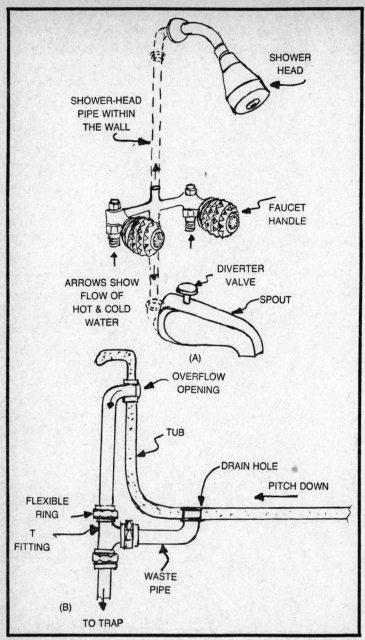

SHOWER
HEAD

SHOWER-HEAD
PIPE WITHIN
THE WALL

FAUCET
HANDLE

DIVERTER
VALVE

SPOUT

ARROWS SHOW
FLOW OF
HOT & COLD
WATER

(A)

OVERFLOW
OPENING

TUB

DRAIN HOLE

PITCH DOWN

FLEXIBLE
RING

T
FITTING

WASTE
PIPE

(B)

TO TRAP

Fig. 9-3(A). Shows tub-cum-shower assembly in addition to the hot and cold water valves. There is a diverter valve at or near the spout. (B) Shows the common drain connection from the drain hole in the tub, and the overflow opening leading to the trap.

valve assembly, and its connection to the cross brace attached to studs. Cover the walls above the plastic side walls with Sheetrock, as before, and complete the paint or tile job. Your modern bathing facility will then be ready for use.

Most manufacturers give complete instructions, drawings, and photographs with the package you buy. Follow these precisely and you will find the work pretty easy to do.

I will just add a few words here about the tub stopper which you seldom pay any attention to. At the flip of a lever or handle located between the tub's faucet handles, the tub stopper closes or opens the drain (Fig. 9-5). The common *trip-lever system* has a metal plug which drops down as the control lever is turned; the plug blocks the drain hole. The lever comes mounted on a metal plate which is attached with two screws to the wall. To take out the system, simply remove the two screws with a screwdriver and lift out.

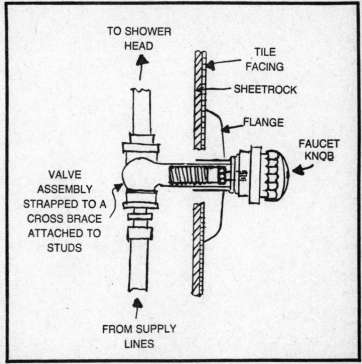

Fig. 9-4. Only the faucet handles show up in the tub. The valve assembly is located inside the wall. Add a removable plywood panel on the backside of the wall to provide quick access to pipes and assembly during future repairs—else the wall will have to be ripped out.

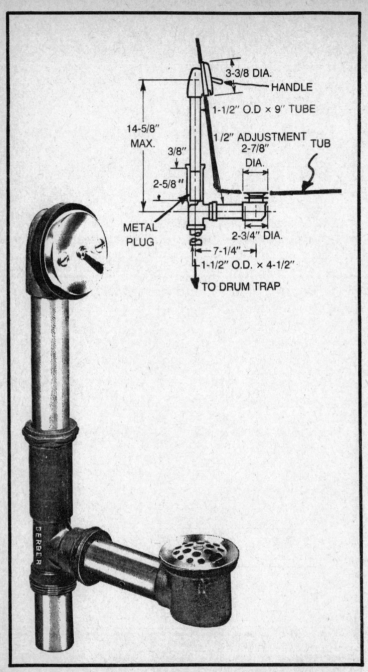

Fig. 9-5. Pop-up waste and overflow assembly. At the flip of a handle, the metal plug opens or closes the drain. Courtesy: Gerber Pbg. Fixture Corp.

INSTALLING SHOWER STALLS

If you wish to install a bathing facility within a limited space, or in an old room with no present shower facility, a prefabricated shower unit is the ideal solution (Fig. 9-6). A 30 × 36 × 75-inch unit is an adequate size. If you like, and space permits, by all means install a larger facility. Some even come with a molded seat.

Installation is not much different from that for the tub and shower combination described previously. Depending on the location within the room, one or two stud walls will have to be constructed for the enclosure. The overall dimensions will depend on the size of the unit; the dimensions can either be measured out or taken from the manufacturer's roughing-in instruction sheets. To install the drainpipe, cut a clearance hole of suitable size in the

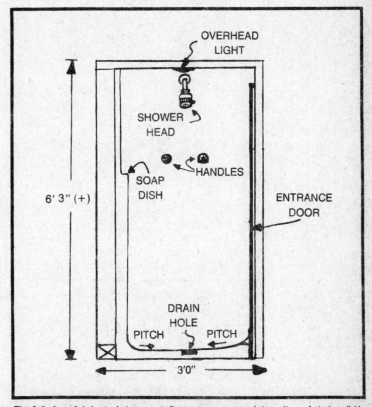

Fig. 9-6. A prefabricated shower stall comes as a complete unit ready to be slid in place—only the pipe and shower head connections have to be made. The enclosure is made of studs resting against the unit.

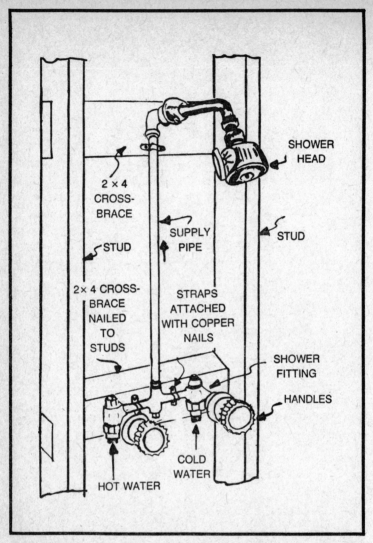

Fig. 9-7. Shower stall setup is similar to that for a combination tub & shower installation except for the faucet and diverter valve for the bathtub. 2" × 4" cross braces attached to the studs hold the shower-head assembly and the valve assembly. Prefab units can be installed in a limited space or in rooms without any bathing facility.

subfloor. For the water connections, stub-outs are installed within the wall along with the valve assembly, the shower head assembly, and the vertical supply pipe (Fig. 9-7). Next, the shower stall is slipped into the enclosure; the drainpipe and connected fittings are

Fig. 9-8. The 'Trinidad' shower bath by Kohler Co.

Fig. 9-9. A unique type of bathroom arrangement.

installed from below through the clearance hole; and faucet handles and the shower head are fitted into place.

Another type of shower stall is constructed in place. A waterproof pan with a drain hole is placed at a suitable location in the room, and walls are built around it. The shower head and valve assembly are mounted in one of the side walls. A fairly large clearance hole should be cut in the sub-floor to accommodate the drainpipe. Determine the exact location of this hole, either from the manufacturer's drawings or by actually measuring the off-sets of the pan. It will be

Fig. 9-10. Kohler's sleeping bath is 20 inches deep—six inches deeper than most other five-foot bathtubs. Its three-foot width and gently sloping back with integral lower back support and arm rests add new dimensions to bathing. The "no-apron" design offers installation versatility; the bath can be installed in a corner, in an island or peninsula setting, or in a recess.

Fig. 9-11. Fig. A unique bathtub and shower control panel. Courtesy: Standyne (Moen).

necessary to cut some structural members if a drum trap is to be used. Since such a trap has to be cleaned at regular intervals, provision should be made for an easy access to it during repairs. The drainpipe is passed through the clearance hole and locked in place both above and below the pan bottom by applying plumber's putty or by using fitting washers. The lower portion of the drainpipe should be connected to the drum trap which in turn is connected to the branch drain or soil stack.

The method for attaching the shower head and the valve assembly to cross braces running between two adjacent braces is the same as that illustrated in Fig. 9-7 for a prefab unit. Brass or copper straps nailed to the cross braces provide the necessary connection. After the hot and cold water pipe connections are made, the walls are finished with Sheetrock and tile facing, or some other waterproof wall covering. To provide easy access to the valve assembly in case of future repairs, leave enough clearance in the wall around the valve stems. Finally, install the valve flanges, the handles, and the shower head.

Some modern showers, tubs, and fixtures are illustrated in Figs. 9-8, 9-9, 9-10, and 9-11.

Garbage Disposers, Automatic Washers, and Dishwashers

Chapter 10

Garbage Disposers, Automatic Washers, and Dishwashers

Appliances like garbage disposers, dishwashers, and automatic washers greatly help reduce the burden of family chores, but they can also lead to serious accidents if improperly handled during installation, operation, and repairs. This fact makes it essential to fully understand the appliances working principles, the manufacturer's specific instructions for each unit, and the requirements of utility companies and the local building codes, before undertaking installation or repair jobs. I don't mean to scare away the do-it-yourselfer, but rather to alert him to the inherent hazards of simple omissions like failing to unplug an appliance before starting to open its interior. Tackling such jobs carefully will result in considerable savings.

There are many different designs of each of these appliances; descriptions that follow are general ones and should be supplemented with manufacturer's instruction booklets which come with the units you buy.

GARBAGE DISPOSERS

Also called *food waste disposers*, these appliances fill an important sanitary need in the kitchen; they dispose of a variety of wastes in seconds. In rural areas and in localities with no pick-up service, garbage disposers are really a boon. For their efficient operation, it is necessary that the septic tanks have enough capacity or public sewers exist in the street. Various designs and models are available in the market with different price tags. Those in the medium price range are good enough to deal with most food wastes including vegetable and fruit peelings, egg shells, steaks, roasts, melon rinds, celery, carrot tops, fats, greases, small bones, tea leaves, pieces of bread, coffee ground, etc. More expensive designs with high-power motors and heavy duty shredding mechanisms can deal with medium-sized bones, corncobs, sea food shells, and similar hard material. Food waste disposers are *not* designed for following type of waste, which should *not* be fed to them:

- large bones
- aluminum foil paper, cardboard, rubber
- rags, tea bags, wires, strings
- chinaware pieces, glass bottles, glass pieces, tin cans
- bottle caps, pieces of plastic, broken dishes
- cigarette filters

If you do discard this type of material in your disposer, it will soon stop functioning. Also, the strong fibers of artichoke leaves and some corn husks can get wound around the mechanism, preventing it from working.

Figure 10-1A illustrates the working of a common type of garbage disposer, and Fig. 10-1B shows the exterior of one such type. In essence it is a shredding device run by a motor which chops the food wastes into very small pieces. The upper portion, sometimes called a *hopper* is mounted inside the sink drain; it replaces the strainer and the flange that come with a sink. The lower portion of the disposer houses the motor mounted inside a metal housing. The water seal between the lower and upper portions protects the motor. The blades or impellers attached to a flywheel batter the garbage and throw it against the stationary shredding element and cutter surfaces. The speed of rotation of the flywheel is 1700 revolutions per minute (rpm) or more, depending on the power of the motor. The waste pipe connection (the tailpiece) is located a little above the water seal. It is connected to the discharge line through a P or S trap, depending on whether the line runs through the wall or the floor.

Garbage disposers are meant to run with cold water because it solidifies the fat and grease content of the waste which can then be easily shredded and washed down into the drain line. If hot or warm

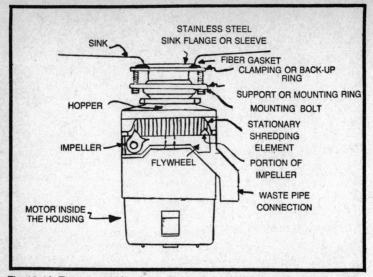

Fig. 10-1A. To remove old garbage disposer, unscrew the mounting bolts. Twist the unit, and pull down. While unscrewing the bolts, brace the disposer from below else it will fall down. Mounting is done in a similar manner. Follow the manufacturer's instructions.

water is running when you operate the disposer, the liquid or semi-solid fats will stick to its inside walls and to the shredding element, leading to possible clogging and jamming.

Installing a Garbage Disposer

Garbage disposers come as fully assembled units ready for installation. They are designed to fit the sink and drain openings without making any alterations in them, and they seldom need much plumbing work. Since both electrical and plumbing alterations must be done during installation, you will be well advised to check both the local and the national plumbing codes to avoid incorrect or defective work which may cause future problems.

To install a new garbage disposer unit in your kitchen sink, disconnect and remove the sink drainpipe and the old sink flange including any gaskets or sealing material. Apply a heavy bead of ordinary plumber's putty around the edge of the sink opening and the underside of the sink flange unit which came with the new garbage disposer.

After inserting the flange from the top into the sink opening, press it down firmly until it grips the putty layer. Do not turn it around or else the seal might break, leading to subsequent leakage. Remove excess putty all around. Everything so far has been done while you are standing, but now you have to sit on the floor and work from the underside of the sink.

On the lower portion of the flange place the fiber gasket and then the clamping or backup ring with its flat side up. Next comes the support ring or the mounting ring, which has three holes with mounting bolts. All these parts should be held above the groove in the flange. The snap ring should be slipped over the flange and moved up until it snaps and fits into the groove. Tighten the three mounting bolts in turn to apply a uniform pressure until they hold the clamping ring and the gasket firmly against the flange.

Fig. 10-1B. A heavy duty garbage grinder with 1/2 H.P. motor—Courtesy: White-Westinghouse Appliance Co.

Now raise the main disposer unit to the sink mounting assembly, and turn the body flange counterclockwise until it engages inside the mounting assembly. Insert a screwdriver into a lug and turn the body flange towards the right until it locks in place (see Fig. 10-1C, step #4).

Now you should make the plumbing connections. A discharge tube will come with the unit. If necessary, use a straight tailpiece instead. The trap should be connected to the disposer discharge tube by a slipnut. Follow the plumbing code requirements for all the connections. Run the unit and check to see if there is any leakage at the joints. Remake a joint if it is unsatisfactory. Some sinks have the space for garbage disposer connection on one side instead of in the center. Always follow installation instructions which come with a new unit; designs and installation procedures may vary somewhat from one to the other.

The disposer should be connected to a 120V 60 Hz, AC supply, unless it is specially manufactured for 200V service. Before making connection, turn the power off. Open the disposer base by removing the electrical cover and pull the electric wires out (Fig. 10-1C, step #6). The BX or Romex cable from the toggle switch should be connected to these wires. Follow the manufacturer's instructions for making electric connections. After insuring that the unit is properly grounded, replace the electric cover of the disposer unit.

Garbage Disposer Problems and Cures

You may expect many years of trouble-free service from your garbage disposer because it is strongly built and can even cope with occasional indiscreet use. The best cure for problems that may arise, though, is preventive maintenance: do not dump into it objects it is not designed to handle (a list of such objects has been given earlier in this Chapter). Always use cold water when the unit is running; cold water solidifies the oils and greases which are then shredded and disposed off, instead of entering the drain line in the liquid state and clogging it. However, grease does build up gradually on the walls of the disposer and it gives out bad odors. Be careful which drain cleaner you use. The regular ones should not be put in a sink fitted with a garbage disposer—use only those which are specifically advertised for use in garbage disposer units. They contain a petroleum compound which effectively deals with clogs and greases, and also acts as a deodorant.

A simple method of cleaning worth a try is to fill the disposer half-way with ice cubes and run it until the cubes are shredded and the noise subsides. Then throw in a few pieces of lemon rind and run the disposer for another minute. This treatment scrapes off the waste material sticking to the walls and deodorizes the unit.

Most garbage disposers consist of sealed units and repairs are therefore not easy to make. It will generally be wise to call the authorized repair service for any serious malfunctions. You can deal with the common troubles like a jammed flywheel, motor failure, slow grinding or shredding, water leaks, drain stoppages, and abnormal noise during running. Before calling a repair man, always compare his charges with the cost of a new unit which, of course, you yourself can install in no time. If the price difference is not much, you will be better off with a new disposer.

If the disposer *hums but does not start*, either it is jammed or its bearings are worn out. Jamming due to misuse is very common. Sometimes when in a hurry, you shut off the unit before it has chewn up the entire load of waste. A hard, solid object like a bone may remain stuck in between the shredding element and one of the impellers. Or you may have inadvertantly thrown in a prohibited object like a rag, piece of glass, a broken dish, cigarette filter, or a piece of string. Try to clean up the shredding chamber as much as possible and then turn the flywheel in a reverse direction after you have taken out the disposer circuit fuse.

There is a special tool for turning the flywheel by hand. You may also make one yourself from a 3-foot length of 3/8-inch drill rod. See Fig. 10-2 for details. If nothing else is available, turn off the disposer, and pry the impeller blades with the handle of a broom or a similar piece of wood. As the particles are loosened from under the moving parts, the impeller will become free. You may have to make several attempts before this happens. Remove the broom handle and press the reset button (which always trips if a jam takes place), and the unit is ready for use again.

It is easy to detect worn-out bearings from the wobbly motion of the rotor shaft and the chattering noise that results if the motor tries to start at all. Replacement of bearings is the logical cure.

If there is not even a humming noise when you try to start the garbage disposer, one of three causes is possible: a blown fuse, a

STEP 1

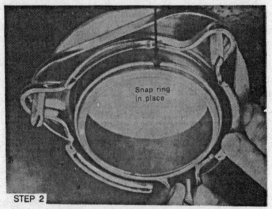

Snap ring
in place

STEP 2

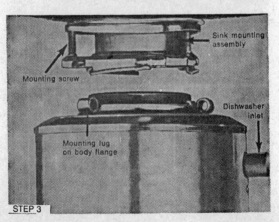

Sink mounting
assembly

Mounting screw

Mounting lug
on body flange

Dishwasher
inlet

STEP 3

STEP 4

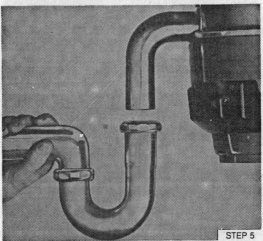

STEP 5

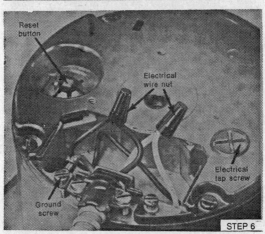

Reset button

Electrical wire nut

Electrical tap screw

Ground screw

STEP 6

Fig. 10-1C. Steps in fitting a new garbage disposer in the kitchen sink. Courtesy: Sears Roebuck & Co.

263.

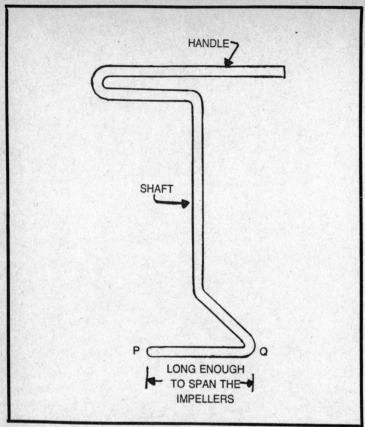

HANDLE

SHAFT

P　　　　Q

LONG ENOUGH
TO SPAN THE
IMPELLERS

Fig. 10-2. You can make a convenient tool from a 3-ft. length of 3/8-inch drill rod, to turn a jammed flywheel. The shaft should be of a length that allows the portion PQ to reach down to the impellers.

defective switch, or a stuck switch plunger. The switch and the fuse can be easily replaced; a stuck plunger should be freed and cleaned.

Little or no shredding and grinding action results from a stuck impeller, worn-out cutting edges, or an excess feed of hard, solid waste, like bones. Shut off the power and check the impellers. If they are jammed, try to free them by removing the materials stuck in them and then apply a small amount of light oil in their pivots. If the impellers are not damaged and they function freely dispite the fact that the shredding action is slow, the stationary shredding element should be changed.

Leaks from worn-out gaskets or plumbing joints can be easily detected and rectified. If a motor seal is leaking, water may enter the motor and burn it out. You will have to study the service manual of your unit carefully before trying to replace the seal.

A blocked drain results from several causes:

1. Large solids, grease, and oil may be stuck inside the drain.
2. Grease trap may be full.
3. Drain size may be inadequate to receive the refuse.
4. Worn-out cutters may be allowing large solids to pass down into the drain without reducing their size.
5. Use of hot water may be allowing oils and greases to pass down into the drain in liquid condition, where they solidify and stick to the walls. A block builds up eventually. *Always use cold water in the disposer.*
6. Septic tank may be full and not taking any more waste from the drain line.

For suggested repairs in each of these situations, see Table 10-1, Garbage Disposer Malfunctions and Troubleshooting Guidelines.

AUTOMATIC WASHERS

The automatic washer is one of the best laborsaving devices in your home, and it takes the mess out of washing clothes. There are many different types of washing machines, but the basic principle of operation is the same. The machines generate a motion between the wash water and the soiled clothes. This motion makes the water run through the clothes so that foreign matter, stains, and dirt attached to the clothes are softened, detached, and washed away. There are four different types of mechanism by which washing machines operate:

1. Vacuum-cups
2. Agitator
3. Top-loading cylinder
4. Front-loading cylinder

Because this is a book on plumbing, a detailed discussion of the various types of machines is beyond its scope.

Installing an Automatic Washer

Portable washers are easily installed. All you need are water, drain, and electrical connections. The installation should be made

Table 10-1. Garbage Disposer Troubleshooting Chart

Malfunction	Probable Causes	Suggested Repairs
Hums but does not start	1. Flywheel or impeller jammed 2. Bearings worn out or out of alignment	1. Remove the circuit fuse and turn flywheel back with a suitable tool to free it. Remove any solid matter stuck in the chamber. Replace fuse and start the unit. 2. Repair or replace.
Does not start. No humming noise	1. Fuse blown 2. Defective switch 3. Switch plunger stuck	1. Replace fuse after checking for short circuits. 2. Repair or replace. 3. Free and clean.
Slow grinding or shredding	1. Excess amounts of hard soilid waste, like bones 2. Worn-out cutting edges 3. Stuck impeller	1. Let disposer run unless it gets stuck; take out a small amount of waste and feed it later. 2. Replace. 3. Free and clean. Disassembling may be required.
Water leaks	One or more joints or fittings loose.	Tighten the loose joints.
Drain blocked or stopped	1. Large solids, grease, and oil stuck on walls 2. Grease trap full 3. Size of drain inadequate 4. Worn out cutters which pass down large solids 5. Using hot water during disposer operation 6. Septic tank full and won't take any more waste	1. Open and clean 2. Clean. (Should be cleaned frequently). 3. Clean frequently or install larger size drain 4. Replace cutters. 5. Clean out the drain and use cold water only. 6. Get the septic tank cleaned
Operation too noisy	Loose joints at the fittings	Tighten the loose joints

NOTE: If you don't feel confident to handle any particular repair, call a professional technician.

according to the plumbing code. Figure 10-3 illustrates two different types of hot and cold water connections. In one system, the rubber hoses are connected directly to the sink faucets, while in the other, separate shutoff valves of the threaded type are used to make the connections. The latter alternative provides a better and independent control. Normally, your new washer will have hoses already attached to it and you will merely need to screw these on to the cutoffs.

To drain off the waste water, a standpipe has to be attached to a nearby drain. The top of the standpipe should be a few inches higher than the maximum water level in the washing machine. It is not necessary to make a permanent connection between the standpipe and the drain hose of the machine; just insert the hose into the standpipe and secure it in place so that it does not fall out and flood the room with waste water. This type of open connection is a safety device; it prevents a cross connection between the waste water line and the water supply pipe by creating a vacuum breaker.

Normally when a separate laundry room or space is set apart in a house, all the plumbing lines are put in. The water supply lines are provided with air chambers which prevent water hammer noises. Otherwise, as the washer shuts on and off several times during one complete operation of washing, there would be considerable amount of water hammer noise. If you are installing a complete plumbing system for your new washer, *air chambers should be provided*.

Automatic washers which have to be permanently installed in one spot require much more installation effort than just the plumbing and electric hookup. Some have to be bolted down to the floor. If you have a concrete floor, drill holes in it with a star drill and install bolt anchors. When a concrete platform is required, it is made of poured concrete. The foundation bolts are set into the concrete during the pouring process (see Fig. 10-4). In wooden floors, the bolts should go right through and get anchored to wooden beams. Where this is not practicable, attach a large sheet of plywood securely to the wood floor by means of a few screws, and bolt down the washer to this sheet.

Washing Machine Problems

Table 10-2 lists some common troubles that might develop in your automatic washer, and provides possible solutions. Only those

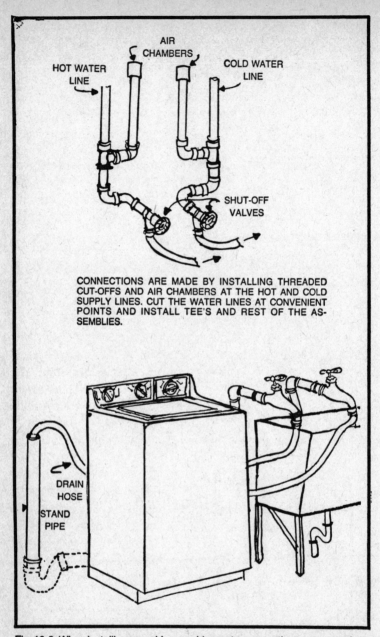

AIR
CHAMBERS

HOT WATER
LINE

COLD WATER
LINE

SHUT-OFF
VALVES

CONNECTIONS ARE MADE BY INSTALLING THREADED
CUT-OFFS AND AIR CHAMBERS AT THE HOT AND COLD
SUPPLY LINES. CUT THE WATER LINES AT CONVENIENT
POINTS AND INSTALL TEE'S AND REST OF THE AS-
SEMBLIES.

DRAIN
HOSE

STAND
PIPE

Fig. 10-3. When installing a washing machine water connections may come from
faucets or preferably from threaded cutoffs (see figure at top) on the hot and
cold supply lines. Air chambers should always be provided to prevent water
hammer noises. The stand pipe should be higher than the maximum level to
which water rises in the machine.

Table 10-2. Automatic Washer Troubleshooting Chart.

Malfunction	Probable Causes	Suggested Repairs
1. Water temp-erature low	a. Water hoses reversed b. Not enough hot water entering the machine c. Thermostat on the inlet valve defective	a. Connect correctly b. Install larger hot water tank. Raise hot water temperature setting at the heater thermostat c. Open up and replace
2. Water not entering the machine	a. Inlet hose crimpled or connecting faucet turned off b. Solenoid defective c. Timing contact not closing d. Water valve out of adjustment	a. Straighten the hose; turn the faucet on b. Replace c. Adjust or replace if necessary d. Readjust
3. Water level too low or too high	a. Float switch defect-ive or out of adjustment b. Inlet valve does not close properly c. Pressure of water incorrect	a. Replace or adjust b. Repair the valve or its seat; replace if necessary c. Change pipe size
4. Water does not drain out or is slow in draining	a. Drain valve clogged with foreign matter b. Lint trap clogged c. Garment stuck in drain casing d. Water pump not working or dirty e. Loose belt	a. Check and clean b. Check and clean c. Remove the mis-placed garment d. Repair or replace e. Tighten
5. Water flows out during working	Drain valve stays open	Adjust or clean
6. Machine vibrates during spin cycle	a. Wash load un-balanced or too heavy b. Shock absorbers or springs loose or defective	a. Reduce the load or balance it b. Tighten them or replace
7. Machine does not stop	a. Timer not function-ing b. Transmission switch has stuck	a. Replace timer b. Unstick switch or replace it

Continued on next page.

Malfunction	Probable Causes	Suggested Repairs
8. Washer tears the clothes	a. Surface of agitator cylinder is rough b. Insufficient water	a. Smooth by rubbing with an emery cloth b. Correct as in item 3
9. Machine gives electric shock when touched	Machine not properly grounded. (Shock due to static electricity)	Install grounding
10. Washing results unsatisfactory	a. Proper washing procedure not being followed b. Washer overloaded c. Incorrect temperature, insufficient rinsing, inadequate water, etc.	a. Follow washing instructions detailed in your manual, or ask dealer for demonstration at home. b. Follow manufacturer's instructions c. Find out specific reason and deal accordingly.
11. Scale deposits on washed clothes	Washer has accumulated lint, soap compounds and water scale	Run washer for 10 minutes with hot water and one pound of Calgon. Then let water stand for one hour and run remaining cycle.
12. Excessive tangling	Improper loading	Feed a mixture of small and large clothes whenever possible
13. Excessive lint	a. Improper sorting and loading. b. Incorrect type of detergent. c. Dirty soap distributor. Long washing time.	a. Feed correctly. Wash clothes with a heavy lint separately. b. Use a standard brand of detergent. c. Clean soap distributor regularly.
14. Odor inside the cabinet	Accumulation of scum on the cabinet due to hardness in water	Clean the cabinet walls with a stiff brush to remove the scum deposit

problems are included which you can easily tackle with a few ordinary tools. Most of these involve just a little change in the use pattern of the machine, or some minor repair. For more serious problems, special tools and professionally trained men are needed; it will be necessary to call a trained repairman who generally deals with the brand of machine you have. Unless you have considerable experience it will not be advisable to involve yourself with repairs involving machinery and electrical equipment.

DISHWASHERS

A dishwasher is another excellent labor-saving device in the home. Its operation is simple—hot water mixed with a dishwashing detergent impinges on stationary dishes, tableware, pots, and pans. After the wash portion of the cycle is complete, the soiled water either drains out or is pumped out, and the load is subjected to a rinsing action with clear water. Finally a heating element dries out the load. This last portion of the cycle may also be used, if desired, to warm up the serving dishes.

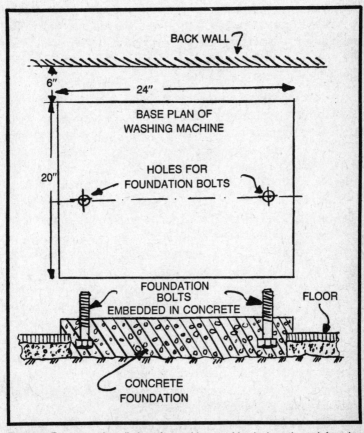

Fig. 10-4. Permanent installation of a washing machine is done through foundation bolts embedded in poured concrete.

Most kitchenware articles carry inscriptions mentioning if they are dishwasher safe. Only those brands of tableware that can stand high temperatures should be placed in the dishwasher. Hand-painted dishes, wooden articles, some types of plasticware, and fine china should *not* be cleaned in a dishwasher, nor even warmed there.

The main operating parts of a dishwasher are: a motor, an impeller placed at the bottom, a watertight tub cover, draining and filling apparatus with a pump, dishracks, and a basket for tableware. In addition, there are controls. As opposed to an automatic washer, a dishwasher needs only a hot water inlet line.

Installing a Dishwasher

A portable dishwasher rolling on wheels has to be placed near a sink at the time of use. It comes with a water hose which should be connected to the hot water faucet through a special adapter. The drain hose of the dishwasher is positioned to discharge into the sink. The soiled water is pumped through the hose into the sink by a motor-driven pump which is housed inside the dishwasher.

Permanently installed dishwashers have flexible water hoses with coarse-thread, female-screw couplings at the end. These couplings are connected to a faucet on the hot water line having garden-hose threads on the spout. Such a faucet does not cost much and can be easily installed. Just cut away a piece of pipe from the line and install a T. The faucet should be attached to this T through a nipple.

Figure 10-5 illustrates the details of connections for an under-the-counter dishwasher. The hot water supply comes from the line leading to the sink. A shut-off valve is provided on the connecting line which is secured to the wall by two clamps. The drain hose from the machine is connected to the sink drain and discharges the waste on the upstream side of its trap. You will have to install a *washing machine T* for the purpose. Open up the connection between the trap and the tail piece of the sink. Swing the trap to one side and, after taking out the tailpiece, fit the washing-machine T. Assemble the drain pipes and you will have a connection with male water-hose threads to which the drain hose of the machine can be slipped on and secured with a clamp. In some cases you may have to reduce the length of the T by cutting it so that it fits.

If the drain hose does not have a screw-thread female coupling, attach one with the help of water-hose fittings and hardware. If, after

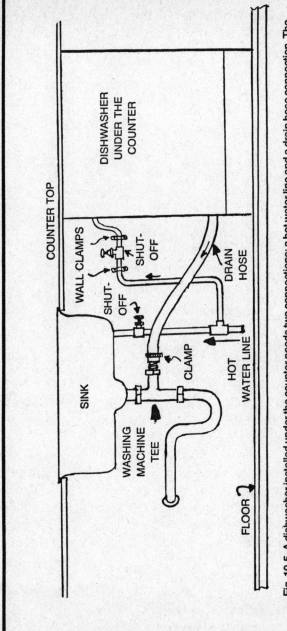

Fig. 10-5. A dishwasher installed under the counter needs two connections: a hot water line and a drain hose connection. The hose is connected to a washing machine T which you will have to install. If your kitchen sink has a garbage disposer, the drainage hose can be connected to it through a short inlet pipe. Most disposers have this inlet pipe. Remove the knockout plug from the disposer with a screwdriver and hammer and connect the hose. For rest of the installation refer to dishwasher instruction manual.

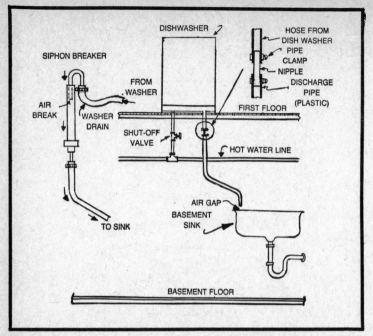

Fig. 10-6. In case there is no sink nearby, the washer drainpipe can be carried down to the basement and discharged into a tub or drain. Leave an air gap above the rim of sink to prevent cross-connection. Sometimes such vertical runs of drain line cause water to be siphoned out of the washer. This can be prevented by providing an air-break as shown in the illustration on left. The drain hose from washer empties into a stand pipe which is connected to the basement sink.

positioning the machine, you find too much hose hanging around, just coil it up and tie it with a string. Don't cut it—maybe sometime in the future you will want to shift the machine to a location which needs a longer hose.

In case there is no sink near the location of the dishwasher, the drain connection may be made to a sink or tub in the basement. Connect a garden hose to provide additional length to the drain hose; use rigid copper nipple to make the connection, and secure it with clamps. Long hose drain line going down to the basement may cause water to be siphoned out of the dishwasher. This can be prevented by providing a siphon breaker (see Fig. 10-6).

In rare cases when it is not possible to discharge the drainpipe from the washer into an existing sink or its drain, you will have to connect it directly to a drainage line in the house. This will necessitate the installation of a trap and possibly a vent pipe. The trap may

Table 10-3. Dishwasher Troubleshooting Chart.

Malfunction	Probable Causes	Suggested Repairs
Door leaks	a. Gasket worn out b. Incorrectly installed gasket	a. Replace b. Install correctly
Impeller on the dasher broken	Some object dropped on the dishwasher bottom or on the impeller and struck against it	Install new impeller. To prevent such mishap in future, install a guard.
Dishes not properly washed	a. Dishes not pre-cleaned properly b. Loading of dishes in the trays not correct c. Soap used in place of recommended detergent d. Incorrect amount of detergent used e. Water pressure low f. Water temperature low	a. Pre-clean dishes properly b. Read instruction manual and load accordingly. c. Use recommended detergent d. Measure out and add correct amount of detergent as per instruction manual e. Normal pressure is 15 pounds per square inch. If it is lower, call the water utility. f. If water temperature is not in the range of 140°F to 150°F, adjust the water heater thermostat
Water leaks at hose connection	Hose connection loose	Shut off power supply and tighten loose hose
Leaky drain valve	a. Dirt prevents valve from closing b. Weak spring c. Linkage gone out of adjustment	a. Flush out with water and work it several times b. Replace c. Adjust correctly
Dishwasher does not fill up	a. Drain valve stays open b. Inlet valve does not open c. Low water pressure	a. Adjust correctly b. Adjust the linkage. If necessary, repair or replace the solenoid c. If pressure is below 15 pounds per square inch, call your water utility.
Slow draining	a. Stoppage in the plumbing system b. Drain valve not opening to full extent	a. Clean the drain line or trap as necessary. Check garbage disposal if dishwasher drains into it. b. Adjust drain valve

Continued on next page.

Table 10-3. Dishwasher Troubleshooting Chart. (Continued from previous page.)

Malfunction	Probable Causes	Suggested Repairs
Inflow of water does not stop	a. Inlet valve stuck open b. Solenoid not working properly	a. Open out the valve; clean and reassemble. Clean out bleed-hole if clogged. b. Repair or replace
Inlet valve leaking	a. Excess lime deposits b. Linkage out of adjustment c. Valve seat or washer worn out d. Gasket or fitting gone loose	a. Clean with a small brush b. Adjust c. Replace d. Tighten
Machine does not start	a. Fuse blown or circuit breaker tripped b. Open circuit developed in the unit c. Timer or switch defective d. Switch linkage gone out of adjustment	a. After checking circuit for shorting and grounding, change fuse or reset circuit breaker as the case may be b. Check the entire circuit with a tester and remove the open one c. Replace d. Readjust

be of a large size, and the washer drain may hang inside it. It is preferable that a permanent solid connection be made between the washer drain and the trap. In case the sewer and house drain back up, a solid connection will prevent any waste matter from flowing out.

Dishwasher Problems

Table 10-3 lists some common problems which may develop in your dishwasher, and it suggests possible solutions. Only those problems that you can easily tackle, with ordinary tools are listed. In most cases the problems will be connected with the inlet-outlet valves which you can remove and clean up or even repair or replace. More serious problems require special tools and professional help, and you will be smart to call a repairman trained to repair your brand of machine if these more serious problems arise. *Whenever you undertake any repair job, however, be sure to disconnect the power supply.*

Planning and Installing a New Plumbing System

Chapter 11

Planning and Installing a New Plumbing System

Whether you are building a new home or modernizing an old one, proper planning of the plumbing system will save on material and labor. For a new house, you will have to choose locations for a well and a sewage disposal system before locating the house itself! Inside the house, planning includes the selection of the right type of fixtures with regard to size, styling and color, as well as the selection of their exact locations in the kitchen, laundry, and bathroom to provide maximum convenience and accessibility. Prior to installation, a plan of the system should be prepared, preferably by an architect or an engineer, which will give the exact requirements of pipe lengths, sizes, and the details of fixtures and fittings. An estimate of the cost can be prepared at this stage.

In a house under construction, the installation of water supply and drainage lines presents no problems. All pipes intended to run inside the walls are placed in position prior to the finishing of the inner surfaces of such walls. If you plan to run pipelines in the open and then box them in, in an old house, not too much breaking through the walls and floors will be necessary. The real breaking through comes when you intend making additions to your existing home and have to run the pipes inside the existing walls and floors. You will have to remove part of the wall covering and flooring, and will also have to cut through some *joists* (horizontal beams supporting the floors), and *studs* (vertical supports for partitions and walls) to run the new lines through them. Most of this work will be required for the larger drainage pipes. The water supply pipes are generally much smaller in diameter, and run alongside the drainage lines in the same space. Breaking through will be much less extensive if planning of the whole sytem is done beforehand.

PLANNING A PLUMBING SYSTEM FOR A NEW HOME

In a new home, you have ample latitute for the selection and arrangement of fixtures. Your precise requirements should be considered and accommodated at the planning and drafting stage if costly changes are to be avoided later on. Not only the fixtures and their locations, but the complete layout of the water and drainage system itself can make a big difference in the convenience of use and the overall cost of construction. Your home has to serve not only you but your growing family for many, many years, and it will be wise to plan accordingly by considering future needs. In addition to the usual kitchen and bathroom setup, the following popular items should be considered:

> additional bathroom
> extra half bath
> toilet in basement
> extra shower in basement
> wet bar in family room
> sink in basement workshop
> outdoor faucets
> sink in yard
> garage drain
> garbage disposer in kitchen
> automatic washer and dryer
> automatic dishwasher

Most of these facilities can be added at a later date but at that time their installation will necessitate opening up wall and floor surfaces, and cutting joists and studs; the delay will thus make installation much more expensive.

Judicious planning of the drainage system results in considerable cost cutting. If the fixtures are scattered all around the house, larger quantities of pipes, fittings, soil stacks, and drains will be needed. The soil stack, which is 3 inches to 4 inches in diameter and extends right from the house drain in the basement up and out through the roof, is the single costliest item in home plumbing. Fixtures should be located in a manner so that only one stack is

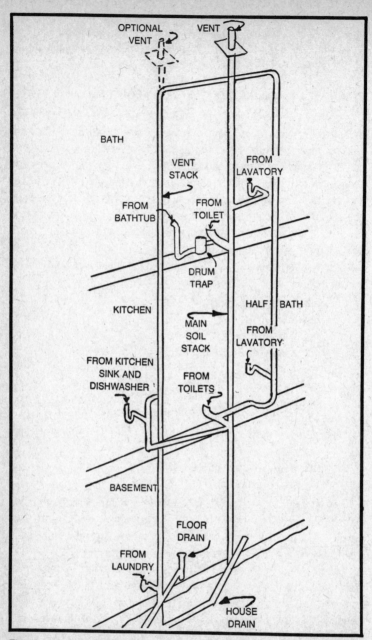

Fig. 11-1. You will save a lot of money by arranging fixtures so that a single main stack will do. Toilets close to the stack should run into it directly. For others run branch drains of the same size as the soil stack and connect to it. In some cases, you will have to provide secondary stacks.

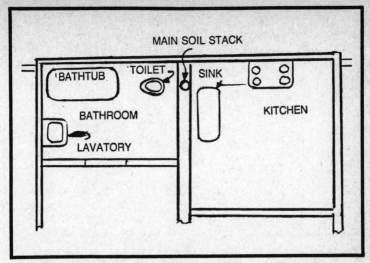

Fig. 11-2. A single mainstack arrangement for kitchen and bath unit.

needed (Fig. 11-1). This, of course, may not always be possible, particularly in large houses. Figure 11-2 shows adjacent locations of the bathroom and the kitchen requiring only one soil stack, while Fig. 11-3 indicates how the various fixtures in a bathroom can be arranged so as to cut down on the amounts of pipes and fittings.

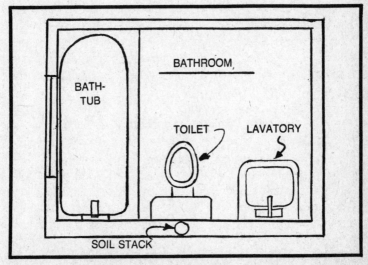

Fig. 11-3. Judicious arrangement of fixtures in a bathroom can save considerable amounts of pipe and fittings.

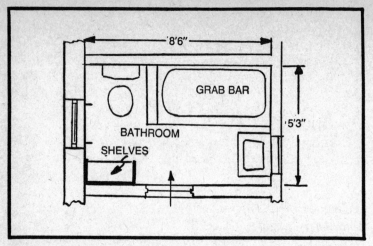

Fig. 11-4. Space has been nicely utilized in this design of a bathroom. It has fixtures against two walls.

Toilets close to the main soil stack should drain directly into it; those farther away need a branch drain of the same size as the main soil stack. Toilets too far away should be provided with a secondary soil stack 2 inches in diameter towards the top and 3 inches or 4 inches below the point of toilet drain connection. Such toilets can also be connected to the main soil stack provided a 2-inch vent pipe leading to the roof top is installed at the toilet. Other fixtures like bathtub, sink, lavatory, and washer can be attached to either the main stack or to a secondary stack. The usual sizes of branch drains are 1 1/2 inches and 2 inches depending on the flow from the fixtures. They should have adequate downward pitch towards the soil stack.

Minimum size of a secondary stack is 1 1/2 inches and it should either be vented right through the roof or through that portion of the main stack which is above the highest branch drain connection in it. If two branch drains connect to the stack at points more than 8 feet below each other, then the lower drain should be provided with a revent to prevent breaking up of the seals in the traps of the lower fixtures due to syphoning out of water when an upper fixture is flushed. Such a revent pipe has to be of the same diameter as the branch drain.

The house drain in the basement or at the lowest floor should be the same size as the main stack, and should slope down to the house sewer. All the stacks should flow into the house drain.

The arrangement of fixtures in a bathroom and the room's location relative to other rooms in the house determine the convenience and comfort you get from its use. If the fixtures are properly distributed over the available space and the bathroom is easily accessible from all other rooms, it is an ideal situation. Figure 11-4 shows good utilization of space in a bathroom while Fig. 11-5 show a bathroom conveniently located across from four rooms. As mentioned before, it is good policy to plan and install your plumbing (including the fixtures) for future expansions. Whenever you add an extra bedroom, an additional bathroom will come in very handy. The original plan should take this into consideration and should leave enough room for these additions. Also consider that a liberal number of plumbing conveniences along with superior quality fixtures greatly enhances the value of a house; if and when you decide to sell this house, you will get a much better price if these features are available.

BREAKING THROUGH WALLS AND FLOORS

For a house under construction, pipes are easily installed without the necessity of breaking through wall coverings and floors, and without too much cutting through of studs and joists. However, once you remove the wall and floor coverings, the remaining work is

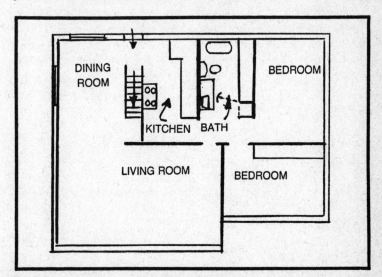

Fig. 11-5. The bathroom in this arrangement is ideally located: Readily accessible to all the four rooms on the floor.

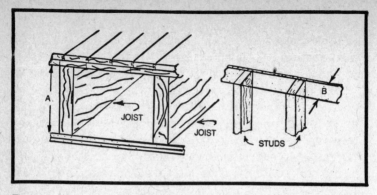

Fig. 11-6. How large a drainage pipe can be run up a partition or under a floor depends on the type of pipe and the dimensions 'a' and 'b'—the depths of joists and studs. Water pipes, being much smaller in diameter, present no problem. They just run alongside the drainage pipes.

practically the same for both new and old construction. The description that follows applies to both.

To run pipelines inside partitions and under floors which have ceilings underneath them, it is necessary to measure out *clear* spaces *a* and *b*, the depths of the joists and studs, as shown in Fig. 11-6. Table 11-1 gives the clear spaces in inches required by drainage pipes of various sizes.

You don't have to take any measurements if you know for sure the sizes of the studs and joists in your walls and floors. From Table 11-2 you will be able to figure out the maximum size of pipe that can be run. Fittings are planned on a pipeline preferably at locations where the most space is available. You will need more room for

Table 11-1. Clear Space Requirements for Drainage Lines of Various Diameters.

Material	Diameter in Inches			
	1 1/2	2	3	4
Cast Iron Pipe	-	4	-	6 1/4
Cast Iron Fittings	-	4	-	6 1/4
Plastic and Copper Pipe	1 3/4	-	3 3/4	-
Plastic and Copper Fittings	2 1/8	-	3 5/8	-

Table 11-2. Approximate Clearance Available at Various Studs and Joists.

Size of Stud/Joist	Approximate Clearance in Inches Available	Maximum Size Pipe It Will Take
2″ × 4″	3 3/4″	3″ copper/plastic
2″ × 6″	5 3/4″	2″ cast iron
2″ × 8″	7 3/4″	4″ cast iron

turning and tightening the fittings on threaded metallic pipes than on plastic and copper pipes.

Notching Studs and Joists

When the partition wall is not thick enough to take a drainage line, it should be made thicker. Add 2 × 4-inch studs after you remove the facing and install the line (see Fig. 11-7). If you are working at an outer wall and cannot possibly break into it due to the type of construction, the required clearance can be obtained by adding 2 × 6-inch or even 2 × 8-inch studs.

The load on a wall is carried by the studs, each one of which shares a part of it. The load on the floor is carried by the joists in the same manner. Notching through studs and joists reduces their structural strength, which should be restored by reinforcing them properly. A notch at the top of a joist should be reinforced by inserting a tightly fitting block; a notch at a joist's underside should be reinforced by attaching a steel mending plate or strap with screws

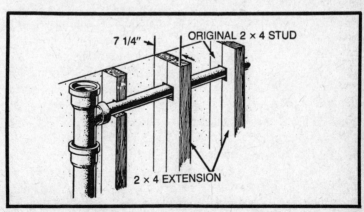

Fig. 11-7. Thin partitions can be thickened by adding 2 × 4-inch studs to accommodate drainage pipes.

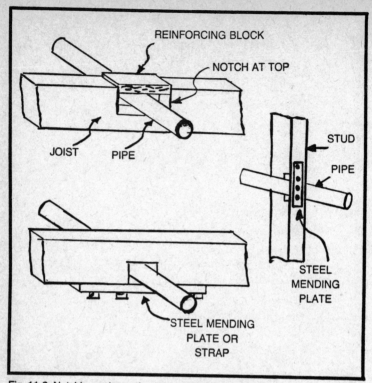

Fig. 11-8. Notching reduces the strength of studs and joists. Reinforcing should be done by fitting a reinforcing block if the notch is at the top of a joist, or by a steel mending plate if the notch is at the underside or at a stud.

(Fig. 11-8). A notch in a stud also requires a metal mending plate. A lesser amount of strength is lost by drilling a hole and threading the pipe through it.

Notches at the top of studs in a non-load-bearing partition wall can be cut up to half the thickness of the studs if only two studs in a row are notched, and at least two more studs are left unnotched. This rule applies if the notching is done in the upper half of a stud's height. If the stud's lower-half is notched deeper than one-third its thickness, it should be reinforced; under no circumstances should notching be deeper than two-thirds the thickness, even if it is proposed to be reinforced. If possible, pipes should run parallel to the joists and in between them, except when you are working either in an attic when the line can be crossed on top of the joists, or at the first floor when it can be crossed below the joists, without the necessity of notching them (Fig. 11-9).

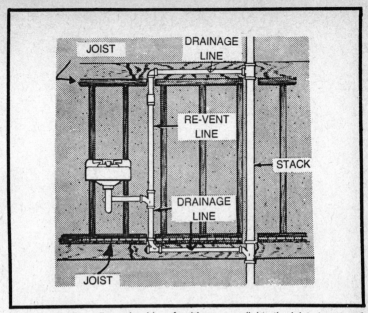

Fig. 11-9. Drainage lines should preferably run parallel to the joists to prevent notching.

Notching of joists can be reduced by running the lines through floors, sub-floors, and stripping. Toilet drains always run in between the joists or below them. When notching does become necessary, make it towards the ends and never in the middle half of the joist (Fig. 11-10). No notch should be deepr than one-fourth the height of

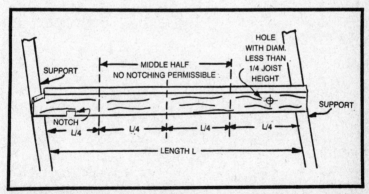

Fig. 11-10. Notching is not permissible in the middle half of a joist. Also notches should not be deeper than 1/4 the height of the joist. Holes are preferable provided they are centered between top and bottom of joist and their diameter does not exceed 1/4 the joist height.

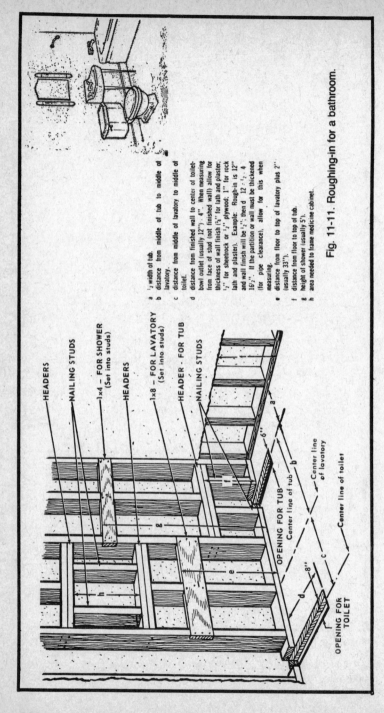

HEADERS

NAILING STUDS

1x4 — FOR SHOWER
(Set into studs)

HEADERS

1x8 — FOR LAVATORY
(Set into studs)

HEADER - FOR TUB

NAILING STUDS

6''

OPENING FOR TUB
Center line of tub

Center line
of lavatory

b

a

f

g

e

8''

h

d

c

Center line of toilet

OPENING FOR
TOILET

a ½ width of tub.

b distance from middle of tub to middle of lavatory.

c distance from middle of lavatory to middle of toilet.

d distance from finished wall to center of toilet-bowl outlet (usually 12''). 4''. When measuring from face of stud (not finished wall) allow for thickness of wall finish (¾'' for lath and plaster; ½'' for sheetrock or ¼'' plywood; 1'' for rock lath and plaster). Example: Rough-in is 12'' and wall finish will be ½''; then d 12 - ½, 4 16½''. If the partition or wall must be thickened (for pipe clearance), allow for this when measuring.

e distance from floor to top of lavatory plus 2'' (usually 33'').

f distance from floor to top of tub.

g height of shower (usually 5').

h area needed to frame medicine cabinet.

Fig. 11-11. Roughing-in for a bathroom.

288

the joist. Holes through joists are preferable to notches provided they are centered between the top and bottom of the joist and their diameter does not exceed one-fourth the height of the joist.

Planning a Bathroom Wall

Figure 11-11 shows an economical and convenient bathroom wall arrangement, regardless of whether it is a new construction or merely an alteration in an old building. All the fixtures—the bathtub, shower, lavatory, and toilet—are placed against one wall; this wall is therefore the only one that needs its finish stripped. The others remain untouched. In a new bathroom the wall should be made sufficiently thick to accommodate the piping; in an old one it can be thickened if necessary as described before.

Figure 12-7 in the next Chapter illustrates how new drainage lines run. The bathroom shower here is in the basement and the drainage runs into the main soil stack close to the house drain connection. Both a main vent pipe and a revent pipe are necessary. Arrangements for baths on upper floors may differ in details but the basics are the same.

INSTALLING A DRAINAGE SYSTEM

When starting the installation of a plumbing system, start with the drainage lines. The smaller diameter water pipes can later be placed beside the drainpipes.

In general the installation sequence will be as follows:

1. Assemble and install the toilet drain.
2. Install the house drain in a trench below the first floor or the basement.
3. Install the cleanout assembly at the point where the main soil stack will join the house drain.
4. Assemble and install the main stack.
5. Install branch drains and revent lines.
6. Install any secondary soil stack.
7. Install the basement drain or areaway drain.

Assembling and Installing the Toilet Drain

Two openings should be cut in the floor, one for the soil stack and the other to take the floor flange under the toilet (see Fig. 11-12). When the bathroom is located above a room ceiling you have to cut an 8-inch wide strip in the flooring starting from the center line

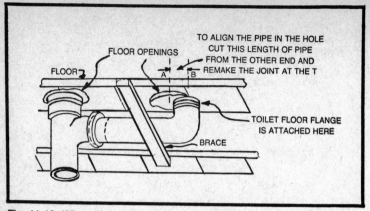

Fig. 11-12. When there is no ceiling underneath the floor, cut two holes of appropriate size for the closet bend and the soil stack. For copper pipe, a quarter bend is used instead of a closet bend.

of the toilet bowl outlet up to the wall against which the toilet will sit (Fig. 11-11). This opening is needed to furnish space in which the stack T and the closet-bend assembly will be installed. If, however, you are working at the first floor, there will normally be no ceiling below and all you will need to cut are two holes of suitable sizes through which to pass the stack and the closet-bend assembly. Installing will be done from underneath, as shown in Fig. 11-12.

When the toilet-drain assembly is made of plastic pipe and fittings, it will consist of a T at the soil stack, a floor flange and a closet-bend under the toilet, and two short pieces of pipe (Fig. 11-13). If copper pipe is used, there will be just a 1/4 bend in place of the closet-bend. In either case, first find the vertical length of pipe needed between the floor flange and the bend. This will depend on the location of the T that you install at the stack. Solder or weld the bend and the pipe together. The floor flange is not to be put in at this time; it is installed later along with the toilet. Hold this assembly of the pipe and the bend in place, and measure out the length B of the horizontal piece of pipe needed to make the connection to the T. Next lay the T, the horizontal pipe, and the bend assembly, roughly assembled together, on the floor with a brace underneath, so that the center lines C and D are parallel. Put guide marks on the pieces. Carefully weld or solder them together according to the marks.

Figures 11-12 and 11-14 show a cast-iron pipe installation which is practically the same as that for plastic or copper pipe. When the assembly stays between two adjacent joists, only a closet-bend and

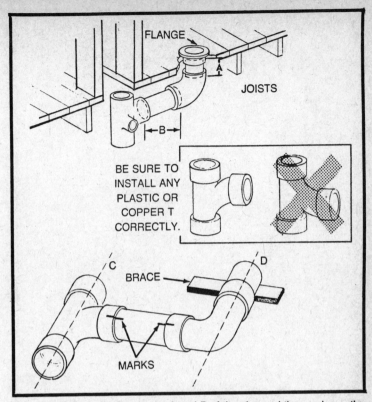

Fig. 11-13. Figure out the lengths A and B of the pipe and then make up the assembly. The welding or soldering should be done after laying it on the floor so that the center lines C and D are parallel. Place marks to insure correct joining.

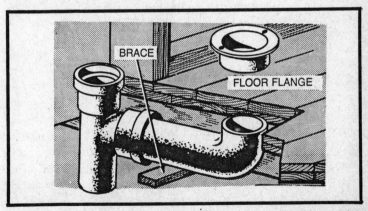

Fig. 11-14. After the toilet drain assembly is installed, it is braced from underneath. The floor flange is attached later, when the floor is completely finished and the toilet is being installed.

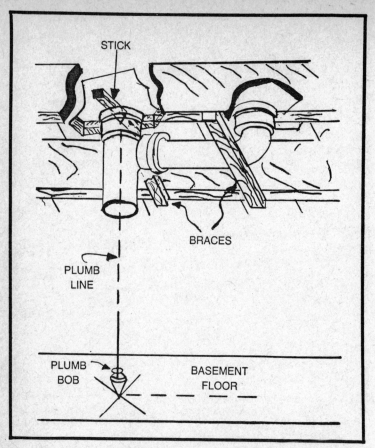

STICK

BRACES

PLUMB
LINE

PLUMB
BOB

BASEMENT
FLOOR

Fig. 11-15. Suspend a plumb bob by a string from the center line of the stack T. The point where it strikes the floor is the starting point for the house drain trench.

T are needed. The length of the bend is adjusted by breaking off a length equal to AB, the distance between the center lines of the pipe and the hole. The two center lines then coincide and the pipe aligns directly below the hole in which the floor flange is installed from above. If an assembly has to run under the joists, you will need a T, a hub-top-long quarter bend, and a vertical piece of pipe. Lengths A and B will be determined as before, and after assembling the pieces the joints will be caulked. Finally the assembly will be braced from underneath so that it will not hang from the toilet, or else the strain may open the joint.

The floor flange will be attached later when the bath room floor is finally being finished and you are ready to install the toilet.

Installing the Building or House Drain

Soil stacks are made of cast iron, plastic, or copper pipe, and are usually 4 inches in diameter for an ordinary size of home. For the house drain, 4-inch cast-iron pipe is used. If the soil stack is made of 4-inch plastic, the house drain may be the same. For connecting different types of pipe, a special adapter is used at the foot of the stack.

The soil stack should run truly vertical between the stack T (from the toilet drain) and its connection to the house drain in the basement or at the first floor. A stick is placed across the upper end of the stack T and a length of string is tied to it at the center line of the pipe. A plumb bob is attached to the other end of the string which is laid out till it almost hits the floor. After the string stops swinging, mark the spot on the floor where the plumb bob is almost touching. This will be the starting point for the house drain trench (Fig. 11-15). Measure out and stake two other points, two feet away on either side. They will serve as a references in case you lose the original point.

The house drain will go out either through or under the foundation of the outer wall and extend to a point 5 feet outside where it will turn into the house sewer. Draw a line from the mark under the plumb bob to the point in the outer wall under which the house drain will exit. With this line as center, dig a trench two feet wide and one foot deep, measured below the surface of the finished floor. Provide a pitch equal to 2 1/2 inches per 10-foot length, to the bottom of the trench, and compact the soil firmly.

When the trench has thus been prepared on the inside, go out and extend it 5 feet to the outside. This is the point where the house sewer starts (Fig. 11-16). The inside and outside runs of the trench should be connected by tunneling through or under the foundation. The grade along the trench bottom should be held constant over its entire length. Trenches should also be dug for any branches like those from a secondary soil stack or the floor drain, which connect to the house drain.

Before laying the pipe for the house drain, make up a cleanout assembly by joining to the drain a Y having a cleanout adapter and plug, and a 1/8 bend, (Fig. 11-17) or a cleanout T with two 1/8 bends. If, however, you are using cast-iron pipe, instead of plastic pipe, the assembly will consist of a test T and two 1/8 bends, or a Y having a cleanout ferrule and plug, together with one 1/8 bend. The parts should be correctly aligned by laying them on the floor as you

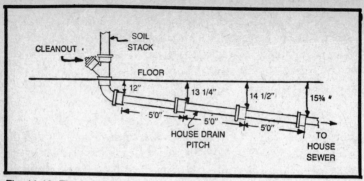

Fig. 11-16. The house drain starts at the bottom of main soil stack where a cleanout should be provided. Depth below the finished floor is 12″ at the start, and increases at the rate of 1 1/4″ per 5 feet. Good pitch helps keep the house drain clean by generating self-cleansing velocity in it.

did for the toilet drain assembly explained previously. Finally the assembly should be caulked or welded as necessary.

Place the assembly inside the trench so that it centers itself correctly under the hanging plumb bob. Brace it and pour concrete to

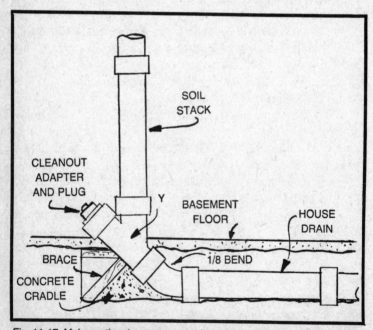

Fig. 11-17. Make up the cleanout assembly and pour concrete to form a cradle under and around it. Then lay the house drain in the trench and out to 5 feet outside the foundation, to connect to the sewer.

form a cradle all around and underneath. After the concrete has set, lay the length of pipe and make joints to complete the house drain up to 5 feet outside the house. At appropriate points install Ys to take the floor and branch drains, which should now be laid under the floor, in a similar manner. The floor drain will have a trap and seal to keep sewer gases from entering the house.

The process is somewhat different for a house drain that is suspended from the roof of the basement, and which, after running down one wall, goes out through the foundation. Often it may go out through the wall without running down it as shown in Fig. 11-18B. It can even be a combination hanging and underground house drain.

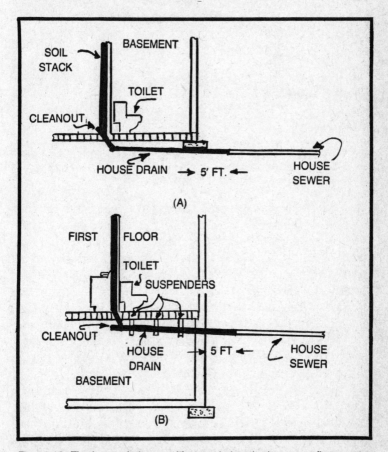

Fig. 11-18. The house drain can either run below the basement floor—or be suspended from the ceiling—illustration B. In either case it runs 5 feet beyond the outside wall and then connects to the house sewer which connects to the street sewer or to the septic tank.

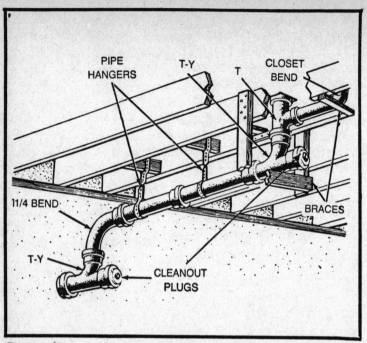

Fig. 11-19. The suspended house drain starts from the foot-of-the stack assembly and is secured in place by hangers and braces. Often you may have a combination suspended and underground house drain.

The size of the suspended house drain can be 3-inch plastic or copper for stacks of the same material. For cast-iron stack it should be 4-inch cast iron. Often two cleanouts are installed on the house drain, one at its connection to the soil stack and another where it goes out through the wall or the floor (see Fig. 11-19). A 3-inch house drain should be stepped to 4-inch size beyond the second cleanout. When only one cleanout is used (at the base of the stack) the entire length of the house drain should consist of 4-inch size pipe.

The steps for installing a suspended house drain are as follows. Make up the foot-of-stack cleanout assembly in the same manner as explained earlier for the underfloor drain. Make all the joints and connect this assembly to the toilet drain assembly. A small length of pipe may be required to make up the length between the two. Allowing a pitch of 2 1/2 inches per 10-foot run, set up a chalkline to find the spot where the drain will go out through the wall. Cut a hole about 6 inches in diameter in the wall and dig a trench outside for a length of 5 feet. Assemble the drain from the foot-of-the-stack assembly to its end, 5 feet outside the point where it will connect to the sewer; complete the second cleanout assembly if it is used. Provide braces to support the house drain, as illustrated in Fig. 11-19.

Assembling the Main Stack

If you have a suspended building drain, you have already connected it to the toilet drain assembly and are ready to start the soil stack. If, on the other hand, the drain is an underground one, the toilet drain assembly is yet to be installed. Figure 11-20 illustrates how it is done. Starting from the house drain cleanout, assemble the length RQ by joining the required number of pieces. The last section, A, will in most cases have to be cut to fit in the space PQ. Now raise the toilet drain assembly for a moment and insert the section A. Make the joints to complete the stack up to the toilet drain. Continue building it up until it goes out through the roof. As you go along,

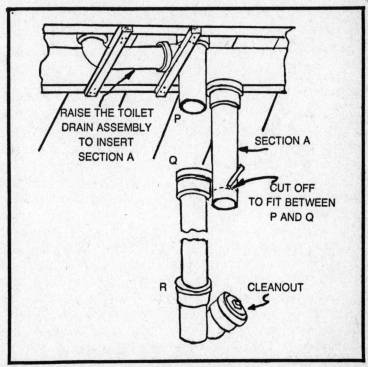

Fig. 11-20. Start assembling the soil stack from the cleanout till you reach the last section, A. Cut it to fit in the space PQ. Raise the toilet assembly and hold it till you insert the piece A. Complete the joints and continue assembling the stack till you come out a foot above the roof.

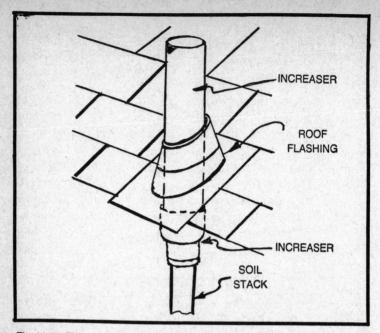

Fig. 11-21. The soil stack extends a foot above the roof top. Often an increaser is used to increase the diameter. A watertight joint is made between the roof covering and the soil stack by means of roof flashing which is adjusted to roof pitch.

include in the line any Ts for drainage lines and vent lines. Take care that these are so inserted that the drains flow *down* into the stack while the vent pipes have a slight *upward* pitch. Use chalkline to simulate positions of drain and vent lines. For a cast-iron soil stack you will need special vent Ts. If there are several floors with toilets, the toilet drain assemblies will have to be made for each one of them and secured in place before the stack is built up to it.

When assembling the stack, you may sometimes come across a roof rafter or some other obstruction. Quarter or 1/8 bends are used to make offsets so that the obstruction is bypassed. The stack should protrude approximately 12 inches above the roof and should be attached to it by means of a watertight roof flashing (Fig. 11-21). This part of the stack may be made larger in size by attaching an increaser.

Installing Branch Drains and Revent Lines

Branch drains connect fixtures like bathtubs, kitchen sinks, and lavatories to the soil stack or to the house drain. Connections to the house drain have already been discussed. Those branches drain-ing into the soil stack are installed by starting from the stack and proceeding towards the fixture. The usual size of branch lines is 1 1/2 inches, and they may be made of plastic, copper, or steel.

The *revent lines* are similar in size and material. Their function was explained in Chapter 1. Sanitary Ts are used to connect plastic or copper revent lines to the branch drains. Revent lines are assem-bled starting from their connection with the branch line, to the inverted vent Ts already installed in the soil stack. When using steel pipe, use a vertical vent T or horizontal vent T, as illustrated in Fig. 11-22, and assemble the vent run starting from the T in the stack. The final joint is made by caulking the unthreaded steel pipe end into the socket of the drainage line vent T.

Installing a Secondary Soil Stack

A *secondary stack* having a toilet connection is installed exactly as the main soil stack was installed, with its foot-of-the-stack clean-out assembly joined, in the same manner, to the house drain.

Installing Basement or Areaway Drain

If the house sewer discharges into a street sewer, the base-ment floor drain can be connected to the house drain. The same is

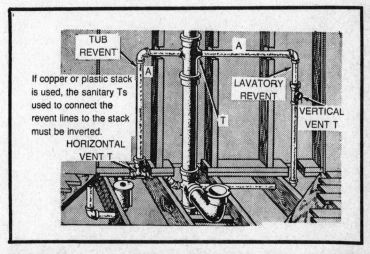

Fig. 11-22. Vent pipes provided for venting fixtures like lavatory, tub, and toilet are connected to the coil stack through a T. Connections at the fixtures are made through a vertical vent T or horizontal vent T. Assembling of the vent pipe is started from the stack T and carried onto the fixture vent T.

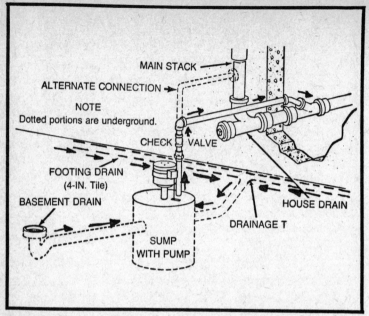

Fig. 11-23. When you have a house drain suspended from the ceiling, a sump at the basement floor is required along with a pump to lift the water up to the house drain. Both the basement drain and the footing drain will flow into the basement sump.

true of any other indoor drain as well as the footing drain. The floor drain will run in a trench just like the house drain if the latter is underground. On the other hand, if you have a suspended house drain, the flow from the basement drain will go to a sump fitted with a pump which will lift the flow to the building drain. The footing drain will also be connected to the sump (Fig. 11-23).

The roof drains and areaway drains may be connected to the house drain or to the house sewer if permitted by the sewer or building authority. Otherwise these can flow downhill like other natural runoffs from the ground. Often a sewer authority will require that the house or building sewer be installed by a certified contractor if connection has to be made to the public sewer.

When you have your own private septic tank and disposal system, do not connect the surface runoff from areaway, floor, footing, or roof drains to it. Instead, employ either of the two alternatives shown in Fig. 11-24:

1. Bypass the septic tank and connect to the building sewer leading to the leaching field. This will call for a larger field.

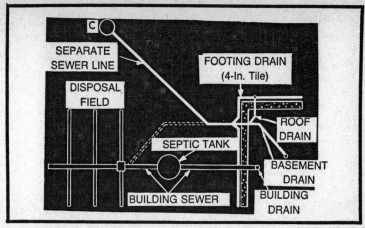

Fig. 11-24. The runoff carried by the roof drain and the foundation drain can either be carried to the disposal field after bypassing the septic tank or it may be discharged into a natural stream or disposed of through a dry well (C).

2. Carry the flow through a separate storm sewer line into disposal system C which may either be a dry well on your property or a natural body of water like a stream, lake, or river.

Figure 11-25 illustrates a typical dry well to dispose of storm runoff. Alternatively, precast concrete galleries may be used.

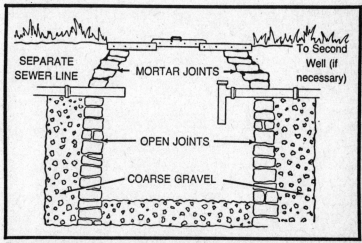

Fig. 11-25. A dry well consists of open-jointed sidewalls of stone with gravel bottom. The storm water percolates into the gravel all around and at the bottom, and then seeps down to the ground water table. More than one well may be required.

INSTALLING A WATER SUPPLY SYSTEM

The house service line brings water to the house from a source which may either be a public water supply main or your own private well. If it is a public supply main, the house service line, including the water meter, is installed by the water authority. The size of the service line depends on the individual water requirements and the normal pressures in the main. When you have a well, the service line will lead from it to a pressure tank from which point the main supply lines will deliver water to the branch supply lines of the fixtures. Sizes of these lines should be adequate to convey flows during hours of maximum consumption which occur in the early morning and late afternoons. Figure 1-1 illustrates a typical water service to a house, while Fig. 1-2 shows the layout of hot and cold supply mains and branches feeding the fixtures. These were discussed in detail in Chapter 1. Water supply systems were discussed in Chapter 2.

In this Chapter, emphasis is placed on how to plan and actually install the drainage and water supply systems within the structural setup consisting of floors, joists and studs, etc. Figure 11-26 shows a typical layout starting from the meter and the main shut-off valve. The cold water main line splits into two—one line going to the water heater and the other to the fixtures. Pipe may run between the joists or across them. It runs vertically when crossing the floors or running from a floor towards the ceiling. Except in the basement, water pipes are concealed within the walls and mostly run alongside the drainage lines. The hot and cold lines run parallel to each other, but are separated by at least 6 inches so as to avoid loss of heat from the hot water line (unless it is insulated). Whenever doing a plumbing job, keep in mind that as you face a fixture like a sink or lavatory, the hot water line will run on the left and and cold on the right. As indicated in Fig. 11-26 the main water supply lines run under and across the first floor joists and are attached to them by means of hangers. Connections between branches and mains are made by union Ts and Ls. Shutoff valves should be provided liberally on the various runs and particularly at each fixture; they come in handy when you have to do some repairs. At the hot water heater and tank, always provide shut-off valves at the inlet and outlet lines.

Union couplings should be provided on threaded pipes at locations where you may have to take the line apart for replacements or repairs to fixtures, like at a hot water heater. All horizontal runs of pipe should slope slightly towards the house service line and a

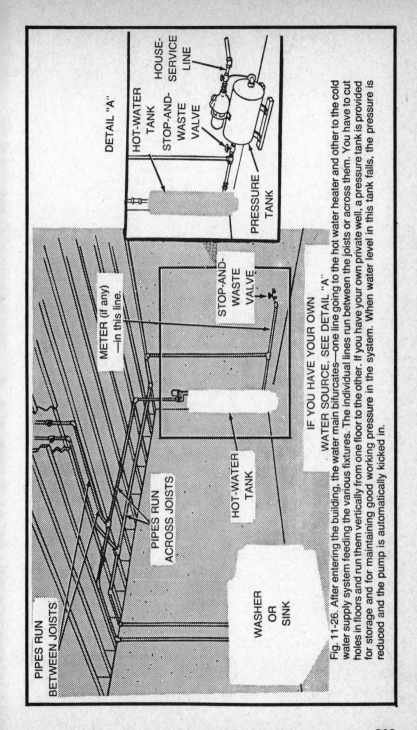

PIPES RUN BETWEEN JOISTS.

PIPES RUN ACROSS JOISTS.

METER (if any) —in this line.

WASHER OR SINK

HOT-WATER TANK

STOP-AND-WASTE VALVE

DETAIL "A"

HOT-WATER TANK

STOP-AND-WASTE VALVE

HOUSE-SERVICE LINE

PRESSURE TANK

IF YOU HAVE YOUR OWN WATER SOURCE, SEE DETAIL "A."

Fig. 11-26. After entering the building, the water main bifurcates—one line going to the hot water heater and other to the cold water supply system feeding the various fixtures. The individual lines run between the joists or across them. You have to cut holes in floors and run them vertically from one floor to the other. If you have your own private well, a pressure tank is provided for storage and for maintaining good working pressure in the system. When water level in this tank falls, the pressure is reduced and the pump is automatically kicked in.

303

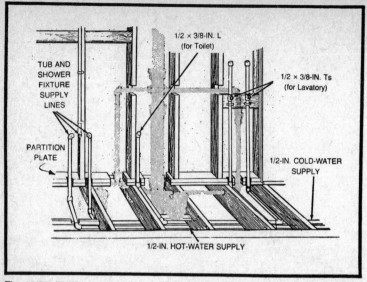

Fig. 11-27. The horizontal runs of hot and cold supply lines go under the joists and the vertical runs leading to the fixtures pass through notches cut in the partition plate. Suitable Ls and Ts are fitted at their ends to take the fixtures. The hot water line is on the left and the cold water line on the right as you face the fixture.

stop-and-waste valve should be provided at this connection so as to allow draining off the internal supply system if necessary. The following sizes of pipe are recommended under normal conditions of consumption:

Branch lines leading to fixtures: 1/2-inch pipe

Main supply lines, both hot and cold: 3/4-inch pipe.

Main line serving both the hot and cold system (starting from the meter up to the point of bifurcation): 3/4- or 1-inch pipe.

Running Lines From One Floor to Another

In the basements, the main supply lines run below the joists and are strapped to their underside. In upper floors this is not possible, so they run across the top of the joists; *notches* have to be cut for the purpose. The lines cross over from lower floors to upper ones through holes cut right through.

A common layout for water supply lines in the bathroom is illustrated in Fig. 11-27. The horizontal lines run under the joists, notched if necessary, while the vertical runs go up through notches cut in the partition plate. On upper floors, the supply lines should preferably run up close to the soil stack and then branch out to the fixtures by running inside notches cut in partition studs.

Installing Air Chambers

If you suddenly turn the flow of water off or on, for instance at a shower or faucet, there is at times a knocking sound. You might have wondered what causes it. Normally it happens on a day when water pressures are high. As you suddenly stop the flow of water, its kinetic energy is converted into high pressure. The force of this sudden pressure acting on the joints and the pipe bends produces banging or knocking noises. In localities which are close to pumping stations or overhead storage tanks, the high pressures of water are brought down by installing pressure-reducing valves. To protect the lines from damage and to eliminate the inconvenience of sudden noise and banging, it is usual practice to install at each fixture a device called an *air chamber*, consisting of a 12-inch to 18-inch high pipe with air trapped at the top. The high-pressure wave generated by the stoppage of flow at a fixture travels to the air chamber and gets dissipated by compressing the air contained therein without causing noise or damage to the joints and fittings (Fig. 11-28). Air chambers should be provided both on the hot and cold water supply lines.

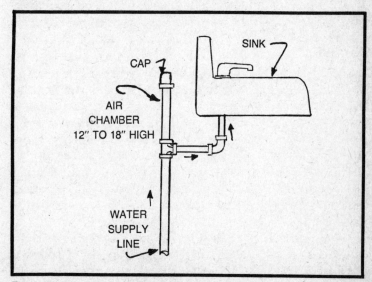

Fig. 11-28. To prevent water hammer noises and damage to joints, air chambers are provided on supply lines at fixtures.

A 24-inch high air chamber placed inside a partition can be connected to several supply lines by installing horizontal connecting pipes within the floor. This eliminates the need for individual air chambers on supply lines of each fixture.

INSTALLING A HOUSE SEWER, SEPTIC TANK, AND WELL

The house sewer is the pipe, usually 4 inches or more in diameter, which runs between the house drain and either the street sewer or your septic tank. When it connects to the street sewer, the installation should conform to the local code. The actual connection at the street sewer is made either by the sewer authority representative or by an authorized contractor. When you are the one laying the house sewer in your yard, make sure you are fully familiar with your local code, and contact the sanitarian or building inspector for any clarifications.

The slope of the house sewer, its depth below ground, and the spot where it joins the house drain are very important factors; you will have to figure these out before starting the work. To generate self-cleansing velocity inside the sewer, lay the pipe with a downward pitch of at least 1%—that is, a drop of 1 foot in a 100-foot length, which comes to about 1 inch per 8 feet. If possible, provide a steeper pitch. This will be no problem since the street sewer usually runs pretty deep and, therefore, the depth of the sewer running below grade—under your front lawn—may be made quite substantial with the pitch much steeper than the minimum of 1 percent.

The house sewer should run as straight as possible between the house and the street sewer. Any unavoidable changes in direction should be gentle and not abrupt. A right-angle turn, for example, should be provided by two 45° elbows and not by a 90° elbow, unless it is a long, sweep elbow with a very large turning radius. Cleanouts consisting of sanitary Ts running straight up from the pipe to the ground surface, and provided with caps and plugs, are installed at 45° or sharper turns and at the end of every 50-foot run. A cleanout installation is always provided on the house drain inside the house. Sometimes there may be two cleanout installations, one under the stack, and another near the outside wall (see Fig. 11-19).

When the foundations for the house are being poured, a knockout may be provided so that the house drain may be installed later on. The knockout may simply consist of a small wooden box wrapped in tarred paper which you insert in the formwork before the concrete is poured. After the house drain is inserted in the hole and adjusted to its final position, the space around it should be filled with cement mortar to make a watertight joint.

The house sewer leading to your private septic tank does not have to run deep. It may only be 2 or 3 feet below grade. The septic tank stays only about a foot below the ground surface. To prevent greases and oils from flowing into the septic tank, a grease trap is sometimes provided on the house sewer near the outer wall. The septic tank may be as close as 15 feet from the house. Its capacity depends on the bedrooms you have. Consult the state health code for further details of the requirements. It will be advisable to get your septic tank and disposal system designed by a professional engineer after he has examined the soil and has performed percolation tests. Many systems soon fail if not properly designed or correctly installed. A detailed description of private sewage disposal systems was given in Chapter 3.

If you don't have the facility of public water supply, a private well will have to be drilled. In order that the well water does not get polluted, the state health codes have laid down minimum separating distances measured from the disposal field. These may range from 75 to 100 feet for different localities. You have to follow the requirements of these minimum separating distances not only for your own system, but for those facilities on neighboring properties too.

The water well should preferably be located at the highest point of your property. However, the *quantity* of water you may get from a well without drilling too deeply into the ground, is more important than its elevation. Depending on the water-bearing strata, underground drilling may range anywhere between 75 feet and 300 feet, so you can imagine the spread in cost. Normally a water yield of three to five gallons per minute is considered to be very good. Test borings at several spots may have to be done until you hit an adequate quantity of water. In fact, as mentioned earlier, you have to decide the locations of your well and your sewage disposal system before locating the house itself. Even when buying land, these things should be considered and properly evaluated. You may hesitate to invest in land if you will have to spend an extraordinary amount of money for your well and sewage disposal system.

Remodelling and Modernizing an Existing Plumbing System

Chapter 12

Remodelling and Modernizing
an Existing Plumbing System

A house can be made more comfortable and elegant-looking by modernizing its plumbing system. The necessary improvements fall under two categories:

1. *Additional facilities* like a half or a full bathroom, toilet, shower, and wet bar in the basement playroom; sinks in the yard and the workshop; garage drain; additional wash-basins; etc.
2. *New fixtures* of modern design in place of old ones.

Such remodelling not only improves the appearance of a house, but also enhances its resale value. Most of the plumbing alternations require work both on the drainage and the water supply lines. You may want to do the entire job yourself or you may consider hiring outside services for a portion of the work.

PLANNING PLUMBING EXTENSIONS IN AN OLD HOME

Before starting to do anything, you should work out a detailed plan of the job. A sketch, however rough, is always desirable. It should show the proposed locations of the fixtures, the routes along which the pipelines will be laid to connect to these fixtures, and the lengths and sizes of the various pipes to be used. On small and simple jobs, it will suffice to make a plan showing the dimensions of the floors and the positions of the walls; but more often it will be helpful and desirable to work out an elevation too. When working on this sketch you will notice several important structural features of the building which you are likely to miss otherwise. The same basic principles of planning and laying out a plumbing system apply to an old home as to a new one. The system should be convenient and yet not overly expensive. There should be a minimum amount of breaking through the walls and floors.

Finding space for additions is the main problem. The greater the amount of reconstruction, the higher the cost of improvements. This fact brings up the question: should you add rooms on the outside of the existing building or confine the remodelling to interior changes only? It is easier to make outside extensions, provided there is enough space. The additions can be planned and constructed the same as in a new house, with almost full freedom in laying out the plumbing system. But from an economical standpoint, interior changes are usually preferable.

Figure 12-1 shows both the alternatives. The illustration on the top shows part of a house with two bedrooms but no bathroom nearby. One bathroom can be put in according to either of the two renovation plans shown. In plan #1, the closets attached to the bedrooms have been converted into an access hallway leading to the new bathroom extended *outside*, the existing building. The bathroom has the usual facilities: tub, toilet, lavatory, and linen closet. The soil stack is placed in the new wall close to the toilet, and the house drain runs straight to the house sewer outside. In plan # 2, the space occupied by the closets has been extended by putting in a new partition wall, and the bathroom has been accommodated in it. One of the bedrooms has been reduced in size. The soil stack can either be placed at position 'X,' inside the new partition wall, or outside at position 'Y,' and boxed in. A new house drain will connect it to the existing main stack or to the existing house drain.

In a single story house, a new soil stack can easily be installed inside a partition and carried up and out through the roof for venting. In a multi-story house the stack will generally run through partitions on the upper floors. This may not always be possible and it may have to be boxed in. Figure 12-2 shows the alternatives for boxing-in, at the first and second floors. When this method is impracticable, one choice may be to run the stack inside an outer wall or to build it completely outside and box it in as in plan #2, Fig. 12-1.

The foregoing example may have given you some idea of the problems that may arise during remodellings. The *old work*, as remodelling work is called, is much more difficult than *new work* for a

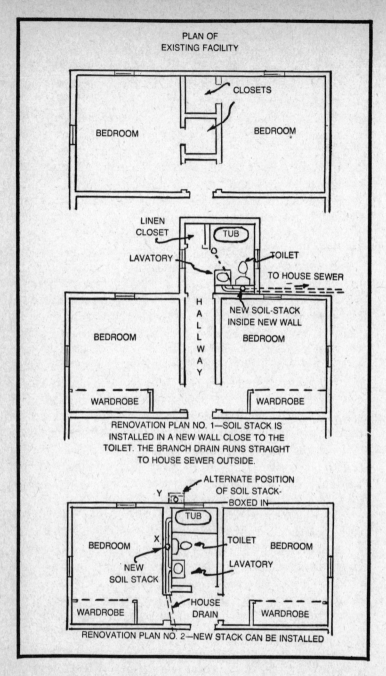

Fig. 12-1. Interior vs. exterior expansion.

house under construction. The framework on a new house is still exposed; you can see all the studs and joists, and run the pipes with much greater ease. In *old work* the pipes are concealed within the walls. The wall facing has to be stripped to expose the water supply and the drain-waste-vent (DWV) systems so that new pipings may be connected. An experienced plumber always tries to uncover as small an area of walls and floors as possible.

Whenever practicable, plan to hook-up new fixtures into a wall which has facilities existing on its other face; this way you can make the connections to pipes which are already there without having to run new lines. When adding a new toilet, you need a soil stack and if you don't want to run a whole new stack right from the house drain in the basement up to the roof, it will be smart to locate the facilities in such a way that the old soil stack may be used.

It is much easier to install horizontal runs of pipes than vertical ones, particularly in the basement or attic. The pipe can go under or over the joists. Other floors can be raised to conceal the piping (Fig. 12-3). For vertical runs you will have to remove the facing material from the walls so that the framing is exposed. Also as for new construction, you will have to cut through studs and joists. The same rules as those discussed in detail in Chapter 11 apply here (see Figs. 11-8 through 11-11). The water pipes, being smaller, run in the same space with the drainage pipes. The hot-water line, unless insulated, is separated from the cold line by at least 6 inches. It is

Fig. 12-2. The soil stack from a basement crawl space or the first floor running up to the second floor can run through closets without being boxed in. Where this is impracticable, place it in an enclosure like a corner cabinet, room divider or a soffit.

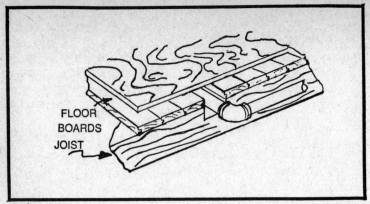

Fig. 12-3. Horizontal runs of pipe can be concealed in the floor (raised if necessary).

better to use plastic or copper pipes in remodelling than threaded pipes which require much larger space for turning around when making the joints. Cast-iron piping of the no-hub type may also be used with advantage. Studs can be added to thin partition walls or over plastered outer walls to allow pipes to run through them. (See Fig. 11-7). All the runs have to be properly supported by straps, hangers, notches in studs and joists, or by any other suitable method.

LOCATING PIPES INSIDE THE WALLS

New pipes can be connected to an old line where it is exposed, like in the attic or basement. However, most of the time it will only be possible and desirable to make connections to pipes concealed inside a wall. This brings up to the tricky problem of locating these pipes. In old houses where plumbing has been altered and remodelled several times, the task is quite difficult, and when you finally discover a pipe you are after, it will probably be in an entirely unexpected location. You can use a metal detector if the home has iron and steel pipes. The device does not respond to copper or plastic.

One straightforward approach is to follow the pipeline from its exposed location, in the basement or attic, and work up or down. When you use a hammer to strike a riser located for instance, in the basement, someone on the upper floor can listen to the sounds and judge the approximate location. You can go from one floor to the other, following the sound.

Another way is to shut and open the flow of water in the line and listen to the noise. A more exact method is to measure the distances of the exposed portion of pipe (for instance in the basement) from two side walls, go upstairs, and measure back the same distances from the same two walls. This way you can pinpoint the location of the pipe inside the wall.

An easy method for DVW pipes is to go to the roof top and observe the pipes' positions in relation to the walls. These can then be located on the lower floors by methods as described previously. These procedures will give you a rough location only. In the case of cast-iron or galvanized pipes, it is possible to determine the exact location by driving long test nails into the wall until they hit the pipe. Be sure, however, that there is no plastic or copper pipe in the vicinity or else you may puncture it and cause flooding.

BUILDING CODE AND COST ESTIMATES

Before starting a remodelling job and even before you order materials, it will be wise to check the building code and find out what you may or may not do, the kinds of pipe and joints allowed for various purposes, the type of supports required, and so on. And finally when you have checked your existing facilities and decided what additions you wish to make, an estimate should be prepared of the number of fittings, the lengths of pipes and new fixtures that will be needed, along with material required for structural work, so that these may be ordered at your plumbing supply store. To select the appliances and fixtures you should consult a number of catalogues from leading manufacturers like American Standard, Eljer, Moen, Kohler, Gerber, General Electric, Hotpoint, Westinghouse, and others, and also go out to large plumbing supply and appliance stores.

ADDING NEW WATER SUPPLY LINES

Water lines do not require any particular pitch. They can be laid horizontal, with a negative pitch, or even vertical, with the direction of flow upwards. The drainage pipes, on the other hand, do not run full or under pressure, and hence they have to be laid with a small downward pitch to create a flow velocity. Normal pitch for drainage pipe is 1/4 inch per foot of pipe length.

Regardless of whether existing water supply lines are made of rigid copper pipe or flexible tubing, the addition of a new line is generally a simple matter. First figure out a convenient point from

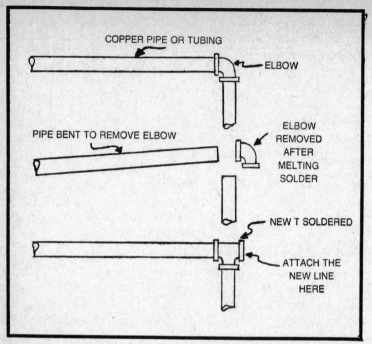

COPPER PIPE OR TUBING

ELBOW

PIPE BENT TO REMOVE ELBOW

ELBOW
REMOVED
AFTER
MELTING
SOLDER

NEW T SOLDERED

ATTACH THE
NEW LINE
HERE

Fig. 12-4. It's possible to remove an elbow and to put in a new T from which a new line can start.

which to start the new run. Most often you will select a junction of two lines connected with an elbow. If one line has a long stretch or consists of flexible tubing, it will be easy to torch-heat the elbow, and bend the line to slip the elbow off (Fig. 12-4). The ends of the tubes, when still hot, should be wiped clean to remove all traces of solder, and should be coated with flux. Clean a new T-fitting and slip it onto the ends of pipes. Make the joint by heat-soldering. You are now ready to start putting in the new line. Consider whether to use rigid copper pipe or flexible tubing. Copper tubing is very good and very convenient if the line has to run through walls, floors, and ceilings. In exposed locations, rigid copper pipe should be used.

It is good practice to install a stop valve on the new line to permit work on subsequent lengths without interruption of the supply on other lines. Otherwise a cap will have to be fitted at the end of the new run after the close of work each day.

When it is not practical to remove an elbow and replace it with a T, or when a new line is to start from an existing straight run of pipe, a small length of this straight run should be cut out and replaced with a similar length having a T-fitting attached to it (Fig. 12-5). Joints at both ends are made with the help of slip couplings which are slipped over two small lengths of pipe on either side of the T. After the pipes are properly aligned, the couplings are slipped over joints A and B, and soldered.

When working on a home improvement job involving the additions of rooms and bathrooms or the expansion of an attic, the new pipes should be installed in place before the inside walls are constructed. Joints and connections which will remain inside the walls, or otherwise inaccessible, should be carefully soldered so as to remain watertight for the entire life of the house. If you wait to install the new lines until after the walls are partly or fully built up, the work may prove to be more difficult, you may end up ripping walls and floors to squeeze pipes through. The advantage of using flexible tubing is that it needs a very small number of fittings and can be bent in any direction desired. In fact, it may only be necessary to provide fittings at the start and finish of each run, which is both convenient and inexpensive. However, in most of the jobs, a combination of the

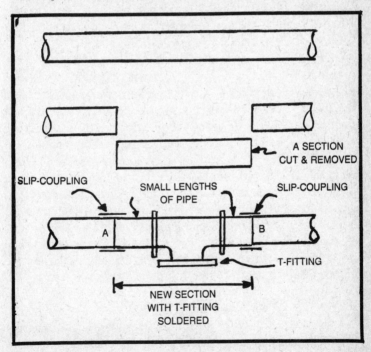

Fig. 12-5. It's also possible to cut a pipe and add a section with a T-fitting where a new line can start.

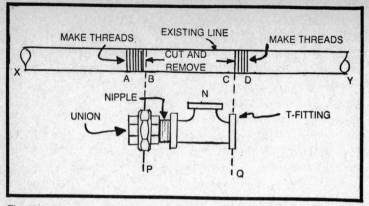

Fig. 12-6. It's necessary to attach a threaded union and T-fitting for running a new line with threaded pipe.

rigid copper pipe and flexible tubing is used. The tubing is not used in exposed locations because it is likely to be damaged. Also, there are a number of bends on it and these bends might cause still-water pockets; hence, all horizontal runs should be given a substantial pitch to drain out this water, when necessary, to guard against the danger of freezing. There will be no problem on vertical or near-vertical runs.

The procedure for running extensions from existing lines with threaded pipes (iron, steel, etc.) is somewhat different. The method is illustrated in Fig. 12-6. Fit together a union, a nipple, and a T-fitting of the same inside diameter as the line XY. Measure out the distance PQ between the center of the union and the center of the outer hub of the T-fitting. From the line XY, cut off a portion BC exactly equal to the length PQ. Unscrew the lengths XB and CY from their joints and thread their ends AB and CD. Screw on the T-fitting at CD and put back the line CY into the system. Now screw the nipple into the T, and the union onto the nipple. Tighten up the assembly. Take the other section of pipe XB, screw it into the union, and put it back into the system. By turning the union around, tighten up and complete the job. You are now ready to assemble the new line starting from the end N of the T-fitting.

ADDING NEW DRAINAGE LINES

Just like when adding water supply lines, you should make sure of the provisions of your plumbing code regarding drainage lines before starting any work on them. A copy of the code may be obtained from the town or city hall. If the existing drainage plumbing in your home consists of plastic or copper pipes, additions and alterations are comparatively easy. With iron or steel pipes, the work is more cumbersome due to the type of the joints and fittings required. A new drainage line from a fixture will have to be connected, by means of a suitable fitting, to an existing soil or waste stack. If its length is substantial another pipe, called a *revent* pipe, will be run from the drainpipe of the fixture to the vent stack above. First you have to figure out the path the new line will follow. Several alternatives will generally be available. For a new fixture like a bathtub, the drainage pipe will probably go down vertically through a floor, running inside a wall until it reaches the underside of the basement ceiling. From that point it will run across to the soil stack, or it may first go vertical for a distance, and then horizontally across a ceiling until it hits the soil stack. Sometimes it may discharge into a waste stack instead of into the main soil stack. In most cases a vent pipe connection will be necessary.

When cutting the pipes, allowance should be made for overlap length at fittings and for the dimensions of the fittings themselves.

Sizes and types of drainpipes are governed by the provisions of the plumbing code. If none exists for your community you may use the following guide:

Drains for sinks, basins, and bathtubs 1 1/2″ to 2″ pipe
Drain for toilets   4″ lead or plastic pipe

Figure 12-7 illustrates how drainage connections for fixtures may be made for a bathroom. The toilet is always located next to the soil stack. From the drum trap of the bathtub, the drain line runs horizontally into the wall, turns right, and is installed in grooves cut in joists. Finally it joins the vertical waste pipe through a Y-connection. The upper portions of the soil stack and the waste pipe act as vent pipes. A revent pipe connects the tub drain line to the vent pipe. This provides proper ventage and prevents the drum trap seal from being broken due to sewer gas pressures.

There is a sink connection to the waste pipe. A cleanout is provided on the small horizontal pipe connecting the waste pipe and the soil stack. This facilitates future cleanups and repairs.

Connecting a Drainage Line to a Soil Stack at a Cleanout

It is an easy matter to connect a fixture drainpipe to the soil stack at an existing cleanout. An additional stack may also be con-

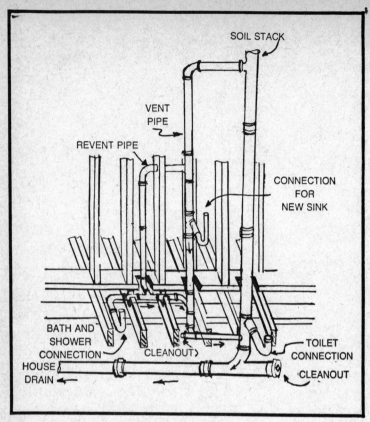

Fig. 12-7. Adding drainage lines for new fixtures.

nected in the same manner. Remove the plug and attach a nipple or short piece of pipe by caulking or screwing it in, as the case may be (Fig. 12-8). Next attach to it a new cleanout with the usual elbow, and you are ready to connect your new drainpipe or stack pipe to it. Screw it on or caulk it in.

Connecting a Drainage Line Directly to Soil Stack

Remodellings almost always include new fixtures, and you have to connect their drainpipes to the soil stack or to the house drain. Often new vent pipes will also be required. Compared to water supply pipe extensions, working on the drainage lines and the soil stack is more difficult and time-consuming. This is because the stack is a much larger-sized pipe. Also, it stays buried inside the walls for almost its entire length except in the basement and the attic. The

320

connection procedures for copper and plastic pipes differ from those for cast-iron or steel pipes.

Connecting to a Cast-Iron or Steel Stack. The connection is made through a *sisson joint*, which is basically a slip-fitting. The upper section of pipe should be properly supported by installing iron straps at least at two joints. Then, with a hacksaw, cut and remove a full length of pipe (see Fig. 12-9). After positioning a Y-fitting, a sisson fitting, and a piece of pipe cut to the required length, expand the sisson fitting and make the four joints secure by caulking. You are now ready to connect the new drainpipe to the Y.

If you are working near the roof, the connection can be made with much less effort. Open out the topmost joint and lift the upper section a few inches; tilt it and strap it securely in place. As before, using a hacksaw, make a cut at B (Fig. 12-10), discard the piece BC and slide AB down into the lower socket. Add the Y-fitting and, after straightening the pipes, make the joints. In cases where you can lift up the topmost section substantially, cutting may not be necessary. While holding the upper portion in its raised position, just slip the new fitting under it and make the two joints. The stack will now stay

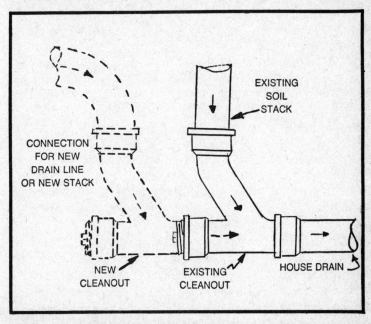

Fig. 12-8. To connect a new fixture drain or a new stack at a cleanout, remove the plug and attach a nipple or short piece of pipe. Add a new cleanout and you are ready to connect the new line.

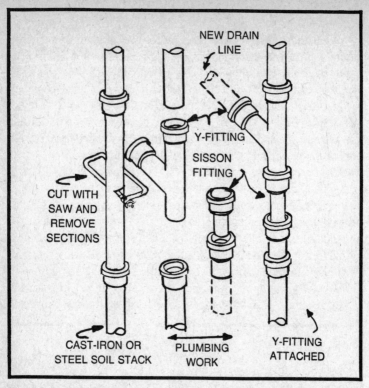

NEW DRAIN LINE

Y-FITTING

SISSON FITTING

CUT WITH SAW AND REMOVE SECTIONS

CAST-IRON OR STEEL SOIL STACK

PLUMBING WORK

Y-FITTING ATTACHED

Fig. 12-9. A drain connection to a cast-iron or steel soil stack is normally made by using a sisson fitting. Cut a length of pipe and remove the pieces after supporting the upper section of the stack by heavy metal straps. Place the sisson fitting and the Y in position. Position a piece of pipe cut to required length below the sisson fitting. Expand the sisson fitting and make all the four joints.

protruding over the roof much more than before, but that is not too bad.

Connecting to a Copper or Plastic Stack. With a hacksaw, carefully cut and remove the required *minimum* length of pipe, *not* a full length as for a cast-iron stack. As before, support the upper portion of the stack to prevent it from sagging or falling out. Install a Y or T for the new branch drain by sweat soldering for copper or cementing for plastic pipe. Make a collar by sawing a coupling in half, and slip it over the lower pipe. Cut a piece of tube a little shorter than will go between the new fitting and the lower portion of pipe (Fig. 12-11). Connect its upper end to the new fitting by sweat soldering or cementing as necessary. Slip the collar up and make the lower joint to connect the short piece of pipe to the lower portion of the stack.

Connecting Fixture Pipes to Branch Drains

The drainpipes from fixtures are connected to branch drains in the same manner as described for soil stack connections. A branch drain is, however, smaller in size, and it runs horizontally. A typical connection of a lavatory through a Y is shown in Fig. 12-12.

During remodelling, there is always the danger of overloading the branch drains. When the system is designed and installed for a new house, the capacities of branch drains are based on the number of fixtures fitted at that time plus any slated for some future expansion. Every time a fixture is added, the capacity is taxed, particularly if the fixture is in the kitchen (like a sink or a garbage disposer) and gives rise to considerable amounts of grease, oil, solid matter, and rinse water. An undersized branch drain will start clogging frequently, giving a warning that it should be replaced with a larger-sized line. Minor overloading will not cause a problem but if the

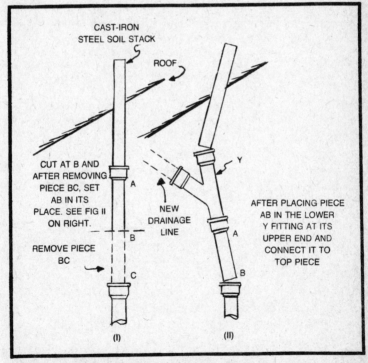

Fig. 12-10. If you are working near the roof, open the top most joint and after lifting the top section of pipe, tilt it and strap it. Make a cut in a lower section of pipe at B. Slip the portion AB down. Attach a T or Y at its top. Make joints after straightening the sections.

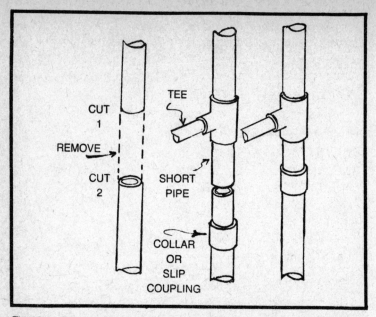

CUT 1

REMOVE →

CUT 2

TEE

SHORT PIPE

COLLAR OR SLIP COUPLING

Fig. 12-11. To add a drain T to a copper or plastic soil stack, cut and remove pipe as shown. Slip a collar or coupling on lower portion. Fit a T with a short pipe and sweat solder (if a copper stack) or make solvent joint (if a plastic stack). Slide up the collar or slip coupling and make the lower joint.

ailment is serious, it is time to do something. All the lines that will get increased discharges after remodelling, should have their capacities checked and should be replaced with pipes of larger sizes if necessary. The pitch should also be checked and, if inadequate, should be increased. Increased pitch means greater flow velocity and less chance for deposits to accumulate.

Working on Lines Within Walls and Floors

As discussed earlier, you have to cut holes in floors and walls to pass water lines and drainage lines, including the stacks, from one floor to another. By careful planning, the carpentry work can be reduced. When a considerable amount of cutting and patching is involved, consider renting power tools instead of working with hand tools. This will save time and labor. The following power tools will come in handy:

- Heavy-duty angle drill with various drill bits
- Large saber saw with a set of blades
- Cat's paw for pulling nails

When assembling the stack and making branch drain connections, the pitch of the drain is very important. If you make the T or Y connections after checking the elevation and the angle of the fitting (from the stack towards the drain pipe) so that a proper pitch is provided, future clogging problems will be minimized.

Running Flexible Pipe

Flexible copper tubing is the most popular material for home plumbing because it can be easily bent in any direction, and long stretches can be laid with very few joints. When you want to run a length of tubing inside a wall from one floor to the other, tie to its one end a long rope with a weight attached. Slowly lower the weighted rope till it comes down to the hole in the wall at the lower floor. Have an assistant pull the weight and the rope out, and haul away as much as required to bring the copper tubing to the desired point (Fig. 12-13). For horizontal runs, use an electrician's snake instead of the rope. Tie it to the copper tubing and let your assistant pull while you feed the pipe into the hole.

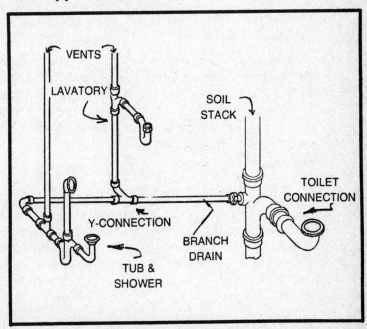

Fig. 12-12. Fixture connections to branch drains are made through Y or T fittings. Proper venting is always necessary.

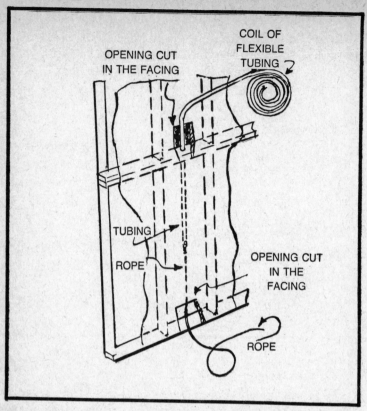

Fig. 12-13. To run flexible piping from floor to floor, within walls, tie a weighted rope to its end and lower it inside the wall till the weight hits the lower hole in the wall. Ask your assistant to catch the weight and pull the rope till the end of tubing reaches the desired point.

SIZES OF DOMESTIC WATER SUPPLY AND DRAINAGE LINES

For home piping systems, the following are more or less standard pipe sizes:

Drainage Pipes

Sewer line	4 inches
House drain	3 to 4 inches
Soil stack	3 to 4 inches
Roof vent	3 inches or more

Branch drains from dishwashers, laundries, lavatories, tubs, sinks and showers   1 1/2 inches.

Water Supply Pipes

Service entrance	1 inch
Branch to water heater	3/4 to 1 inch
Hot and cold mains	3/4 inch
Branch lines to dishwashers, laundries, tubs, showers and sinks	1/2 inch
Branch lines to toilet and lavatories	3/8 inch

When you are joining pipes of the same material but of different size, use a *reducer*. You can buy reducing elbows, reducing Ts, and reducing couplings.

When the pipes to be joined have the same size but are of different materials, an *adapter* is required. Adapter elbows, adapter Ts, and adapter couplings are available.

If you wish to join a copper DWV pipe to a cast-iron pipe, get a transition fitting. Caulk it into the cast-iron pipe at one end and solder it to the copper pipe at the other.

Very often you will need to connect plastic pipe to cast-iron pipe. Just place the spigot end of the plastic pipe into the socket of the cast-iron pipe, and seal the joint with a special compound made for the purpose. You can buy it at your plumbing store.

SELECTING AND ADDING FIXTURES

Almost invariably a remodelling job will consist of installing new fixtures in place of the old and obsolete ones. If a new fixture is to be fitted in practically the same location as the old one, the job is very simple. You already have the water supply and DWV pipes, and will merely switch the connections from the old to the new fixture. If, on the other hand, the location of the new one is substantially different from that of the old, the DWV fixture branch may have to be remodelled so that it conforms to the maximum wet-vented run allowed by the plumbing code in force. It will be necessary to extend the water supply lines, too.

The details for making new fixture connections have been discussed in various preceding Chapters, and reference should be made to them:

sink and lavatory	Chapter 6
toilet	Chapter 7
faucets	Chapter 8
bathtub and shower	Chapter 9
washer and dryer	Chapter 10

A fixtures' size, quality, color, and general finish should conform with the general decor of your home (see Figs. 12-14 and 12-15). The best quality fixtures may cost about one-third more than the average ones, but they add considerably to the value of your home.

Bathtubs

Large-sized bathtubs seem to be preferred nowadays. The minimum size for comfort is 60 × 32 × 16 inches. Do not accept a tub less than 16 inches in depth. A larger depth gives extra convenience. If a square tub appeals to you, get at least a 4-foot square with a seat at one or both ends. The best material for a bathtub is

Fig. 12-14. Fixtures in this modern bathroom all blend with the decor.

Fig. 12-15. Or, here's another version of a modern bathroom design. Courtesy: Kohler Co.

acid-resistant, enamelled cast iron. It will not chip or scratch. Steel tubs are somewhat cheaper, and have equally long life, but some of them may very soon show scratches. An oval, large-sized bathtub with matched setting does give a luxurious look (Fig. 12-16). You may also consider a whirlpool bath attachment (Fig. 12-17), or the raindrop personal shower put out by Kohler or others (Fig. 12-18).

Sinks and Lavatories

The size of your washbowl or lavatory should be large enough to allow convenience in washing hair or a new baby. A 20 × 24 inch bowl does not cost much more than the common 17 × 19 inch size. The best material is vitreous china. Figure 12-19 shows one large sized sink, and Fig. 12-20 shows a space saver.

Toilets

The choice of water closets or toilets is a very important one. Wash-down toilets are the cheapest and noisiest. Somewhat more expensive are the reverse trap type, and the best ones are those

Fig. 12-16. An oval bathtub surrounded by geometric shapes of counters carrying the sinks and other facilities, can look luxurious. Courtesy: Kohler Co.

having the siphon-jet flush action. Toilets which are quiet in their action and efficient in self-cleansing are the best. The wall-mounted ones which hang completely above the floor eliminate the usual floor-cleaning problem. A one-piece toilet and tank gives good appearance, too. Coming into popularity is a toilet and bidet combination, as shown in Fig. 12-21. A bidet is used for feminine and male hygiene, sitz baths, etc.

Faucets and Shower Heads

Faucets and shower heads are generally considered to be bathroom trim or fittings. They come in various shades, lusters, and

Fig. 12-17. Easy to attach to your tub, a hydro whirl (whirlpool bath attachment), simulates the whirlpool message which you could only get at a health spa. Courtesy: Kohler Co.

Fig. 12-18. A raindrop personal shower can provide a gentle massaging action. Courtesy: Kohler Co.

price ranges. Most of these will shine at first, but the cheap ones soon rust or tarnish and develop leaks and drips requiring occassional repairs and washer changes.

You will find three different grades of fittings offered by various manufacturers. The most expensive ones may have a polished gold or chromium surface, or a brushed satin finish. The average type is almost half the price of the first group, and yet offers good service and appearance. The least expensive fittings are those that soon develop rust or tarnish, leaks and drips.

You should buy faucets and shower heads which go with your lavatory, sink, and tubs. It is not necessary to accept the fitting you see attached to a particular fixture in a showroom. The two parts are manufactured separately, and most fittings will go with almost any fixture.

When you visit your plumbing supply store, ask the dealer to show you various qualities of faucets and to point out the differences between the cheaper and the more luxurious brands. You will find that while the good quality ones are made of heavy brass with a copper-nickel-chrome finish, the light weight brands consist of zinc or aluminum die castings. The best proof of good quality is a well-known manufacturer's name stamp. These companies will not stamp their names on their cheapest quality line; the most you will find on the cheaper fixtures will be a fancy emblem which means nothing.

Shower nozzles come in several qualities and with or without convenience features like *volume* spray control (to give coarse or

Fig. 12-19. The Lakefield sink, from Kohler, is a self-rimming, enameled, cast-iron sink. It measures 33 by 22 inches, slightly larger than many sinks requiring metal frames. This means that it can often be installed in existing countertops without replacing the entire counter.

Fig. 12-20. A single bowl kitchen sink with an integral elevated garbage disposal compartment meets the space limitations of a smaller sized kitchen. Courtesy: Kohler Co.

fine spray) and *spray direction control* provided by a ball joint inside the assembly. Nozzles with a self-cleaning head are suitable in areas with hard water supply. Cheap quality shower nozzles often clog or corrode and need repairs.

You may want to go in for two very important safety devices at your shower:

1. Temperature-control valve
2. Automatic diverter control valve (not the manual type)

While taking a shower, you must have had the unpleasant experience of water suddenly turning scalding hot or freezing cold. This happens when some other member of the family starts using water at another fixture or fitting, thus diverting water from one of the lines. A *temperature-control valve* maintains the shower water at a constant temperature and eliminates the possibility of a sudden rush of very hot or very cold water. Two types of valves are available; a thermostat mixing type and a pressure controll type. The latter is usually preferred. Installation instructions will come with the unit you purchase.

Another hazard is a sudden spurt of water falling from the shower head of your combination bathtub-shower, when you enter the bathtub and open the faucets. This happens if the last person to use the shower forgot to pull down the shower lever that diverts water back to the tub spouts. By the time you turn the control you might get scalded. Most manufacturers provide a manual control with the bathtub assembly instead of an *automatic diverter control* which automatically turns the supply back to the tub spigot after the shower is turned off. If your system does not have such a control, it

Fig. 12-21. A Caravelle bidet and a Rochelle toilet are companion fixtures for the bathroom of the sophisticated: Courtesy Kohler Co.

may be a good idea to buy one. The installation is not difficult and complete installation instructions come with the unit.

Like bathtubs, showers come in various sizes, shapes, and colors. Prefabricated fiberglass showers are very common; they come in a compact package ready for installation which takes only a few hours. Two-wall models are available for corners and three-wall units for other locations.

Colors

Floor tiles, coverings, fixtures, and fittings come in a wide spectrum of colors. Light colors are usually preferred in baths located in the northern and southern sides of the house because these rooms get little or no sunlight. Baths located towards the east and the west may have deeper shades of color. It is an accepted fact, however, that dark colors make a room look smaller than it is. Light pink, yellow, or mauve will look nice in any bathroom. You may want to avoid exotic colors because they usually go out of fashion quickly. Once a color scheme is installed, you have to live with it. If the scheme is weird or unusual you may lose out some time in future, if you have to sell the house.

Hot water heaters are generally white. Kitchen sinks are usually metallic in color, being made of stainless steel sheets. The colors of your dishwasher, garbage disposer, automatic washer and dryer should blend with the general color scheme of the rooms they're in.

Plumbing for Swimming Pools, Gazing Pools, and Drinking Fountains

Plumbing for Swimming Pools,
Gazing Pools, and Drinking Fountains

Water systems are not just limited to supply and drainage in a home. Many houses have swimming pools, gazing pools, or drinking fountains, too. And each of these items involve a different kind of plumbing.

SWIMMING POOLS

More and more homeowners are installing swimming pools every year. In fact, in-ground pools are even more popular than the above-ground ones.

Proper operation and maintenance of a pool requires that the water be circulated, filtered, purified, heated, skimmed, chlorinated, and at times drained off and refilled. These practices are accomplished by different types of pipes, fittings, and mechanical equipment.

Figure 13-1 illustrates the layout of an in-ground pool. Its equipment mainly consists of the following parts:
1. Skimmer-feeder
2. Pump and motor
3. Filter
4. Water heater (optional)
5. Hydro-stairs (optional)
6. Piping and valves

The pump lifts water from the pool through the skimmer and delivers it to the inlet side of the filter where it gets purified by

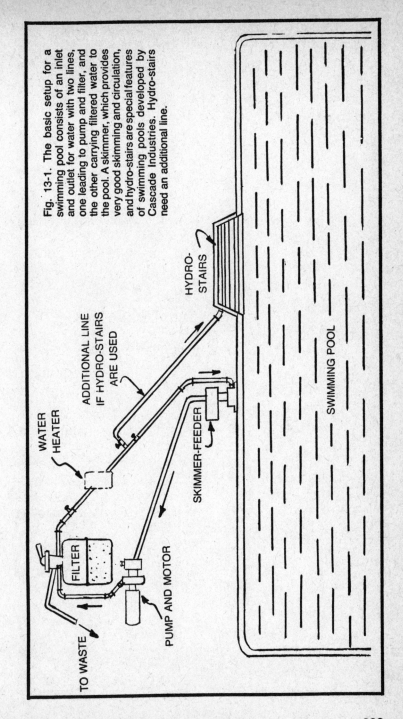

Fig. 13-1. The basic setup for a swimming pool consists of an inlet and outlet for water with two lines, one leading to pump and filter, and the other carrying filtered water to the pool. A skimmer, which provides very good skimming and circulation, and hydro-stairs are special features of swimming pools developed by Cascade Industries. Hydro-stairs need an additional line.

WATER HEATER

ADDITIONAL LINE IF HYDRO-STAIRS ARE USED

HYDRO-STAIRS

FILTER

TO WASTE

PUMP AND MOTOR

SKIMMER-FEEDER

SWIMMING POOL

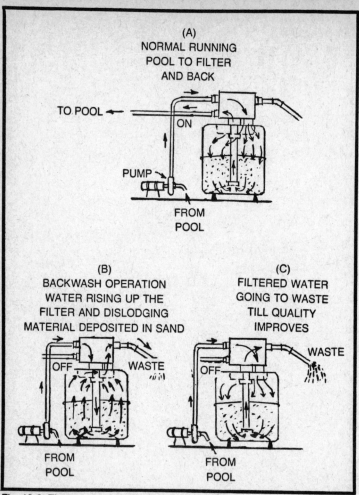

Fig. 13-2. Three cycles of filter operation.

passing through a sand and gravel bed. The filtered water rises through the central pipe and goes back to the pool. The three sketches in Fig. 13-2 illustrate the normal filtering action (Fig. 13-2A), the backwash process, and the waste process. During a normal run, water goes down through sand and gravel and rises through the central tube (Fig. 13-2B); in the backwash cycle it enters at the top of this tube and rises through the filtering media (Fig. 13-2B).

Every time the pool is started for a new season, it takes a while before the filter begins to give out good quality water. The filtered water has to be wasted for some time. Figure 13-2C shows this operation.

There may be two return lines to the pool, one leading to an inlet in a side wall of the pool, or to the stairs, and the other connected to the underside of the skimmer where the filtered water enters the pool through a nozzle. The high velocity sheet-like jet from the nozzles causes a very effective skimming action (Fig. 13-3).

A water heater is a convenient optional feature in a swimming pool setup. It can be placed in the usual plumbing system. (See Fig. 13-1).

Emptying the pool is necessary in areas where winters have sub-freezing temperatures. Some towns do not allow thousands of gallons of pool water to run into roadside drains and sewers. Nor is your private sewage disposal system designed to take so much overload. The only choice you have for emptying is to gradually sprinkle the water over the lawn and let it seep down.

The inground pool has a waste line in its plumbing system near the filter (see Fig. 13-1). Attach a garden hose or sprinklers to this line and let the pump run a few hours each day. As the water spreads

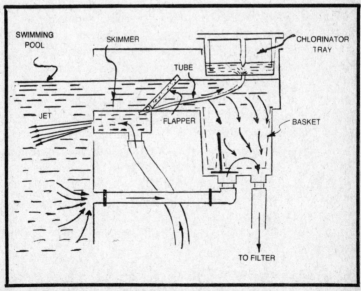

Fig. 13-3. All water from the filter passes through the skimmer and shoots in a jet into the pool. This provides an excellent skimming action and circulation. It is a nice feature provided by Cascade Industries. The pool water both at the surface and at about one foot of depth flows through the basket into the inlet pipe of the pump and filter.

over the lawn, it will improve the grass and the evergreens, and will gradually percolate down to the ground water table.

For emptying an above-ground pool, you should buy a small centrifugal pump with an electric motor. There is no pump in the plumbing system of this kind of pool; such pools are filled simply by running water from a garden hose. Attach an intake hose to the inlet end of the pump and to the outlet end attach the usual garden hose. Every time you wish to start the pump, it will have to be primed. After attaching the intake hose to the pump, fill the hose completely by pouring water into the other end; hold that far end closed with your thumb. Lower this end well into the pool, remove the thumb, and start the pump (Fig. 13-4).

A couple of days before you intend to begin sprinkling pool water on your lawn and evergreens, stop feeding chemicals to the pool water. There is a chance that some of these may be injurious to plants. A waiting period of 48 hours is long enough for the chemicals to get dissipated. To be perfectly sure the chemicals are gone, fill a sprinkling can with pool water and empty it over a very small, out-of-the-way area of the lawn, preferably in the evening, and check it the following morning. If the grass is as fresh as before, the water is safe and you can start the job.

Some basic precautions have to be taken when installing the plumbing system for a swimming pool and when operating it. No cross-connection is permitted between this system and the municipal or community water supply even if you intend to install check valves or any other protective devices on such a connection. For the same reason, the pool should not be filled directly from the public supply. An open tank should be filled up with water first, and this water should then be transferred to the swimming pool.

If you observe closely, you will find that the treated water from the filtering system enters the pool at its shallow end while the water returning to the filter is drawn from the deep end. The inlets and outlets should be arranged so that there is proper circulation of water without the formation of still-water pockets. In some cases, it may be necessary to make changes in the locations of existing inlets and outlets.

GAZING POOLS

Depending on the topography of your land, a gazing pool may either be located on level ground or at a high spot with the ground sloping away from it. If located on level ground, the gazing pool's

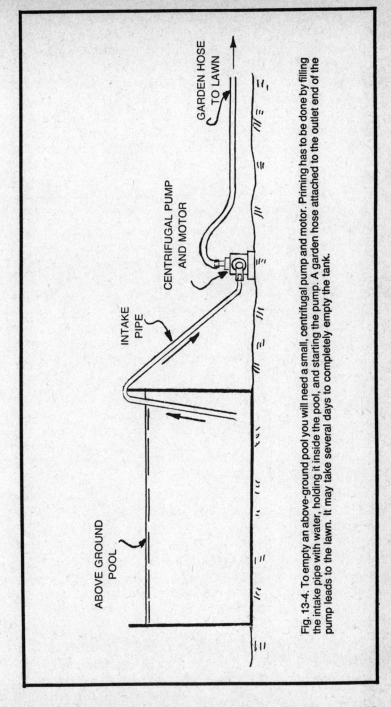

Fig. 13-4. To empty an above-ground pool you will need a small, centrifugal pump and motor. Priming has to be done by filling the intake pipe with water, holding it inside the pool, and starting the pump. A garden hose attached to the outlet end of the pump leads to the lawn. It may take several days to completely empty the tank.

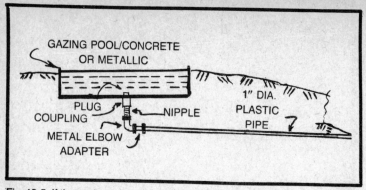

Fig. 13-5. If the gazing pool is on level ground, pumping is normally required to empty it. If on sloping ground, as in this figure, a plastic pipe can be run at a suitable pitch till it comes out of ground near the lawn. A metal-to-plastic adapter shall be required. The plug in the pool bottom is taken out when emptying.

contents would have to be pumped for emptying purposes, just as for an in-ground swimming pool. When located on high ground, as illustrated in Fig. 13-5, the gazing pool may have a pipe buried underground at a suitable pitch so that the pipe's lower end comes out of the ground near the lawn or at some other suitable spot. A 4-inch plastic pipe will be quite suitable. The plug in the center of the pool sits on a coupling attached to its bottom. The pipe is connected to the coupling through a metal-to-plastic adapter, a 90° elbow, and a small nipple.

The plug is taken out when the pool is to be emptied, and the line stays open during winters. This does not allow water from rain or melting snow to accumulate and cause damage to the pool sides in case it refreezes. In regions of very severe winters, a fiber pipe should be used instead of plastic pipe.

FOUNTAINS

If you have an artistic temperament and would like to watch multi-colored lights playing on a fountain in your yard as the evenings turn into nights, take up this project. You will find that it is pretty simple to execute. All you need is a pump and motor and two plastic pipelines with T connections. A small waterproof enclosure for the pump and motor will be needed. You can probably get a pre-cast concrete fountain from a concrete specialty store (Fig. 13-6).

Buy a fountain pump unit from a good garden-supply store or from a large plumbing house. If you are ambitious, you can even use an old washing-machine pump or get an ordinary centrifugal pump

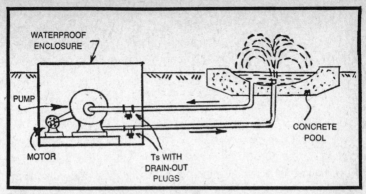

Fig. 13-6. Fountains are generally made of concrete. A motor and pump can be purchased at a garden-supply shop. A waterproof enclosure protects them from weather. The two lines have a downward pitch with Ts and drain-out plugs to drain the fountain.

with a matching motor. If you can get hold of a submersible unit, no piping will be required.

You should try to locate the pump so that its axis stays a couple of feet below the bottom of the pool. This will keep it primed and ready to start at any time.

Fig. 13-7. A Buster Crabbe Pool in free-form shape. This model incorporates a patented skimmer-feeder as standard equipment. Courtesy: Cascade Industries and Parco Pools, Stratford, Connecticut.

Electric power to the motor and to any night lights at the pool should be carried by waterproof cable placed in a trench at least 1 1/2 feet deep. Check with your local electric code for guidelines. Alternatively, a flexible waterproof cord may be used if it can be attached to an outdoor electric outlet.

Fountains, like swimming pools, use the same water again and again, and may have to be drained and re-filled a few times every season. The two pipelines should be pitched towards the pump. This will help in draining out the fountain quickly. The Ts will have to be opened for the purpose of draining. The pitch on the lines will also help in constant priming of the pump provided, of course, that the pump is located lower than the fountain bottom.

Figure 13-7 shows a full-featured backyard pool.

Preventive Maintenance and Vacation Shut-Down Procedures

Chapter 14

Preventive Maintenance
and Vacation Shut-Down Procedures

A properly installed plumbing system gives almost trouble-free service for a long period of time. The span of life of each individual fixture and fitting, however, depends on its quality and on the type of use it receives. Inconsiderate and rough use may result in breakdowns, cloggings, leakages, and flooding problems. If one discards the wrong type of materials into the toilet and the garbage disposer, cleans the surfaces of sinks and lavatories with hard abrasives, or ignorantly sets the thermostat on the hot water heater very high or very low, only trouble can be expected. If you follow the basic maintenance procedure outlined in this Chapter, though, it will go a long way to give you good service and to prevent the expense of unnecessary repairs.

PIPELINES, FIXTURES, AND FITTINGS

Major portions of your water, drainage, and gas lines are concealed within the walls and the floors. You will find the exposed portions only in the basement, the attic, and in some closets. Whenever moving or storing furniture, appliances, or heavy objects, be careful not to hit and damage any of these lines.

Sinks, lavatories, tubs, and toilets will continue to shine if their surfaces do not get spoiled by the use of harsh abrasive cleaners. They should be cleaned occasionally with soap and hot water. If a commercial cleanser is used, it should be of a nonabrasive variety.

Do not cut or chop vegetables and other items in the kitchen or on the drain board; it will leave scratches which cannot be easily removed. Also, avoid scraping metallic objects like spoons, forks, or utensils against these surfaces. Although some kitchen sinks are made to resist staining, continued contact with citrus fruit pulp and juice, vinegar, tomatoes, mayonnaise, yogurt, ketchup, cottage cheese, tea leaves, coffee grounds, etc., tarnishes the enameled surface. Remove such items as promptly as possible by throwing them in the garbage can or washing them down into the garbage disposer if one is fitted under the sink.

The kitchen sink drain, if not fitted with a disposer, is likely to get clogged if pieces of food, oils and greases, tea leaves, and coffee grounds are discarded into it. As you wash your pots and pans in the sink, some grease and oil will always go into the drain and will tend to deposit against its walls. Food particles and other matter like tea and coffee grounds, when washed down into the drain, will stick to the grease on the walls. This will ultimately result in a clog and a back-up of the flow into the sink, or at least a sluggish drain. If you pour drain cleaners into your sink and lavatory drains on a regular basis, they will remain clean and will not require large-scale unclogging procedures. Two types of such chemical cleaners are available—acidic and alkaline. Acids are more effective but should be used with extreme care so that they don't touch your skin and burn it. Brand name cleaners like Clobber and Bust-Loose cost about $4 a quart. Both acids and alkalis dissolve grease, but only acid is effective for hair.

Among alkaline cleaners, Lye, Drano, and "99" are common brands. Care should be taken not to mix the acid and alkaline cleaners in the drain or else they may produce a violent eruption. Unless you can completely drain out one type, do not pour in another.

Your bathroom lavatory has a slight advantage over the kitchen sink; it has a pop up drain plug which stops large objects from going down the drain. This should be lifted up occasionally and cleaned with a brush or cloth. Articles in the medicine cabinet should not fall down into the lavatory, keep them properly arranged. If a corrosive substance does fall down on the surface of the lavatory, promptly clean and wash it. It is a good idea to fill both the sinks and lavatories to the brim after plugging the drain opening and then to suddenly release this water. If done frequently, the flushing action will help keep the drains clean.

Fittings like faucets, tub and shower assemblies, and toilet-tank handles are normally chromium plated and retain their shine for a long period of time. Wiping with a wet towel, or washing with soap and water is all you have to do. Sometimes you may want to clean them with a special liquid cleaner manufactured for the purpose. If the surface of a fitting has been damaged by misuse, it may start corroding and you may observe some green spots. To prevent further deterioration, remove the spots by rubbing them with very fine emery paper or a powder cleanser; then apply a thin layer of wax.

Keep an eye out for drips or leaks at faucets and other water outlets. Sometimes there is a continuous leakage from the toilet tank into the bowl which you do not see; only your water bill goes up. To check for a suspected leak, get a dye from your hardware store and drop some of it in the tank so that the water in it gets colored. Watch for a few minutes without flushing the toilet. If the colored water appears in the bowl, there is a leak. To repair the leak, refer to information in Chapter 7. In most cases, a new rubber ball will have to be installed.

Every fall, drain the outside faucets and pipes, and shut them from the inside to prevent freezing during the winter. This way you won't have any pipe bursts.

WATER METER AND VALVES

Normally the water meter is owned by your water company and you don't have to do anything about it except to know where it is located and report to the company if the meter is malfunctioning or has stopped.

The various stop valves on your water supply lines should be in good working order. It is recommended that tags be tied in the basement to all the valves, the hot and cold water lines, and the gas line. This will identify each one and enable you to work the right shut-offs when the supply has to be stopped in a hurry, for instance in case of a burst line or broken joint. It is equally important that all family members know exactly where the main shut-off valve for water is located and how it can be reached.

WATER HEATER

Normal setting for the thermostat on your water heater is between 140°F and 150°F. Unless you specifically want water at higher temperature, keep the setting as near to 140°F as possible. This will keep the heater working for many more years and will also effect a saving in your gas or electric bill.

Complete details on water heater maintenance and repairs were given in Chapter 1. As mentioned there, clean the sediment buildup every other month by opening up the drain valve and letting water run out till it gets clean. When doing this, it will be a good idea to check the safety relief valve mounted at the top. It is either a pressure type or pressure-cum-temperature type. Check to see if it is in good working order and not corroded or stuck. This valve opens in case of excessive pressure buildup inside the tank, and thus prevents possible explosions. Work the lever by hand several times and observe if it turns freely. At times you may use a thermometer and observe the water temperature in an adjacent hot water line to see if the thermostat is working properly. If not, proceed according to the recommendations in Chapter 1.

ROOF AND YARD DRAINAGE

You should inspect the vertical downspouts from the roofs periodically, particularly after a heavy downpour, to insure that they do not have any leaks and are properly conveying the roof water away from the house or into a dry well. If they connect to ground pipes or to a dry well, open up the connection at ground surface and inspect the ground pipe—often you will find that it is partly or fully clogged with leaves, dirt, paper, and other matter. Direct a jet of water from your garden hose into the pipe. If water backs up, it clearly indicates a clog exists and should be removed. The water from the roof in such cases backs up into the ground and the substructure of the house, leading to a wet basement. The clog can be removed with a heavy flush of water or with cleaning equipment. In extreme cases, the line may have to be opened.

If you or your neighbors have trees in the yard, the dry leaves are likely to lodge inside the roof gutters. Check the gutters periodically and remove the leaves and debris. You may want to eliminate this task by completely covering the gutters with 6 inch wide wire screens made especially for the purpose. These can be bought at most hardware stores.

Proper grading in the yard of a house is important. If there are any local depressions or low spots, especially over the septic tank or the disposal field area, fill them and regrade the ground so that all water flows away from the property along natural drainage lines. Water standing anywhere close to your house, particularly next to the foundation, is likely to seep down to the basement and make it wet. The ground all around the outer walls should slope away so that no rain water flows towards the house itself. It is not a good practice to dig flower beds next to the walls — when you water the plants, the excess will find its way down to the foundation and cause a wet basement.

SEPTIC TANK AND DISPOSAL SYSTEM

With proper care, your septic tank and disposal system should give long service. The following suggestions will help keep it in good order:

1. Do not overload the system by running several appliances simultaneously.
2. Do not use strong bleaches and detergents in your washing machine. They slow down the bacteriological action in the septic tank.
3. Do not wash several loads of clothes in a row without giving the machines and the system some rest.
4. To prevent grease from entering the septic tank, install a grease trap on the kitchen line if possible.
5. Strong chemicals, acids, paints, varnishes, etc., should not be discharged into the drainage system.
6. Because the capacity of the system is designed only for the flow from the house, no rain water from the roof or yard should find its way into it.
7. Do not discard into your sinks, toilets, etc., articles like: wrapping paper, paper towels, cooking oils and fats, coffee grounds, cigarette butts, and old rags.

As the family size increases, there are heavier demands on the disposal system. If you are experiencing problems you did not have before, probably it is time to redesign the system and install a few more lines of trenches, seepage pits, or galleries. Consult a professional sanitary engineer for advice.

Mineral sludge goes on collecting at the septic tank bottom and, depending on the size of your family and its habits, cleaning may be necessary at intervals of from two to five years. It is good practice to open the top cover every year and measure the depth of top scum, the bottom sludge, and the liquid in between. When the combined depth of scum and sludge increases to half the total depth of the tank, it is time for cleaning. The depths are measured by a special stick which septic tank servicemen carry. Septic tank cleaning should always be done by professional septic tank cleaners. The best time for this action is during summer or spring. If done in winter, the new bacteria will take some time to grow, unless a small amount of old sludge and liquid is left behind for seeding purposes. Some people use septic tank cleaning chemicals but their usefulness is somewhat doubtful, and in any case they cannot take the place of good care and regular cleaning.

Trucks and heavy vehicles should not be allowed to move on top of the septic tank and absorption field because they may cause structural damage. Also, shrubs and trees should not be planted over them—the roots can go down through the joints and clog the pipes. There is no objection to growing lawn grass in the area.

PREVENTING FROST DAMAGE TO YOUR PLUMBING

Chapter 5 described methods for insulating exposed pipelines, and Chapter 8 provided full details for installing and maintaining year-round, freeze-proof service in non-heated buildings and garages.

It is recommended that you inspect all the water supply pipes in the attic, unheated basement and garage, and any new addition to your home. Pipe insulation may have been damaged in some spots, or someone might have forgotten to insulate the pipes in the addition. Sometimes you will find uninsulated pipes running close to an outside wall with no insulation in it. Insulate all such pipes according to the methods given in Chapter 5. There may be some radiators near open windows. Either close the windows or open the radiators a little to avoid their getting frozen. Sillcocks should be opened and completely drained off after closing the inside stop-and-waste valve.

If you have no time to insulate exposed pipes when very low temperatures are forecast and a deep frost is expected, certain things can be done in a hurry. One of these is to keep water running continuously in the uninsulated line, letting it go to waste. The arrangement, though expensive, will reduce the likelihood of a pipe freeze, which is more expensive. Another is to place several electric bulbs along the exposed pipeline and turn them on. To avoid losing the heat, enclose both the bulbs and the pipe within an enclosure made of aluminum foil. Take the usual precautions against electric shocks.

CLOSING THE HOUSE DURING WINTERS

There may be a time when your home or vacation cottage has to remain vacant for a few months. If this period is expected to include the winter season, and if the heating system will not be running, it is important that the plumbing system be drained of its water and thus prepared for the cold spell, if damage is to be avoided.

First shut off the cold water supply to the house by closing the main shut-off valve in the basement. Then take the following steps to drain off most of the water contained in various pipes and fixtures:

1. Starting at the top floor, open all the faucets and the valves. After water stops running, take out the plug from the main shut-off valve, and collect the remaining water in a bucket.

2. Flush the toilets to empty their tanks. Remove any remaining water in the tanks by means of a sponge tied to the end of a stick.

3. Drain out water from all the traps under tubs, lavatories, and sinks by opening their cleanout plugs. Those not provided with such plugs should be dismantled and, after all the water is drained, reassembled.

4. Pour a non-volatile liquid like kerosene oil in the toilet bowls and in all other fixture traps including the one in the basement floor drain. The seals will prevent sewer gases from entering the house. Add automotive anti-freeze solution to the seals to prevent them from freezing.

5. If the radiators are the hot-water type, drain their water.

6. Drain the water from the boiler, the pneumatic tank, floor tanks, expansion tanks, and other containers.

7. Empty the hot-water tank by opening the bottom drain valve and the cock in the pipe at top which lets air in. Check to be sure that it is completely emptied, including all horizontal pipes. If necessary, pipes can be opened at joints to drain the water.

8. Washing machine, dishwasher, pumps, and other equipment that has some quantity of water inside, should be completely drained.

9. To drain the insides of all the valves, open the small screw-plugs on them.

10. Shut off the curb stop-valve and open the service pipe just close to the basement. Uncouple it so that it is open to atmosphere.

11. Uncouple the water meter from the line, and tilt it to drain off water.

12. Wrap the main shut-off valve, and as much of the main supply pipe as possible, with insulating tape.

When you have your own well water supply, let the water from the lines run back into the well by opening all the valves. The pump should be left dry, or water contained in it will freeze and damage it. If the pump is a submerged one, don't do anything; but if it is reciprocating or rotary type, drain the water out of the casing. The water tank should also be drained off.

When reopening the building which has been closed for some time, if you just close all the outlets and turn on the water supply, you will trap a lot of air in the water lines and the tanks. When you open the faucets, this air will rush out and water hammer will occur. To avoid this, you should first open all faucets and valves throughout the building and then open the main supply valve gradually. Air in the lines will be pushed out slowly through the faucets, which should be closed progressively upwards as the water rises in the pipes and flows out each faucet for a few minutes. Air should be allowed to escape from the storage tanks and other containers of water. Air chambers for preventing water hammer should be checked to see that they are in working order. If air has been sucked out of them, open up the caps, let them fill with air, and then replace the caps.

Bibliography

Alth Max. *Do-it-Yourself Plumbing*. Harper and Row, New York, 1975.

Anderson, Edwin P. *Audel's Home Appliance Service Guide*. Theo, Audel and Company Publishers, New York, 1960.

Arco. *Handy Man's Plumbing and Heating Guide*. Arco, New York, 1973.

Babbit, Harold E. *Plumbing*.

Blendermann, Louis. *Design of Plumbing and Drainage Systems*. The Industrial Press, New York, N. Y. Second Edition, 1963.

Brockwell, Percy T. *Major Appliance Servicing*. McGraw-Hill Book Company, Inc. New York, 1958.

Brann, Donald R. *Plumbing Repairs Simplified*. Directions Simplified, 1973.

Crouse, William H. *Everyday Household Appliance Repairs*. McGraw-Hill Book Company, Inc., New York, 1952.

Daniels, George. *Home Guide to Plumbing, Heating, Air Conditioning*. Popular Science Publishing Company. Harper and Row, New York, 1967.

Day, Richard. *The Practical Handbook of Plumbing and Heating*. Arco Publishing Company, Inc., New York.

Ehrenkvanz, Florence and Inman Lydia. *Equipment in the Home*. Harper and Brothers, New York, 1958.

Francis, R. J. Sr. *Home Owner's Plumbing Manual*. 1971-72.

Geiser, Charles J. *Practical Information, Care and Repair of the Plumbing and Heating System in Your Home*. Chas. J. Geiser and Sons, Inc., 1963.

Gerber. *Tips from your Plumber*. Gerber Plumbing Fixtures Corp., 1958.

Grosset & Dunlap. *Manual of Home Repairs, Remodelling and Maintenance*. Grosset & Dunlap, New York, 1969, 1972.

Hawkins, Harold J. *Your House*. M. Barrows & Company, New York, 1943.

Lane Publishing Company. *Basic Plumbing Illustrated*. Lane Publishing Company, Menlo Park, Ca. 1975.

Lee, Frankl. *Home Repairs Made Easy*. Nelson Doubleday, Inc. Garden City, New York, 1949.

Manley, H. P. *Plumbing Installation and Repair*. Frederick Drake Publishers, Chicago, 1972.

Matthias, A. J. Jr. *How to Design and Install Plumbing*. American Technical Society, Chicago, 1971.

Oravetz, Jules. *Question and Answers for Plumber's Examination*. Theodore Audel and Company, Indianapolis, Indiana, 1973.

Peters, Frazir Forman. *Buying a House Worth the Money*. Little, Brown and Company, Boston, 1950.

Sears. *Plumbing, Planning and Installing*. Sears, Roebuck and Company, 1967.

Starbuck, R. M. *Standard Practical Plumbing*. Norman W. Henley Publishing Company, New York, 1927.

The Home Pro Plumbing Guide. Minnesota Mining and Manufacturing Company, 1975.

Watkins, A. M. *Building or Buying the High Quality House at the Lowest Cost*. Doubleday and Company, Inc., 1962.

Watkins, A. M. *The Complete Book of Home Remodelling, Improvement and Repair*. Doubleday and Company, Inc., Garden City, N.Y., 1963.

Index

Index